jan cremer writes again

by JAN CREMER
Translated by Jon Lulius

GROVE PRESS, INC., NEW YORK

Dedicated to   Jan Cremer + Nana M.
my dog Vodka
Everyone who Hoped
Begged & Prayed
That this Book
Would Never Appear
& to all the Faithful Readers
of my First Book

Written in the United States of America 1966
On Sphinx paper & an
Underwood Touch-Master II (11-8270019)
While enjoying Van Nelle's Strong Shag

All situations and persons portrayed in my book are solely the products of my depraved mind

— J. C.

Love is a pastime, love is a sport
A one-eyed sailor coming into port

The Marquis de Sade is dead
Arthur Rimbaud is dead
& I'm not feeling too hot myself

There's just one Jan Cremer
and that's me!

Jan Cremer

He who travels far and wide
can tell many tales

Grandpa Moses

Dixi et vendidi animam meam

french fries & a sour pickle

. . . the year is 1961. Fall, and the leaves are falling from the trees. One cool morning Our Hero saunters along one of Paris' sunbright boulevards. By the bounce of his step, tan skin and blond hair, by those steel-blue eyes that pierce passing women who follow the playboy in his bright blue suit and cloud of expensive aftershave lotion with longing in their eyes, we recognize that phenomenon Jan Cremer. . . .

146

I'd been hanging around Paris, the money running short, staying at an obscure but cheap hotel where I was supposed to meet Barry. Barry was due in any time now, hitchhiking up from Barcelona. But he hadn't shown up yet. I was afraid the worst had happened but decided to risk it anyway and hang on for a few more days. If the French police had picked him up and if he'd given them my address, they'd be coming to pick me up too.

I spent the days looking in at art galleries, then the Pigalle shooting galleries or sitting behind an expensive beer, bored stiff, in some dark bare-ass joint staring at the strippers. I sat the nights out either at some brightly lit sidewalk café or a neon-lighted bistro or in some of those small cafés with all the red lights around the Place Pigalle. Looking for old girl-friends or pals from my Parisian Period.

I'd tried to call. I'd called Janette a hundred times. An old girlfriend who worked the Place Pigalle. No luck. A shame because I was short on money, hard up for love, and after all, she'd promised to be faithful to me always.

> *Stopped off in Paris once*
> *Had me a ball*
> *Took in the Moulin Rouge*
> *Best of all*
> *Danced with Jacqueline*
> *You there everybody!*
> *Never seen*
> *Paris? Come with me*

147

I was in the Moulin Rouge neighborhood one night and decided to stop in at the bistro where Janette used to pick up her clients and where we had first met. The place was packed. A dozen bored whores were propping up the bar and a few quiet winos were parked off in a dark corner getting high on their cheap sweet wine.

When I walked in, the whores perked up like vultures and passed on the news that the big-shot spender was back in town. A cross-eyed, half-ton Negro woman blocked my way; propping up some of her weight on a thin umbrella, she leered at me suggestively. I shoved her aside and mounted the stool between two chicks at the bar: to my left a little French brunette swimming in perfume, a hand-job expert, leaned into me; to my right a beautiful king-sized blonde in a blue leather suit and knee-high, fire-engine red boots. I ordered Napoleon's favorite, a Cointreau, and asked the bartender if he knew where Janette was.

"Who?" he asked, sore about something, and brought me a greasy glass which he poured about three-quarters full. "Never heard of her. That'll be five francs."

"That'll be what?" I said. "For those three drops? Fill it up."

He filled my glass up to the brim, reluctantly. But I wasn't done with him yet. I took a fifty-franc note out of my pocket, let him have a good look, then tucked it back in. Then I tossed a franc on the bar, pointed to the price list painted on the mirror and said, "You better get your eyes fixed," and stared at him defiantly. He had sleek black hair buttered down flat and a little Rudolf Valentino mustache. He moved off, swearing to himself, and I thought: he won't be much help now, that's for sure.

The king-sized blonde turned, her big breasts nudging my arm, and said, "You looking for Janette?"

I said, "That's right, honey. You know where she's hanging out, or in, or all hung up on?" We laughed, and if there was any ice, it was broken.

"You mean Danish Janette?"

"Yes."

"She left town for a few days with her boyfriend."

I swore. So she'd been unfaithful after all. I'd had a feeling she would be. It had been more than a year since I'd last heard from her. Even though she'd promised to write that last time I saw her on my way to Spain with Barry. She'd even suggested maybe she might join us in Ibiza, after saving up some money and paying off the last installment on her TV set. And that's what I wanted to get engaged to!

"What'll you have?" I asked the blonde giant.

"Mind if I have a cocktail?" she asked. "All that whisky's just about shot hell out of my stomach."

"Fine," I said, very nicely and at the same time thinking that would be another ten francs.

"You know where Janette's living?" I asked. "I'm a cousin of hers from Denmark."

"I could tell by your accent you came from somewhere."

"Yeah. I'm on vacation. A few days in Paris having a ball. Just back from the tropics. No good, the tropics. Too many mosquitoes, too many fleas. And all those black girls!"

The bartender took down an unlabeled bottle and filled up her glass. "Wait a minute," I said, and took a sip: cold tea. I gave the glass a wide swing, sloshing it to him. He ducked fast.

"Don't ask for trouble, Dad," I said. "You may get it," and I socked my fistful of rings into my open palm. It hurt. Still, he looked scared, so it was worth it. Big Blondie, trying to cool things off, said it was all her *fault,* but I just glared at the bartender and said, "Let's have a cocktail this time and no more of that horse piss, and don't bug me again or you've had it!" He nodded like a good lackey. I felt like a hero.

If I'd come into that place wearing tight pants and a leather jacket, I would have been lying out bloody in the gutter a long time ago, but I had big rings on my fingers and wore a nicely tailored suit, so I was treated with respect. Once again Capitalism carried the day!

So then I snapped my fingers and said, "Let's have a cigar, the fattest one you've got, and fast. Plus a cocktail for my fiancée," pointing to Blondie, "and a real one this time." I was laughing while I said it, but with a snarl to show I meant it. He was back in no time with a whole box of cigars. I took two, tossed one back on the bar and said, "It's yours, Mac," for which he thanked me kindly if not quite from the bottom of his heart. "Anyway, don't eat your heart out," I went on cordially, stripping the cellophane off my big fat cigar. "Cool is in now, and after all, we all made our little slips in the last big war."

I bit hard at the tip of my black Havana and spit it out as far as I could, just like I'd seen the gangsters do in American flicks. It plopped right into Blondie's glass which had just been refilled.

"Don't worry, tulip of my eyeballs, rosebud of my fly," I said and emptied the glass out on the floor. I nodded to the bartender who sprinted over with the bottle.

"What do you say, Hero? Want to make some love?" Blondie was pinching my arm while she put her question to me. I studied her for some time, making a thorough survey. She was a good piece, big and with plenty up front or at least what looked like plenty. A nice, tough face

3

with not too much make-up. She looked broad and firm and in her blue leather outfit and bright red boots she looked born for bed.

"How much?" I asked in my business voice.

"Fifty, and I'll take care of the room."

I took my big Havana out of my mouth and sneered, "Blow it. You got a golden cunt or something?"

I wanted her but not for fifty francs. That wouldn't leave me much to get back to Holland on.

"Look," I said, "for fifty I could screw my way up one side of rue Saint-Denis and down the other with everybody's grandmother thrown into the bargain. Anyway, how do I know how good you are? You look great with your clothes on, but flat out with nothing on you've only got two holes, don't you? Twenty. That's my limit."

"It's the union," she said slowly and thoughtfully. "They won't let us work for less than the minimum. But I like you. You're going away, and maybe I'll never see you again, and I might have missed a big chance with you. They say boys back from the tropics have a lot saved up. So what say we have a few more drinks, and I'll have a bite to eat, and then we take off and make up for lost time?"

"A girl after my own heart," I said. "A few more drinks and then I'll let you see what I've got. Or feel it, I mean," I said, quickly correcting myself.

The deal was made, and the bartender filled up our glasses again, and I said, "Have one on me, Mac," thinking one more drink to pay for wouldn't make much difference.

Blondie and me made a cozy couple. Which didn't much please the little brunette who'd tried to interest me at the start and who sat there now pouting and staring off into space. I puffed a yard of smoke into the stack of her hair and when she suddenly focused on me with a mad look in her eye, I said, "What are you having, dear?"

She didn't quite know what to make of that but she said she'd like a cognac, so I ordered her one through the smoke clouds.

"Live and let live," I explained to Blondie.

Every once in a while new chicks came in but none worth looking at. They stood by the glass door fishing for men walking past on the sidewalk. A pimp would come in every once in a while too, shyly make his way over to a table with his whore, order drinks, sit for a while drinking— and then take off with or without her. A trio of gorillas had come in whom everybody there seemed to know. Noisy, big, wearing leather jackets, their hair and their mustaches slimy with brilliantine.

Before they could start playing games with me I stood a drink to the biggest and ugliest of the bunch—a pock-marked guy with a face like a

4

baboon and a frayed fringe of blond hair on his upper lip and a set of the worst crossed eyes I'd ever seen. He'd already given Blondie and me a nice bloodthirsty stare. But my standing him a drink melted his primitive heart. Got to be smart, I thought. Only one suit to my name, and I want to show it off in Amsterdam.

When I'd had enough of that place, I told Blondie I thought we should clear out.

"By the way, what's your name anyway?" I asked her. I thought I should know the name of what I was going to be laying it into soon.

"Annie."

"Lovely name—Annie. Must be nice to be called Annie. My mother's name was Annie. Small world, isn't it?"

"Oooh-la-la!" she said. "Don't turn around. Look. One of my tricks just came in. I had a date with him tonight."

I looked over my shoulder. A huge punk was shuffling in on blue suede shoes. His hands as big as shovels, he was headed our way. Sitting down on the other side of Blondie, he started talking to her in a low voice, just low enough for me not to hear what he was saying. Suddenly they were arguing. He wanted her to come with him. When she refused, he snatched up a glass and smashed it against the counter, then swept the tips-saucer off the counter. Annie was trying, with no luck, to calm him down. "He wants me to go with him," she said, turning to me. "What do you want to do? Come back tomorrow?"

I stepped back from the bar. I was furious.

"Well, what do *you* want?" I said. "Me or that thing?" And I looked at the giant as if I wanted to flush him back down where he came from.

"With you, naturally," she said.

That settled that. So now I have a good piece of ass to look forward to, I thought, and I'm not going to let it go without a fight. "Something wrong, mister?" I said to the giant and at the same time let him have the syrupy Cointreau right in the eyes. Yelling, he reached for his eyes with one hand and swung at me blindly with the other. The whores were howling all over the place. The bartender was making an end run around the bar with a stick in his hand. I had already loosened my watch band, and now the silver was stretched tight over my knuckles. I got in one fast slash at the bastard's face, leaving a long white stripe that suddenly turned red with blood. He screamed, then grabbed me by the throat with his enormous claws. I could hardly breathe. Even though Annie was pounding him hard with an umbrella now, he wouldn't let go. "That's what you get for being gallant to ladies," I thought while I struggled to break his grip. Then Cross-Eyes, my good old baboon, jumped the giant from behind and got *him* by the throat.

"Lay off my buddy!" he screamed. "You mess with him, you mess with me!"

He gave Jumbo a few solid punches on the back of his head. Jumbo let go of me. He staggered back. Like an arrow from a bow, my hand shot out in front of my body and into the giant so hard I almost passed out. Cross-Eyes and his pals took over from there. Behind the bar again, the bartender was clubbing out at whoever he could hit. Cross-Eyes was still swinging like a madman but, owing to the weird fix his eyes were in, he kayoed a few innocent bystanders. His friends were helping him out, and before long the place was a mass of tangled, fighting, screaming people. Bottles and tables were flying through the air, the whores stabbing away with the tips of their umbrellas.

"Let's go," I said to Blondie. "Let's get out of this place. I hate violence."

148

The sleepy clerk at the hotel was a Dutchman. I could tell that because when I signed the register Jan Janszen, born April 20, 1940, Amsterdam, he smiled in recognition. When we found out we both came from the same city, we introduced ourselves gaily. Fellow countrymen far from home. He went to a hotel school and was putting in his apprentice year in Paris.

In Dutch, so Annie couldn't understand, I asked him what he knew about my fiancée.

"She's good," he said. "Never had any trouble with her. And that says a lot. Every other day, murder or manslaughter. Some of those pimps'll steal the dirt out from under your nails. The Yanks, especially, get robbed every time."

While he was handing me the green rubber pear with the key on, I whispered, "Tell me. How do you say sixty-nine in French?"

149

It was a dark room with a colossal bed. Red roses on the wallpaper, dark red velvet curtains. Annie removed her blue jacket and hung it up on a peg next to her umbrella. I felt like it looked. As a matter of fact, I was so hot I'm surprised the sheets didn't catch fire.

"Come on," I said. "Off with that cowhide," and I was out of my own clothes in no time. Naturally I hung up my suit nicely. My mother had taught me to do that. Otherwise, wear it three times and it's only fit for the ragman. Stark naked, I threw all the blankets onto the floor and jumped into bed. I left the lights on. I wanted to see what I was doing.

When she was in the bathroom, I wedged a Bible I found in the night table in behind the mirror that faced the bed. I tried it out; I had fixed it just right. The white surface of the bed was fully reflected in the big mirror. The Lord willing, I'd have a great night.

While waiting for her to come out of the bathroom, I lay there twisting my pubic hairs into curls. Then in she came, wrapped in a cloud of exotic perfume. She had taken her sweater off and put her leather jacket back on so I could only see half of her huge bosom. A very erotic sight. And nothing phony about the half I saw either. No falsies. Not this one. At the foot of the bed, she stopped and struck an inviting pose.

"What do you think of them?" she asked and with one hand she reached in under her jacket and brought out one very large tit. She displayed it proudly. The stiff, light pink, pointed nipple was aimed straight at my mouth like a cannon.

"Not bad," I said. "Not bad at all." I was lying relaxed, my hands folded behind my head, trying to act nonchalant, though actually I was about ready to jump out of my skin. I hadn't seen boobs like that for ages. But you have to keep your cool.

"Pretty small, huh?" she teased.

"Oh, they're not as bad as all that," I said. "Shape's nice, but I've seen bigger in my day."

That made her a little angry, so she snapped back, "If I ever catch a broad with bigger ones, I'll cut them off!"

They were tremendous. In the Tit World Series they came off on top. Compared to these whoppers, Anita Ekberg had two pimples. Cunningly, she kept her jacket half closed so I couldn't quite see the whole works. Then suddenly she jerked it back and lifted both breasts up with her hands, pushing them out. A double-barreled erotic thrill!

"Darling," she said, "for another ten francs, I'll take it all off."

"Oh no you don't," I said. "We made a deal and we'll stick to it. Business is business."

"Five," she said, still trying.

"Not even five," I said, "but look, I've got an idea. You give me ten francs back and you can keep your boots on. How's that? For all I care, keep on everything except your panties."

She looked puzzled. Then she said, "I've got something very special. Something I only use with men I love. Something very nice. But it costs a little extra."

7

Out of her shiny crocodile leather purse she took a big wooden prick. It was a fine piece of wood carving, that glistening purple monster. She swung it back and forth temptingly in front of me.

"Oh come on," I said impatiently. All this bargaining was starting to get on my nerves. "Give me all or nothing. After all, I got you out of that fight, didn't I? And anyhow, I'm just a poor soldier left standing at attention all alone."

With a laugh, she threw me a kiss, flung her jacket onto the floor and knelt there still in her boots on the side of the bed. She wriggled her shoulders and the mountains of flesh dangled and swayed. They came down practically to her belly-button they were so big. Then slowly, her tight leather skirt slipping down over her hips and thighs, she edged closer to me. My mouth was watering. She let her breasts brush over my belly and then started pressing down. What sweet torture as her fingernails scraped and clawed their way over my skin.

Then she lapped up my cock between her bright-red lips, and I couldn't help thinking of the song "Tea for two," while her lips moved up and down along my cock, slow at first, then faster and faster. For at least a quarter of an hour she lay there tickling and fondling my balls until at last I let out a triumphant yell.

"Hosanna on high!" I roared.

"What's that, honey? A poem?"

"Yeah," I said. "By Voltaire."

"Beautiful," she murmured and started in again.

When it started to hurt a little, I whispered to her that my balls weren't lollipops, but there was no doubt about it, she liked to see me suffer. Since I didn't want to come, I kept thinking of the dirtiest things I could, like vomit, vomiting people, gory car accidents, oysters. I wanted this to last for at least another couple hours.

"Hey, wait a minute," I said, and, bending over, fought a shoelace out of my shoe. I gave it to her to tie around my balls. Like that you can go on for hours because the sperm can't get out. It hurts a bit because the sperm's trapped inside struggling to get out and your prick can't relax.

While I lay back for a second, exhausted, she stood up and squirmed out of her skirt, letting it slip to the floor. With her dark blue net stockings held up by a black leather garter belt, she looked like a pre-war courtesan. There were tiny dimples on her butt, and her belly came out in waves around the belt. Her black panties had a cunt-slit embroidered on one side with a red rose. But the ass! That ass was a modern masterpiece! Her muscular, net-stockinged legs were unusually long for her torso.

I was speechless. I hadn't seen anything like this since God knows when. I thanked my lucky stars. To me, this Blondie was the embodiment of the French tricolor: the blue of the veins pulsing through her breasts, the white of her abundant flesh, the red of her vagina lips. She sat down on the bed, the soles of my feet up by her cunt, her booted legs alongside my shins.

With skilled fingers she then opened up the red lips of her cunt, her green fingernails contrasting sharply with the color of that tender flesh. Groping carefully, she opened it wide up and then let the wooden work of art slide in. She wielded the dildo expertly, in and out, in and out of her fleshy slit until ecstasy started making her shudder. In a German film this would have been the cue for a shot of flowing, murmuring waterfalls.

I couldn't take it any more. I wrestled my way on top of her and then in. I rammed away at her like a madman. With all that sperm shoving to get out, my balls hurt like hell. In the meantime she was coming in wave after wave. "More, more. Now! More! Oh darling, honeybun, sweetheart."

The leather of her boots was cold against my back, her garter belt digging into my belly. She just kept sighing and moaning from coming each time and clawing at my brown skin with her green fingernails. I suddenly couldn't take the strain and, ripping off the shoelace, shot off an endless warm stream straight into her.

"Oh sweetheart," she cried. "That's so good, so good, so good."

Carefully pulling the boots off her long legs, then undoing the garter belt, then slipping her stockings off, I nestled comfortably in the perfumed hollow between her legs. Entwined like that, we fell asleep after she had kissed and licked me all over and whispered and laughed: "You sure know what you're doing, don't you?"

"I sure do," I answered casually.

"Tell me you love me," she sighed in my ear.

She kept on biting my ear until I said it.

Why not?

150

I woke up early the next morning after a light sleep. I looked her over thoroughly. No doubt about it, she was one of the Creator's finest. Her Mount Venus, the largest I'd ever climbed, was luxuriantly overgrown with dark blonde hair and jutted up like a boulder under the surf. Her breasts were so large they lay next to her on the sheet like two separate bodies, their big pink nipples pointing expectantly upward. Then she woke up and looked at me with her pale blue eyes. I thought she was very beautiful.

Through the closed windows I could hear Paris waking up too. "Let's get up and get some breakfast," I said.

We dragged our weary bones out of bed. While she was making herself up in the bathroom, I couldn't hold my piss in any longer, so I practically filled the bidet in the room. Then out she came looking as fantastic as ever.

I felt very proud walking down the street with her, all the earlybirds on their way to work turning around to stare or whistle. We stopped in at an American-style self-service place for a hamburger with onions, mushrooms on toast and a Coke. We were both starved.

We decided we'd spend the day together. It was great weather, fall weather. We strolled through the Luxembourg Gardens, sat on a bench, watched the pigeons pecking away at the bread crumbs. We poked around a big department store looking things over, then got into an automat booth to take some six-for-a-franc snapshots of ourselves. It felt very good to have her big ass across my lap in that tiny booth. Love was wonderful all right. I was crazy about Annie. No nonsense about her. Simple and honest, the kind I go for. Now that we were out of bed, she insisted on paying for all the R & A—refreshments and amusements. We spent the afternoon in a little art-film house cracking up at old Laurel and Hardy films.

Back out on the streets again, I suddenly wanted to have her again. We weren't far from my hotel and I wanted to see if Barry had made it there yet. Also I wanted to show her my room. So up we went and straight to bed until eight that night.

That's one of the nicest things in life, I think: when you're tired and a bit on edge from not having had enough sleep, to settle down in bed with some well-built sexbomb in the middle of the day in a strange city full of crowds and noises with the curtains wide open so the sun shines in and the sounds of the working city keep you half awake.

Then I walked her back to the brightly lit Pigalle region. While she went home to change, I stepped into a nearby amusement gallery to try my luck at pinball and a game of automatic poker. In three shots I'd picked up a present for her: a shabby little teddybear. We had a drink together at the bistro and I had some French fries at the Place Pigalle and then it was time for her to go back to work.

I had her phone number. She had mine.

151

I went back to my hotel late that night. On the spring-busted couch in the hall, his knapsack tucked under his head, there lay Barry, fast asleep.

He was hungry and thirsty, so we took off for a sidewalk café where we sat eating sandwiches and drinking beer while we told each other what we'd been up to. All of a sudden a familiar figure walked by, a guy we thought was off in America studying music on a scholarship. But there he was—Piet Ijsbeer, the pianist, flat-broke in Paris, making the rounds looking for work in nightclubs. He said he'd finally found a job that was supposed to begin the next night, accompanying an American combo at Le Chat qui Pêche.

We celebrated our reunion by putting away more whisky, beer, and wine than we could hold. We boozed our way through the night in all kinds of flea-ridden Algerian bars and nightclubs. We wound up, our money gone, drunk as a trio of one-legged owls. Piet Ijsbeer was staying at another hotel. We walked him home, then he turned around and walked us home. Through the deserted streets of Paris at dawn, the three of us walked arm in arm singing at the top of our lungs. My hotel was on a corner above a Chinese restaurant, the entrance on the side. Piet passed out right in front of the hotel, stretching out on the pavement staring up into space with a dazed look in his eyes. Barry and I tumbled into the lobby. The nightclerk didn't seem very glad to see us. And then Barry pitched over in front of the desk, just managing to wind up on the couch.

"La clé de la chambre seize!" I roared and, clutching the rubber pear with the sixteen carved in white, I staggered upstairs.

My room was on the first floor, overlooking the street. The window was right over the corner where we'd left Piet gazing up into space. I thought I'd better check up on Piet and tried to open the windows. They stuck for a minute, then opened so fast I sailed right out after them, over the balcony rail and down to the sidewalk. I rose slowly, feeling no pain, and lumbered back into the lobby.

Barry and Piet were sitting side by side on the couch. Once again I asked the clerk for the key to number sixteen. He blew his top, said he had just given it to me a minute ago, and who did I think I was. I hiccuped, aimed a finger heavenward and finally came out with, "What the fuck? Can't I leave by my window if I want to?"

152

Those were the Laughing Roaring Howling Days. With no money and no food, we tried to sell whatever we had, including some things I'd invested almost a year's income in. No luck. And I'd hoped to make thousands of guilders off that stuff. Then we planned, down to the last detail, to break into the place where a young Dutch actor was staying, clean him out and beat it. Another fiasco.

So then I put all my hopes on the return of a female Dutch painter who had a studio in my hotel. She had the art-world figured very nicely. She painted imitations of Abstract masters like Alechinsky and Appel and, at the same time, bought her way onto the staff of an avant-garde magazine. Her father was a filthy rich nylon stocking manufacturer in the east of Holland who was worshiped by many moderns as a collector and big-shot philanthropist. He was the one who promptly footed the bills for whatever quasi-revolutionary ideas his daughter wanted to publish; he also was a steady customer for the works of her various teachers. Thus did his darling daughter purchase that fame and glory she craved in her career as an artist. My idea to wangle some cash out of her was to give her a few personal hours of instructions—with the flesh brush instead of the paint brush. Another fiasco. She didn't show up.

Barry and I felt the call of the Fatherland. We had to get back. I tossed my suitcase out the window one night, Barry and Piet caught it, and off we went in Piet's old jalopy to hunt up a ride in Les Halles. The driver of a meat truck from Holland said he would take us along—for twenty guilders.

We fasted the whole trip—nothing to eat, nothing to drink—and made it over the Dutch border the next evening. When we told the driver we couldn't pay for our trip, it was too late for him to do anything about it except rant and rave and drive us to Rotterdam, where we called up old friends who brought us the money to pay him off. We waited for them at the Café de Fles, where we sat with our sulky driver filling ourselves up with pop and beer.

Anyway, we were back in Holland. Barry took off for Amsterdam; I stayed on in Rotterdam. A few days of peace and quiet after all the strain.

153

When I was a kid, I used to sneak into the "For Adults Only" movie matinees. The bosoms and legs of Ginger Rogers, Jane Russell, Zsa Zsa Gabor—I adored them. I used to collect pictures of all the stars, and I had a mammoth collection of Doris Day. Football players and Olympic champs didn't interest me at all. I traded their pictures for my heroines of the silver screen.

After school let out, and on my free afternoons, I used to work with a fish peddler. I stood there in a rubber jacket twice my size selling fish, dill pickles, and French fries, selling mackerel, shrimp, codfish, red herring, pickled herring, salt herring, and more dill pickles.

"French fries with mayonnaise and one dill pickle!"

"Pickled herring and onions!"

"Mackerel and fresh French fries!"

*When school friends came by the stand, I let them have the works: "Step right up for dee*elicious *and I mean dee*elicious *red herrings. Two for a quarter. Not for ten guilders, not for five guilders, not for one guilder but for only twenty-five cents, five five-cent pieces, twenty-five pennies, one little quarter! You there, lady—tell me, were they good yesterday, were they dee*elicious *yesterday, weren't they the best you ever had? All right, you kids. Away from the counter. You're just blocking the traffic."*

I had a knack for business. I soldered a silver ten-cent piece onto a cheap copper ring and wore the ten-cent piece on the inside of my hand. I'd count the change out on the palm of my hand before handing it over and always come out ten cents ahead. I pocketed the ten I saved because I thought I'd have a fish stand of my own someday.

After supper I'd go around collecting old newspapers, piling them into what was left of an old baby carriage. I'd tear the papers up, page by page in halves and sell them to the fish peddler for five cents a pound. If we sold them off to another peddler, we'd pee on the pile first, then cover up the wet sheets with a stack of dry paper. It weighed more that way. After all, during the war the guys in the black market pissed all over the bales of tobacco and wound up rich. Why shouldn't I?

When the first cigarette machines got to Holland, they hadn't perfected them yet. Every evening I had to go out to pick up a pack of Bond Street or Miss Blanche for my mother. I quickly discovered that for the price of one pack you could get two if you pulled two knobs at the same time. Pretty soon I was going with a broomstick stuck up under my jacket. With a broomstick you could work the whole panel—eight packs for the price of one!

You could fish all kinds of good things out of an Automat with just a quarter on a piece of string: salads, croquettes, meat balls, chewing gum, peppermints, chocolate bars, egg rolls, sausages. Our street gang. The Red Bulls, made the Automat a dangerous place for anyone else when we were there. We scared off prospective customers and then had the whole place to ourselves. Since fishing with a quarter never failed, we would have ourselves a feast and then eat cookies or candy all the way home. We couldn't resist playing a practical joke every once in a while—like putting pebbles in the meat balls and putting them back in their cage again, or taking a bite out of an egg roll and, after covering it up with the wrapper, putting it back for the next guy.

I had my own circus. Circus Matador. Friends down the block were the horses and lions; I was the manager and lion tamer. Dressed up in rags and blankets and wearing colored masks cut out of shoeboxes and me with an old bowler hat on and a big black mustache, we used to take off on our free afternoons for the blocks where the rich people lived.

We'd put up our tents in an empty lot, stacking up orange crates and throwing blankets over them. Then I drew a thick line in the sand which nobody could cross without paying. If they tried, they got a few cracks of the old cat-o'-nine-tails which my father had brought back from Africa and I'd found in the attic.

Besides managing the circus, I was also the Master of Ceremonies, star stunt man (I rode a bike with the handle bars turned around backwards), and fakir (the fakir Ayakkes Ahum was my name). For a penny kids could run across my chest or dance on my belly while I lay stretched out on the ground. When some of them went too far, the Manager would suddenly get up off the ground and let them have it.

154

After a long trip across various continents, I was home again. What *I* called home anyway. The whole city was home to me. I tried around at various girlfriends' houses. I rang Sandra's bell. The latch slid back from the lock, I opened the door and there at the top of the stairs was a big, black, naked Surinamer.

"Good morning," I said. "Sandra home?"

"Whadjawanherfor?" he growled, looking ready to barrel down those stairs any minute.

"Just tell her Jan's back from Spain, will you?" I said, and just then out came Sandra into the hall, acting as if she was delighted to see me, and the Negro plunged back into the room.

"Why didn't you write?" she whined.

"I just came to pick up my clothes," I said, "especially my herringbone suit."

If I'd ever remembered Sandra as beautiful, the memory was melting fast. Standing there in her nightgown, dirty, sloppy, her hair hanging down in long greasy strings, she looked a mess. Her dull, blank eyes looked very sleepy. It didn't look as if I'd be able to spend the night there.

"If you want me to tell Tommy to go," she said, "I will."

Which is what I call true love. Sandra was one of those girls who always had to have somebody in her—black, yellow, red, or white—it was all the same to her.

"Let's skip it," I said. "I've got some girls outside waiting for me and I needed some clothes so I said to myself why not drop in on my old fiancée?" Then, with my suit over my arm, I slammed the door behind me, cutting her off in the middle of a three-ring temper tantrum.

Still looking for a place to sleep, my next stop was at the house of an old girlfriend who worked at a delicatessen. Her mother opened the door. She gave me a cup of tea and a cookie while I sat waiting for Anita to get back from seeing a doctor.

"I thought you'd forgotten all about us," said her mother.

We talked—about the cat having kittens, about Anita's sister who'd married a Negro and gotten divorced three days later (all she wanted was to become an American so she could understand movies better), about Anita's brother who'd just been fired and was living off unemployment. "And," she went on, "then there's the baby. It can come any day now."

"Baby?" I said, stunned.

"Didn't you know? Anita's pregnant."

"Jesus," I said, "I almost forgot. I've got to be at the post office before three. A registered letter. Look, if I don't see Anita this time, give her all my best, will you, and I'll see you soon." I got out of there fast.

Well-dressed but flat broke, I roamed the streets like a stray tomcat. All the stuff Barry and I had planned to sell for a fortune turned out to be worthless. Most of it we gave to friends, a little we kept for ourselves, the rest went into the garbage can. Congolese tea, anybody? The market was flooded with it.

I spent the nights sleeping on bare floors in the houses of old girlfriends or in bed with vague acquaintances. One girl I wanted to find was Marina—an Indonesian ballet dancer, tall, slim, with light brown skin and beautiful blue-black hair. I'd gone out with her a few times before taking off for Ibiza and we'd had great times together.

I stood outside the ballet theater a couple of afternoons, waiting for her to come out. She never did. Then I got her old address from the management. I'd been to her place a few times when we first knew each other. Now I wasn't sure how to start things up again. Though I was crazy about her, all we'd really had together was a superficial friendship. What I needed now was love and warmth. And those Indonesian girls have plenty of both.

One chilly, foggy evening, I patrolled her block for hours hoping to bump into her on the street. I rehearsed everything I was going to say when we met. Then, working up my courage, I went up the stairs to the door of her house. A new nameplate on the door—a stranger's name and then her maiden name. Married! Why hadn't she waited for her true love Jan? Hadn't we always been meant for each other? Life is tough.

155

Beebee's mother, Anastasia, had a whole floor in a house on a canal near Hotel Mongolia and the Square. I lived there with Beebee. We called the place the Witch's Cauldron. There Anastasia, the Duchess of Leyden Square, held court, surrounded and waited on by her crackpot retinue. They were a pack of lice and mice who nibbled away at the fringes of the arts, junkies, hopheads, ether-sniffers, glue-sniffers, greasy-haired poets and prospective artists. Limping Gerry, Lunatic Lou, Soggy Noodle, Hairy Hans, and Lenie Hookhand lay or sat around on the floor day after day smoking their joints or playing chess or monopoly or bullshitting for hours about Literature and Art.

Beebee and I slept in a room in the back that was wallpapered with newspapers. Beebee was a little Simone Signoret in show business, a sweet thing and a good playmate. She had a good sense of humor and, fortunately, had worked out pretty well in spite of her mother. Anastasia, who'd passed fifty a long time ago, was an old bitch whose favorite sport was wandering around the house in dirty pink underpants smoking through a very long cigarette holder and followed everywhere by dozens of cats.

The Witch's Cauldron was a reservoir of misery. With a little help from Anastasia, broken marriages could be shattered beyond repair. She saw to it that lonely people got even lonelier. Everybody from the Square was welcome. If you had problems, if you didn't have anywhere to sleep, if you felt rotten, if you wanted to laugh or wanted to cry, or if you were yearning for "contact"—Anastasia was the woman to see. She'd see to it that whatever shit you were in you got in deeper. Giving advice and making trouble was her profession and in her line she was tops.

The house had a pungent stink all its own: uncastrated cats and cat shit. At night when we were trying to sleep, Anastasia would either be plastered and roaring or else barking away for hours with her deep asthmatic cough. Worshiped by the arty and the homeless, she reigned supreme as the Duchess of the Square.

An "artistic" couple lived in the annex—a professional Negro, American, and his wife, who fought every day like clockwork. Sometimes chairs came flying out of their windows, sometimes even the oil stove. Three times a week a repairman had to come to our room with a shaky ladder to put in new panes in the windows just across from us. Up in the attic, Heibel, a sweet kid with a beard and goat-hair socks, lived in blissful sin with the Soggy Noodle's wife Elise.

Every morning the Noodle would come stumbling upstairs and you could hear Elise telling him to get the hell out. It always ended up with the Noodle clanging around putting on water for tea and then angelically lugging three cups upstairs where Heibel and Elise were still snuggled up together in a sweaty bed. Tea was what the Noodle was hoping would win him back his wife's love. "We've all got to be nice to each other in this world," he would say.

But sometimes it got too much even for him. He'd sit on the edge of our bed bawling his heart out. "Write a book," I suggested. What else could I say? And he actually did.

Anastasia wallowed in that misery like a sow in mud. When the atmosphere was vibrating with hate and resentment she beamed with joy. She lived off Beebee's fame in show business and when she realized Beebee really liked me, she put me on her shit-list fast. I used to spend afternoons down in the Square with Barry doing nothing or talking about women or going to a movie. Once when I got back to our room in the evening I found Beebee sitting on the bed crying. Through the closed doors of Anastasia's apartment we could hear marching songs and dancing and all hell breaking loose.

"What's the matter?" I said. "What are you crying about?"

"Maumau's dead," she said.

"Maumau? Who's Maumau?"

"My cat. My favorite cat. He had such nice eyes."

"What happened? A car hit him?"

"No. Mommy butchered him."

One evening when I was alone there—the whole pack of them had waltzed off stoned and Beebee was out of town doing a TV show—the bell rang and Lenie came in. Lenie Hookhand. She was a sweet, dark-haired girl who'd run off from a girls' home and hid out in the city. When she was a kid, she'd played around with the cutting wheel of one of her father's meat slicers (he was a butcher in the south of Holland) and gotten both hands chopped off. She became what psychologists call a "problem child" and was put in the girls' home after getting pregnant at fourteen.

One of her hands was an iron hook; it was magnetic and sucked up all the silverware in restaurants. The other—bakelite in a black leather

17

glove—she'd had to leave behind in the girls' home when she made her getaway.

She was beautiful. The depressing thing was that most of the boys she liked couldn't stand the sight of that hook and as for the ones that wanted her just because of her hook, she couldn't stand them.

There was some cheap rum in the house. We finished that off. We soon started talking about sex and her problems.

They were singing a song on the radio:

When you hear me ringing my bicycle bell,
Then you know what I'm after, you know very well.

We were necking on the bed like mad. Rum makes you potent. It was a short trip we took together but very passionate and when we came back, I was in seventh heaven under a skyful of satin clouds. Then I let out a yelp. Lenie was digging a hole in my back with her hook.

156

At night Barry and I roamed the Square. We cadged money for beer and finally wound up in the Lucky Star, a great place always full of beauties and at least a few easy touches. Especially easy for a big tan lad whose hair had been bleached by the briny deep.

There was one girl I'd been crazy about after seeing her only once. Gorgeous, dark-haired, a young Ava Gardner. Well-built, voluptuous, motherly, with a beautiful broad face. Dressed in an expensive black leather coat, her hair long, blue-black, glistening. She was an usherette at the movie house on the Square and her name was Claudia and the only problem was she was married and had a baby.

I'd seen her the first time just a few days before when Barry introduced me to her on the street. It was the next Monday night when I came into the Lucky Star alone and there she was, sitting at the bar, lonely, only a Coke keeping her company, staring into nowhere. When I saw her there, my heart flipped. When she saw me, she smiled and motioned for me to come over. I went.

"Hi, Jan," she said. "It's good to see you. I was feeling pretty low."

I told her I didn't have any money, so she bought me a drink and then we danced and talked and I thought she was marvelous. When she said she had to go home, I walked back with her. It wasn't far. Saying goodbye to her at the door, I suddenly felt I was in love.

"Well, I'll see you around," I said nonchalantly.

"Yes?" was all she said then.

157

One evening when Barry, Piet Ijsbeer and I were all about to pass out at the Lucky Star, in walked Claudia with a girlfriend. I didn't have any place to sleep since I'd walked out of the Witch's Cauldron one night when Beebee was out. I'd gotten into a short nasty argument with old Anastasia, who started calling me a parasite and a pimp, and after telling her to shove it I left.

That's why, when the bars were getting ready to close, I was making my usual rounds trying to find a bed. With luck, a bed for two with a friendly chick, otherwise on the floor in a friend's house. I wasn't having any luck this time though. I'd tried several times and had gotten nowhere and was thinking maybe I'd have to ring the bell at the Cauldron after all. Beebee wouldn't let me down. Still, I didn't want to risk facing her nightmare mother again. Barry, who didn't know how I felt about Claudia, said, "Wait a minute. I'll ask Claudia if you can sleep there tonight. They've got a big couch where they let me sleep sometimes." He asked her, came back and said the answer was yes.

Just before putting the key in the door, Claudia said, "My husband's not in, Jan. He's gone to Paris for a few days." I don't like to break up a marriage, but all I thought then was "aha!"

I was madly in love with her. With the way she walked, talked, laughed, and looked. She lived in a large dark green room in the back of a house on the second floor. A big room with a big bed, a couch, a kitchenette and, in the corner behind a red-and-white striped curtain, a crib.

"Sssh," she whispered, finger to her lips, "the baby's sleeping."

We tiptoed across the room, and she put on water for tea. Watching her move, I thought, Cremer old boy, it's high time you either got married or settled down with a woman. You need a home, otherwise you'll be shit out of luck.

She got sheets out of the linen closet and took a blanket off the bed. I lay down on the couch. She got into bed, then turned out the light. We lay with half the room between us holding our breath, each waiting for it to happen. I wanted her badly. Everything she did, the way she did it, the way she looked, made me want her. Why is it, I wonder, I always fall hardest for women who are either married or about to get married?

Claudia coughed. I coughed back. Like little children. My heart was thumping like a clock gone mad. I was afraid she would hear it. To cover the noise, I started breathing heavily as if I was fast asleep.

"Jan?" she suddenly whispered.

Her voice came out of the pitch-black dark.

"Jan, are you asleep?"

"Mmmm?" I mumbled as if I was just waking up.

"If you're not comfy there, you can sleep with me here," she whispered, "but just like brother and sister."

My heart was in my mouth. Feverishly I scanned the situation from all angles. Seconds of thought that seemed to take forever. I wasn't sure what she thought of me or how she felt about me and I didn't want to break up her marriage. Though we'd sometimes talked for hours about other things, we'd never talked about how we felt about each other. And I didn't want to just pile on top of her, have intercourse with her, and then drop her. Or have her drop me. I lay there, torn.

If I said I was all right on the couch, maybe I would miss my chance and feel like a cretin the next day. If I got into the bed with her but didn't touch her, I'd feel just as stupid. But if I got into bed with her, there was always the chance that I might touch her and that I wouldn't feel stupid at all, so that's what I chose to do.

I made my way across the dark room to where I guessed the bed was and banged my shins against the coffee table. I swore at the pain shooting through my leg but kept it low so as not to wake up the baby. When I reached the big warm bed, I very carefully stayed as close to the edge as I could. And she stayed as close to her side as she could. Pulling the blankets up over her body, she wished me sweet dreams.

Then, "Lie near me," she whispered, "but just remember, I don't want you to make love to me."

We'll see, we'll see, I thought to myself and tried to fall asleep.

But if I do fall asleep, I thought, I might roll over and in. It was hard to keep myself from touching her. Then suddenly the bed began shaking. I heard her sobbing softly.

"What is it?" I said. "What's wrong?"

"I just feel so lonely and depressed all the time. It's like I don't know anybody at all, and yet I feel I've known you for a long time. Even though I'm married I feel so alone. And it gets worse. It gets worse all the time."

"I feel all alone too," I said, helpfully.

Feeling cautiously under the warm blankets, I lay my hand on her belly. Her whole body shook with sobs. Then she held my hand and caressed it and led it up to her breasts. Big breasts. I stroked her all over gently and now her hand passed down over my belly. Her caresses shot through my whole body. I slid closer and the next second we lay mouth to mouth. I sucked in her breath and kneaded her tongue with my lips. We lay twisted together, our hands exploring each other's bodies.

She moaned when I came inside her and when we came together again, she clawed my back, her sharp nails slicing me down from my shoulders to buttocks. In all my years I've never known a woman who gave me so much the first time. It proved we were meant for each other. Wrapped in each other, we fell sound asleep, tired but satisfied now.

It had been a long time since I'd fallen asleep with a woman in my arms. Everything about her felt warm and sweet. I didn't have the usual feeling of fuck and forget. I wanted to stay with her. I wanted to lock myself into her heavenly body. But I couldn't put away the sad, wistful feeling that she wasn't mine, that she belonged to somebody else, that she was married. There was a piece of paper somewhere that said she was somebody else's property. She could tell I was worrying about something.

"What is it? Tell me. I want to help you. With everything."

I mumbled and said no, really, nothing's the matter, but I still felt sad.

"Are you going to stay with me?" she whispered unexpectedly. "I want you to stay."

"But you're married," I said, "and we hardly know each other."

I could feel her body shake with despair.

"I want you to stay. I'm so happy with you. I want to stay with you. Forever."

"How can you say that?" I said. "I'm just a stray who gets to nibble a luscious bone whenever somebody throws one my way."

"I don't want you to be lonely ever again," she said. "If you want me with you, I'll stay with you."

"But dear Claudia, you've got a baby, a husband, a decent life, and I'm just a tramp. I mean it. I don't even know who I am. I'm still looking around for myself. I've been looking for years and I don't want to drag anyone else into the misery still ahead of me. Stay here and forget about me. It was very good, the two of us, even if it didn't last long. At least it did happen."

I grew glummer and glummer. I didn't know what to do. What had I got into anyway? Not just a woman and a baby but myself too. I convinced myself that by the next morning I would have forgotten all about what bothered me now and only remember what a fine night it had been. But I couldn't really convince myself. I instinctively felt something new had been born—a link between Claudia and me.

If I wanted to break that link, the only thing to do would be to take off early in the morning and stay out of the country again for some time. Out of the country at least I wouldn't see her or bump into her on the street. Amsterdam's one of those cities where, sooner or later, you're bound to meet everybody. So I would have to leave. Leave her behind and just hope she would come to understand why. Understand that a life together would be hopeless.

I kidded myself into actually thinking I could pass up this chance—a chance I'd been waiting for all my life, of having a woman, a mother, a house, of building our nest up in poverty. Hell, I thought, at my age to start feeling like that about a woman? To settle down? I resolved to forget all about it the next day.

Kissing Claudia's ear, I whispered, "Do you love me?"

"Yes," she said. "Tell me you love me too. Tell me you'll never leave me."

"Tomorrow I'll tell you anything you ask," I said. "But if I asked you to leave everything behind and live the miserable kind of life I do, would you actually do it?"

"Yes," she said, and she sounded very definite.

Worried but happy resting there against her soft warm body, I fell asleep.

The next morning I got up early, raring to go as they say. For once I woke up without any kind of hangover at all, mental or physical. Instead, charged with energy, ready for new worlds, a new life, a new future.

Claudia was moving around in her flowered housecoat that showed off her lovely legs. She'd already gotten her daughter up and the child was perched in her highchair. While Claudia was frying eggs for me, I fed the child her porridge. Breakfast was delicious. It really seemed as if we were off to a new start. That morning I too wanted to lead the serious life of a man with a wife and a child and a house and a car and the TV set that goes with it.

Her brother and sister-in-law dropped in for a visit. Her brother was a traveling salesman. Sanitary napkins was his line, and he'd brought along a supply of those plus plenty of diapers. I got up as if I'd just dropped in for a minute and said, "See you soon and thanks for the coffee," and left.

I spent the afternoon at the matinee in the place on the Square where she worked. The movie was a third-rate Italian film with lots of screaming, spaghetti, and sweaty undershirts. I went there every afternoon, and when she was ushering in the balcony, I'd sit in the balcony and when she was downstairs, I was downstairs too. When she passed by in the dark, she'd shine her flashlight on her face and float by with a smile for me.

I fell deeper in love with her every day. She looked great walking by in her uniform. She had a great sense of humor. An English whodunnit film was showing there once, and she took some people to their expensive seats who were rude and didn't tip her. So when they filed by her to sit down, she whispered to them who'd done it.

Late at night I'd wait for hours out on the Square for the show to be over, for her to come out. If it took too long, I'd saunter into the lobby and look at the pictures there. I could feel the glances of the other usherettes boring holes in the back of my neck. They knew what was going on, of course. Sometimes I was a little ashamed of myself for making out with a married woman, but then you only live once, I'd say to myself. It's bigger than the two of us, and you can't argue with fate.

158

One afternoon, Barry, Piet Ijsbeer, and I went swimming in the public pool. I'd just come out of the shower room when they started whistling and clapping like mad. I couldn't figure it out. Then I realized my back must be covered with welts where Claudia had clawed down my back. They sounded very jealous when they sang out in chorus, "You lucky bastard."

159

When Claudia was through work, I picked her up, and we set off in Piet's jalopy for Willemstraat. Nowadays every self-respecting artist claims he was born somewhere along that street. The bars there are always bursting with students and crackpots—middle-class kids pretending they're getting back to the people, watching how the Common People live. We tanked up on beer, danced the polka and the foxtrot to the pumping accordion of old Uncle Koos, and we swung to the records of Paul Anka and Sam Cooke.

Claudia, more in love with me every day, said she didn't ever want to leave me. I had no objections to raise to that. Her marriage was completely on the rocks and her husband was cracking up too. He was a nice guy who'd just graduated himself from the school of life on the Square. He wore a smile that looked as if you couldn't sandblast it off him—an eternal smile, and he did everything he could to hold onto Claudia. She'd had her fill of him though. He'd taken the first train back from Paris where he was working on a film after the landlady had phoned him and given him all the gory details about Claudia going out with "some provo in a blue suit" every night and sleeping with him. She said she could hear it and she probably could since she slept right under Claudia's room and probably climbed on top of her linen closet so she wouldn't miss a single twang from the bed springs. Anyhow, I'd made up my mind: I was meant for Claudia and she was meant for me. And she'd made up hers just the same. I didn't even look at other girls any more. I just thanked my lucky stars I had her.

We'd go out at night, just the two of us, and I'd bring her home late, and her husband would baby-sit the whole time we were gone. The situation was getting unbearable. Claudia slept at home; I slept at friends' houses on a rug by the stove. I was terribly jealous, especially when I had to take her home. I knew she loved only me and the only man she wanted to sleep with was me, but she was married and her husband did all he could to break the two of us up. I could understand that. After all, she was his wife and he had a right to fight for her. I fought too. I did all I could to win her for myself once and for all.

Lots of friends started getting nasty to me when they saw how serious things were. I felt guilty myself sometimes. I'd taken a wife away from that dear sweet boy who spent the whole day in some corner staring off into space or getting smashed or making scenes or bawling like a baby every hour on the hour.

Suddenly Claudia disappeared. Her husband had to get back to Paris and without any warning he'd made her come too. I felt terribly lonely and worried. Maybe she'd never come back to me. Though she'd sworn she wanted to stay with me, her husband had his chance now to talk her in or out of anything.

I spent those bleak days nervously haunting the Square. At night I sat in the smoky bars where Claudia and I used to go when we wanted to be together. I drank to get drunk. Every time the leather curtain by the door swayed, I hoped it would be Claudia coming in. A few days later I got a postcard from her. All it said was, "I'll always love you," which encouraged me. I waited.

One evening when I was out on the Square, I suddenly saw Claudia— Claudia and her husband. She flung out her arm, ran toward me and hugged me while her good little man stood off to one side staring into a bank window as if nothing could be more interesting.

"We've talked it all over. We're going to get a divorce. I'm going to stay with you. Do you want me to?"

"Yes," I said, and I meant it.

I wanted to work hard for her, to build us a nest of our own. We would get the daughter. She'd live with us. For Claudia's sake I was ready to become a Respectable Member of Society. I would work for her. I'd try to paint and then sell my paintings. After all, I'd already had more than fifty exhibitions throughout Europe and my pictures were hanging in countless museums. Or I would write a book. If I had to, I could even put in an honest day's work like everybody else. I could work on the docks if I had to—and get my thumb smashed when they let down the hatch and collect health insurance for months. I would show them all what kind of man I was.

I was very happy and the prospect of falling asleep every night next to Claudia's warm flesh was comforting. After all, winter was coming. What's better than trudging through snow on your way back to a warm room, a beautiful girl, and a good book? Nothing, and you can even leave out the book.

Those were hard times for us. Her sweet little man said if she wanted to live with me, he didn't want any waiting around. She'd have to clear out. Meanwhile, until we found a place to live, he'd take care of the baby.

Most of the time we had to sleep apart. I got her fixed up at an old girlfriend's house while I usually slept on the floor at friends' houses or in one of those sightseeing boats that were tied up at night in the canal just across from the central station. The only trouble there was I had to get up by six in the morning when they came to clean up.

I had to keep her away from her acquaintances and "friends." I knew they'd try to break us up. How could that Cremer do such a thing— make her run off and leave that poor dear boy all alone with the baby? We shot all over town asking people if they knew any place we could stay. We'd be at the office of *Het Parool* every afternoon at two when the late edition came out to look through the ads. I had some money coming in, enough to take care of a couple weeks' rent.

Then we got the key to the attic room where Claudia's sister had lived with her Negro boyfriend. That was before she ran away to be an elephant tamer with a circus. It was a cubbyhole down an alley in the center of town on the third floor in the back with a view of gray rooftops and TV antennas. That Saturday her husband brought over Claudia's clothes and the baby. It was time for domestic life to begin.

It was a low bare room about nine by nine. We put two mattresses down on the floor, one on top of the other, and that was our bed. What is a bed? The most important thing in life, the place where everything starts and everything ends. There was hardly any room for the crib. Then there was a dresser and a record player on top of the dresser. Her sister had left the record player along with the recording of *West Side Story*.

We lived there for weeks. Every time we'd just about had enough because we could hardly turn around in that place, we decided to stick it out. We knew that husband of hers—so sad and calm but at the same time so clever and determined—was just waiting for us to break up. He was convinced we would. "That kid off the streets," he used to call me, "he'll drop you as fast as he picked you up."

That's what everybody thought. Or that Claudia would drop me. But it didn't happen. There was a bond between us and even though we lived in abject poverty, we had a fantastic time together. I had to make sure there was a bottle of milk every day for the baby, and as for us, we got along on a bite here, a hamburger there. Sometimes I managed to pry

25

loose some cash from friends after long arguments and making all kinds of promises. Then we had a feast—home-fried potatoes, steak with relish, a pitcher of beer.

We loved each other; that was enough. No poverty, nothing, could come between us. We had each other and that's what we lived off. Two very mixed up kids had finally found each other. We had fun, we laughed a lot, sometimes we laughed until our sides split just from looking at each other across a bowl of porridge and water. So this was the great life normal people lead! It seemed pretty meager to me sometimes.

Sometimes it got too rough for Claudia. As a married woman she hadn't had a luxurious life, but it had been comfy enough with her own spending money, enough to eat, nice clothes. And from all that she'd been dragged off into a dark hole not much bigger than a jail cell, heated by a stinking oil stove, where there was hardly enough food to keep her baby alive. That could be too much for anybody to take. Still, she had me and that was enough for her. Every day I loved her more. She never let me down and through thick and thin we shared whatever we had.

There was a junk shop on the ground floor of our place and next to the junk shop a delicatessen. All those good smells came right up our staircase—the smell of meat. Every day I had to haul the baby carriage up and down three narrow flights of stairs. The guy who rented us our room was a friendly old Communist who read the party paper *De Waarheid* and smoked cheap Cuban cigars. Red lived right under us and let us use his kitchen. Saturdays he'd give Claudia money to buy our groceries. She cooked. We could eat with him if we felt like it. Simple food—usually potatoes with cabbage or else carrots, onions, and bacon—because Red wasn't rich. Long past sixty, he worked hard down on the docks and got up at six every morning—his tea-kettle whistle waking up the three of us— and, after drinking his cup of tea, off he went in the dark to the harbor.

You could tell he was home in the evening by the smell of cigar smoke. He was a lonely quiet man. When we spent an evening together— eating, having a glass of beer, playing cards—he'd always start talking about Communism sooner or later. He tried to convert me. On the faded flowery wallpaper of his little room, between pictures of his late wife (a stout woman wearing the old-fashioned costume of Zeeland) and of his children (who'd all emigrated to Australia), hung big photographs of Stalin and Lenin against a background of the Red flag. All the money he didn't need for himself he gave to the Party.

"They can use it," Red said. "As long as I have a good cigar and square meal a day I'm satisfied. What more do I need? I'm old. I've had my good times. I've seen everything. But if you want to know what the real thing is, it's Communism, hey—Communism. Those pigs riding around in their big American cars! Capitalism—it's a plague in this country. One of the richest women in the world, our queen. And old Wilhelmina, so rich it was coming out her ears. Prince Bernard, stinking rich. And the workers? We work our ass off just to keep those big shots stuffed with caviar. We work our hands to the bone and what for? For nothing, that's what.

"Look at our government. A bunch of dummies stuffed with straw that couldn't hammer a nail in the wall but went to all the right schools, come from all the right families, all holy as hell on Sunday at least. They pull a few strings and there they are, the half-assed bunch of them, sitting together in the Cabinet. They've all got their fingers in the pie. They all go home in their Cadillacs and then sink down in a fat easy chair to smoke a cigar that would cost a man a full day's wages, and then tring-a-ling, pull the string and in comes James the butler. Champagne, James, and caviar. Who pays for it? The workers pay for it, that's who!

"You take Smurf, for instance, that fool with a mustache. He can't even tie his own shoestrings without making a mess of it. And what does he do for us? For the people? Off he goes, a new trip every week. Smurf in Indonesia dancing with the Papuans in a pair of shorts. Smurf in Africa with his arms around a couple of naked girls with lips down to their chins and holding spears. Smurf in America wearing a warbonnet and smoking a peace pipe. Smurf back in Volendam in his farmer's cap and wooden shoes.

"That's our representative abroad, and what do we look like sending a thing like that around the world? Not much. Still, he rakes it in all right, stacks of money. And what for? For acting like some king of the carnival, and with a face like that! You ever notice the suits he wears? Swallow-tailed coat and nice striped pants that must cost a fortune. And who pays for that, and all these trips he makes? We do, that's who.

"So after three months in the tropics with the monkeys and champagne, back he comes, steps off the plane at Schiphol with his big tan and his white linen suit, and what does he say on TV? 'No comment.' And most of the people think that's just great, but then our comrades from the Party come and want a little more information. 'Excellency,' they say, 'besides all that belly dancing you were doing over there, just what *were* you up to in the tropics, if you don't mind our asking?'

"And all Smurf can do when he finally does say something is let out a whole string of foot-long words in that solemn voice of his so that after about three minutes the whole country's saying, 'Sounds nice, but what's he saying anyway?' And, wham, before you know it, all your money's gone off to the tax man. And they get up all those statistics and charts to try to prove Smurf is the most popular man in Holland. Popular? My ass."

We had our little feast, drank our fill of beer and sometimes I even lit up a Cuban cigar. But I never got involved in a discussion with him. I file politics straight up my ass. When it comes right down to it, I guess I'm always for the winning party anyway.

160

I tried selling some paintings that were still left in my old studio. I didn't have much luck. Collectors and museum directors are generally a kind of art-pimp. Before taking off for Spain a year back, I'd taken most of my oil paintings, drawings, and watercolors to a well-known gallery. While I was away, the owner organized a "Survey of the Works of J. Cremer: 1956–61." It was a big success. He pulled in a ton of money and left the change for me. I was an awful businessman; the contract skinned me alive.

Anyway, all the critics agreed I had a lot of talent and maybe was even a genius. From my former enemies on the daily and weekly papers, suddenly nothing but the highest praise. The honey flowed like water and my paintings sold like hotcakes. From the Municipal Museum in Amsterdam to the Museum of Bagdad, it was the same story: Cremer, besides having a big mouth and being an Art-Provo (a term I'd coined in 1958), could also paint. I could have been dead and buried they were so nice to me. Even the Department of Education bought itself a series of my works.

Back from Spain, I went to the gallery (the first Dutch newspaper I'd seen in a year had a big spread of full praise for my style, the *Peinture Barbarisme*) to ask if any of that money he was making was mine. When I walked in, he nearly fell through the floor. It'd take him some time to figure it all out, but then surely I was leaving the country again soon, wasn't I? He was working hard trying to build my image up as a serious, hard-working artist, which was some job considering all the nasty things I'd said on the radio and TV in the past about art and anti-art, and art lovers and art critics don't forget fast.

Apparently they loved my work but couldn't stomach me. Even in this century the artist has to suffer. How could Rembrandt have known, when he cut his ear off, that he was going to be famous for those Tahitian women and ballet dancers he painted before he went blind? I sent off works to the municipal purchasing commission and, in desperation, finally started calling important private collectors. Who were they? Fat men in the tobacco business, fat men in wholesale clothes, fat men in the nylon stocking line.

"Hello? Is this Mr. Flit van de Fartwheel? This is Jan Cremer. I'm calling about that painting you wanted to buy last year for a thousand guilders. At that exhibition, remember? You were interested but thought a thousand a little too steep."

"Oh yes, of course, old boy. You mean that pink and black thing, if you'll excuse the expression? The tit-work? A splendid piece of work. Splendid. Yes. But priced too high. Fine mood in that picture. Very colorful too."

"Well, I'm hard up right now and I'd let it go for less."

"You would? How much less? You see, I'm in a bit of a squeeze myself. Just bought a Picasso and we're redoing the house."

"OK. For half-price. Five hundred guilders."

"That's a good deal of money and, as I say, I just bought a Picasso and we're having the house redone."

"How much would *you* say then?"

"Now don't get me wrong, Cremer. I think a great deal of your art but I simply can't afford more than, say, a hundred this month and another hundred next month and that's all. Just like to help you out, that's all."

"Well, Mr. Fartwheel, that's extremely kind of you. Even if you do sometimes have a hard time making ends meet, you're still a loyal patron of the arts, aren't you, Mr. Fartwheel? When can I bring it over?"

And I thought, that son-of-a-bitch millionaire counts out an armored truckful of bills for a scribble signed Picasso but picks up my pictures for no more than a big tip for him and then brags about it to his friends. Like: "No, no, wasn't easy to get him to part with it. Certainly cost me enough. Those young painters—much too conceited about their talent. Still, if you want it that much you can have it for what I gave him for it, but it'll hurt me to see it go."

Still, those hundred guilders are much better off in my pocket than in Fartwheel's stuffed wallet. After all, we've got to have bread and we can't make a meal out of canvas and paint. My time is coming, Fartwheel! And if there's no other way, then I'll screw your wife for you, since she's sexy and young and thinks artists are so very interesting, while you're out hustling crap in your gentlemen's apparel shops.

When I get home, there's a feast. The baby gets canned baby food, peas and carrots, applesauce, mashed potatoes, and a bunch of bananas. For Claudia there's a sweet-smelling bar of Maya soap, a carton of cigarettes, and a bottle of fine perfume. I give her twenty-five guilders for groceries and treat myself to ten packs of Van Nelle Strong Shag and Lucky Luke comics. Barry babysits while we take off for the movies—seats in the stalls at the Tuschinski—then off for meat balls at the Czech place in the alley, then up to the Square, where we dance at the Lucky Star and, finally, in a taxi, ride home. I buy a half pint of gin and a handful of fat cigars for our old friend Red, which I leave in front of his door. He brings the cigars back in the morning, won't smoke "cigars that have come from a capitalist's earnings," so I have a puff myself. I keep right on puffing even though Claudia's turning yellow from the stink and the baby's red from it, and I'm turning green myself. They cost fifty cents a piece, those cigars, and it's a shame to give them away. Never give anything for nothing—that's the rule I live by.

arty vermin and
kindred killers

161

I soon learned you can't live on love alone. The stomach complains. When the baby didn't get her food or milk, she yelled all day long. Since staying home was cozier and cheaper than going out for a walk (five minutes on those freezing streets and you wanted a glass of beer or a cup of coffee we couldn't afford), we stayed home all day bumping into each other every time we turned around in that small stuffy room stinking of diapers, porridge, piss, and stove. No cigarettes any more and nothing to drink but water or tea.

To set a good example for the baby, we were up bright and early every morning. The baby slept at the foot of the bed. We couldn't even pay the five guilders a week rent. Welfare didn't want to have anything to do with me, and I didn't want to beg from the government's commission set up to help artists in need. I hadn't fallen that low yet. After all, I'd written too many manifestos predicting the immanent death of Art and its whole crew of shriveled up, mustached, bearded, and bespectacled bunglers.

Red downstairs told me there was always work in the harbor and gave me the address of a contractor near the central station. I went down there that same afternoon, filled in a card and was given the address of a shipping company. I was told to report there early the next morning. Seven-thirty on the nose. There was plenty of work and, even as an unskilled worker, a good salary.

162

A clatter on the wood stairs woke me up. Red was coming to make sure I was up. Through half-shut eyes I looked at the clock. Six! I disentangled myself from Claudia who crooned softly and tried to keep me there beside her in that nice warm bed. I wanted to stay but work is work.

"I love you. You'll be back soon? I'll miss you," she crooned.

"I love you," I said. "Keep the faith. I'll see you soon. Goodbye."

31

I shuffled out the door and went downstairs still half-asleep in spite of splashing my face with cold water. Red and I had a cup of coffee together, and he lent me a thermos and filled it with coffee. I wore dungarees and a thick turtleneck sweater and combed my hair straight back so I'd look like a real dock worker.

We walked through the still dark, quiet streets to the place where he parked his motorbike. Sitting behind him on that sputtering thing on our way to the ferry, I had to laugh at myself. A month ago on a wonderful island with sun, grapes, honey, and loads of beautiful women, and now on the back of a motorbike, with stinking cigar smoke blowing back in my face on an ice-cold morning, setting off to work for a woman. The ferry over to work was packed. The whole boat smelled of Sunlight Soap and strong shag, and when it landed there was a sudden deafening noise as hundreds of cars and motorbikes started up.

Another ten minutes of jolting and we were at the docks. I said good-bye to Red at the gate, since he worked farther down. We'd meet each other at five, and I could save the bus fare riding back with him. It was getting light now. The sun was spraying her first rays out across the cold morning air still hazy with mist when suddenly the sirens cut loose with an ear-splitting blast. I was just on time.

Since I was a newcomer, I had to report at the registration office. We all waited in line until we were called into the little wood-frame office. About ten of us. Older men with stubble beards and patched clothes plus big kids my age or younger. I rolled a shag and waited my turn. The line got shorter slowly.

The man behind the desk looked up at me when I handed him the papers the contractor had given me. He opened a drawer, took out a sheaf of papers and carefully slipped in carbons between the sheets. When he was finally done with that, he asked, "How old are you?"

"Twenty-three," I lied as if inspired, because I remembered you got paid about half as much if you were under twenty-one.

"Married?"

"Married," I answered casually.

"Any children?"

"Three," I said poker-faced, and after glancing at me he said, "You didn't waste much time, did you?"

"No," I said.

"Unskilled worker, I see," he said after another glance at my application.

"Well, that all depends on how you look at it," I said, suddenly feeling sure of myself.

I had just noticed a sign tacked up on the wall behind him asking for welders and riveters and I thought since I was bluffing the whole thing anyway with all that about having a wife and three kids why not go all out? It might be cheating but it would make a big difference on payday.

"Actually, I'm a riveter," I said. "But I've been working on a tramp out in the Orient, and now the little lady wants me ashore because she's expecting another one soon."

"Where did you work as a riveter?" he asked.

"Well, let's see now," I said, racking my brains for the name of a shipyard. "Oh, at Wilton Feyenoord and Verolme in Rotterdam and in Groningen at De Ruwe, but that was all more than a year ago, before shipping out."

"Well, I don't suppose you've forgotten your trade. You're on as a riveter. Better pay for you anyway. And with all those kids, you'll be needing it," he said with a wink that should have cheered me up.

I thanked him, got my punch card and a requisition slip for work clothes, and he tore a page out of his notebook and signed his name to it.

"Punch in first, then pick up your clothes, then find Boss Blokker. Tell him you're the new riveter."

"Will do," I said, and left.

After sprinting over to the gate to punch myself in, I slowed down for my walk over to the clothes shed. Now that I was punched in, I was officially employed by the company and every minute counted. Every minute I stuck it out meant money for food and clothes. I was feeling pretty proud of myself. Off to work, just like that—while my father's old saying, "Work is for those who don't know any better," echoed faintly through my brain. What did he know about work? He never did an honest day's work in his whole life. He didn't know what he was missing.

Work—the greatest thing under the sun!

163

The area down between the buildings, the docks, and the ships was swarming with activity. Hundreds of men in blue or white uniforms were walking down the wharves in big gangs or small scattered bunches. Big green trucks with their tailgates down so you could jump on for a ride headed slowly down to the docks.

There were Swedish ships. Norwegian ships, German ships, freighters and coasters, tremendous works of iron art. One of the Norwegian ships was cut right in two as if a huge knife had sliced it up like a cake. Hundreds of midget men in white suits were scuttling around in the hull with pails, booms, or acetylene torches. With those sparks sputtering up all over the place it looked like a colossal fireworks display.

The place hummed and crackled with activity. This was industry, big industry—the hellish screams of big drills boring in, the noise of steel against steel as they drove holes in the sides of a ship, the thump and throb of hundreds of sledgehammers, the painters with their long-handled brushes tarring the barnacled rusty bottoms of seagoing vessels and painting them over with red lead, the rhythmic beat of the horde of men lined up on their scaffolds scraping the rust off in a shower of flaking paint, then brushing their scrapers off on their overalls.

It looked like a city all of its own—an Atlantis of Activity, but still above water.

A big beehive at work, and all over signs saying, NOT RESPONSIBLE IN CASE OF INJURY OR DEATH.

In the clothes shed I was issued a pair of blue overalls—since I was a riveter (most of the others were wearing white)—that were much too big for me. I tried on one pair after the other while the man behind the counter watched me distrustfully, and finally found a pair that fit. Then I got a pair of goggles, a pair of thick gloves, a cap, and a pair of rubber boots which I stepped into shoes and all. I was ready to go. Of course, I didn't know the first thing about riveting, but I did know what rivets were. I'd seen plenty of rivets in my time. When I shipped out, I saw them all over the steel sides of the ships and on the doors of the ship's brig too.

I finally found Boss Blokker, a middle-aged man in a gray business suit.

"I'm the new riveter," I said.

"OK," he thundered in the hoarse voice of church bass or a guy who shouted his lungs out at every Saturday night football game. He assigned me to a group. Hard-boiled types, all older than me. In fact, one of them well over sixty.

"Report to Dock F," Boss Blokker sang out, "then pick up where the asspatchers left off last week. Attach them to the left noselock and firm the downsnore good and hard. Just be sure the pisspong stays clear for the outgoing hump and the hull survey. Knijpers over here knows the way," and he nodded toward the senior citizen in our group.

"Absolutely," I said. "Come on, men. You've played enough pocket pool, let's get a move on." I thought, being in charge of a crew like that, I'd better show them what a regular guy I was, especially since they were going to have to teach me the fine art of riveting.

They all picked up what looked to me like miniature cannons, hung them around their necks, then took up all kinds of tongs, lifted buckets full of rivets, and off we went on our way to Dock F. The road dropped down to the dock along steep moldy green steps, then up we went across swinging scaffolds, shaky ladders, and big ropes into the hold. It was the center hold, big as a dance hall. Men were walking around in oil-soaked clothes with pails of sawdust and oil.

I'd worked in a harbor before. Cleaning out tankers. They dropped me down through a hole in the top. My job was to scrape the crusted oil off the sides with a putty knife, fill a pail with the stuff, which my partner then hoisted up and emptied. The mess inside was awful and the stink made your eyes and throat smart. The air was suffocating and the only light you had to see by came from a few dim lamps strung up in that huge iron cylinder. The trick was to stay down until your lungs were just about ready to burst. Then you scrambled up top and took an hour's breather.

The most dangerous part of the work was walking the catwalks inside the tank, more slippery than ice from all the oil. One slip and down you went for a ten-yard dive. I lasted a day. I could hardly breathe and spat my lungs out the whole next morning. Then I was put on another job which was even messier and naturally, therefore, better paid. With a rope around my waist I was let down between the inner and outer walls of the ship—a space not more than two feet wide. My job was to wrap cork linings around the pipes after dipping the cork into a pail of red hot asphalt. The cramped space, of course, didn't help much. It wasn't long before I slopped red hot asphalt all over one foot.

I got two weeks' extra pay, plus sick leave. I lived a glorious life of leisure, hobbling around with a cane, my foot all bandaged up. I felt sorry for those guys who had to do all that dirty work. They were mostly down and out, Spaniards, Greeks, Italians, willing to do anything for a wage that hardly paid for bread while the dirtiest work their bosses did was working their fat cigars out of their cellophane wrappers.

When we got to the place, we were supposed to start work. I casually asked Knijpers, "What system do you use here, anyway? A-quadrals or B-quadrals?"

"A-quadrals or B-quadrals?" he said blankly.

"Yeah," I said. "In Rotterdam we always riveted either B- or C-quadrals."

"Well now, I never heard about that, but this is how we do it here," and he picked up a big steel gun that looked more or less like a bazooka with a wooden butt and a trigger and a round disc on the barrel, and said, "Throw me a nail."

I figured a nail must be a rivet. There was an iron bucket in the hold with red hot coals and rivets, so I picked up the tongs and pulled out a glowing rivet.

"Let's have it," Knijpers said and he whistled. Instantly another pair of tongs shot out from around the other side of the steel wall.

Cautiously I gave the still glowing rivet to the boy who was in charge of bucking for the rivets driven into those hundreds of holes bored into the ship's side. Knijpers took his time, sat down, lifted the automatic riveting hammer like he would a machine gun, laid its snout on the rivet head, pulled the trigger and wham, in a deafening blast the spinning barrel had flattened the bolt flush with the steel.

"I see," I said. "Well that's what we call B-quadrals. Here, let me try one."

He handed the gun over to me. It weighed as much as two bazookas. "Throw me a nail," I said.

Knijpers whistled and the boy behind the barbecue flipped a rivet out of the bucket and down on the floor in front of Knijpers who picked it up, looking like the expert he was. When I tried to whistle for a rivet, all I got out was a soft hiss. It just didn't seem to be my day. When the rivet was set in the hole right in front of me, I aimed my hammer at it, holding it loosely and like an old hand, just as I'd seen Knijpers do, and then pulled the trigger.

The shock smashed me in the shoulder and back I shot for about three yards before landing with a smack in the sawdust. Knijpers and the rest of the crew were howling with laughter. I laughed too, but like a farmer with a toothache, as we say in Holland.

"You see?" I said, getting up and brushing off my overalls, "that's what happens when you don't hold the damn thing tight enough. Men," I went on, "I can't tell you often enough: when you hold it, hold it tight; hold it like it was a machine gun and you're out there fighting for queen and country. Hold it tight and don't let loose. Grab it like you'd grab hold of a sweet piece of ass on a Saturday night."

I turned to Knijpers, the old guy whose job was passing the rivets and who probably thought riveting was the greatest thing in the world (he was staring at the big machine in my arms as wistfully as a kid at Christmas looking at a department store window), so I said, "You really like riveting, don't you, Knijpers?"

"I'll say I do," he said. "It was my job for ten years, but now they say I'm too old for it, that's what they say up at the office. And those things cost plenty too. You break one and there's hell to pay."

"You know what?" I said. "I'm going to take that risk with you. I trust you, Knijpers, like I trust my own brother. Go ahead. I'll keep an eye out to see if anybody's coming and roll myself a shag. Go ahead," I said cheerfully. Live and let live, I thought.

"I'll pass you the rivets. But if a foreman comes around, you give it back to me fast, right? I don't want any trouble."

He gratefully lifted the heavy gun out of my arms. I even saw a tear in his eye as he took the steel giant up in his arms, like a baby. In any case I'd made an old man happy—my good deed for the day.

It was biting cold. After all, it was nearly winter. So I had to stay close to the fire to keep my hands warm. To keep the crew on my side I told one joke after another. Then the pain in my ears from all that drilling and hammering got so bad I decided I'd better see the doctor about a pair of earplugs. Knijpers warned me I'd better look after my eardrums; besides I'd punctured one once when I was a Navy frogman laying magnetic mines.

Fortunately I still didn't know my way around this huge industrial area so it took me more than an hour to find the infirmary. The doctor wasn't in; I decided to wait. I noticed some bicycles standing outside; all the bikes parked there were the same reddish brown color. When a worker passed by, I asked him what they were for. Company bikes, he told me, so I picked up the best of the bunch and took a spin along the docks, admiring the bustling industry of men working on ships.

It was a great bike, a Fongers, and I was riding (look, Ma!) no hands in no time. After I'd shot around all the buildings and sheds a few times, I put the bike back in its stand and asked if the doctor was in yet. Too bad. He was. He gave me two little rubber plugs to put in my ears.

As soon as I got back to my steel walls and men, the whistle blew. Noon. We knocked off for half an hour and I milled my way through the throngs to the canteen, had a muffin and a cup of coffee. Like a fool, I'd left my orange lunch box (with sandwiches) and my thermos (with coffee) in the locker room where my clothes were locked up in an iron locker which you couldn't get into until after work.

Knijpers sat down next to me. He opened his lunch box. Three sandwiches wrapped up in wax paper. He opened up the first one, took a look, mumbled, "Goddammit, peanut butter," and gave me half. It tasted fine. He took a long time getting his half down. Then he opened a second and swore louder this time, "Goddammit anyway, peanut butter again, every goddamn day, nothing but peanut butter!"

I thought, the old guy's right. Works his fingers to the bone, the least he deserves is something good on his bread, with his wife at home probably putting away a slab of roast beef. One peanut butter sandwich I could understand, but *two?*

When he opened his third, he really let loose: "God-god-god-god-god-god-*damn!* Wouldn't you know it? Peanut butter again!" I was as mad as he was; I could just see that fat fishwife reaching out at home for another slice of fresh bread and then stacking it with mackerel and sandwich spread and who knows what else.

"Knijpers," I said firmly, "I just met you today, but I admire your working spirit. You know what you've got to do? You've got to give that wife of yours a hiding she'll never forget. Nothing but peanut butter? It's mad! You've got to put your foot down, Knijpers!"

He looked over at me in surprise.

"What wife?" he said. "What foot down? What do you mean? I make my own sandwiches."

164

Those next few weeks were rough. The roughest part was getting up so early every morning and then that ride down to work on the motorbike. Still, I'd found a nice place at work where I could catch up on my rest. There were piles of bamboo mats in the hold and, after posting one of the boys as a lookout, I'd stretch out and fall sound asleep.

The others took turns in the afternoon. Or else we'd play cards between the packing crates and the bales of straw. Or we'd slip out for a cup of coffee on board one of the ships tied up at the dock. Though it was strictly forbidden to take any kind of reading matter to work, you could always wrap your lunch in a newspaper. I usually packed mine up in *The Laugh, Piccolo,* and *Lord Listers.* When I'd read them through, I'd pass them on to my men, my lads, my chums, my comrades, or swap them for whatever pornography they had on hand.

Dockworkers—they don't make better men than dockworkers. Good as gold. Honest. Never break open a crate of beer or whisky, even if they trip right over it. Always ready for a game of cards—an honest game or the usual kind, either one. They'll always give you a bite to eat if you're short, and if you're having a hard time on the job they'll lend a hand. On weekends, they invite you out for a game of billiards or bridge and you're always welcome for dinner. You can even bring your wife. Honest people, simple people, goodhearted as the day is long.

I hadn't been working there long when Boss Blokker gave me a word of warning. He'd noticed my crew was working too hard. Such things were not permitted. There was a work schedule and you had to keep to that schedule. If a ship came in for cleaning or repairs it brought in 50,000 guilders a day on docking charges alone. Well then, keep it there as long as possible—that's what the big bosses wanted. Every day another 50,000. Just for sitting there. Furthermore, if a job can be done by a hundred men in two days, then according to the bosses' schedule it has to be done by a thousand men in twelve days. Because over and above the docking charges the owners have to pay the salaries of the workers too. So what are the foremen there for if not to slow things down and make sure there are plenty of workers—those Common Men who never get paid more than 150 guilders, not much more than $40 a week.

The fact that *my* group was reprimanded says a lot. Most of the day we lay around on bamboo mats, playing cards, swapping stories. We knocked off early—at four-thirty. I spent hours gazing down at the waves slopping in or taking off to other ships to look for something to eat or drink or a good game of twenty-one. I provided Scandinavian seamen on duty aboard their ships with the addresses of "fokkie fokkie" girls and the best dancing bars along the Zeedijk. And picked up my small rewards in return.

I told Knijpers to take it easy. Riveting gave the old guy a kind of childish thrill. When the sirens went off at five, he'd be the only one still going; we had to yank the riveting gun right out of his arms. Sometimes we had to knock him down to make him hand it over. He was always the first one there bright and early in the morning. Even before the gate-keepers. Nice man, Knijpers.

I let three weeks go by before falling into the hold. Damned hard to do it right though. I fell in four times without anybody seeing me. The fifth time I tried, Knijpers noticed me down there and wanted to help me up, the fool. I was sent home on sick leave.

Adieu, dear docks. Adieu, comrades. I'll miss you.

165

A nice cigar-smoking inspector in a leather jacket arrived early one morning, filling our little room with his paper-fat briefcase. My plunge into the hold was no mystery to him and after two mugs of coffee and some Cuban cigars Red had left on his last visit, he filled in "Unfit for work for unspecified period due to accident incurred during working hours." He knew it was all so much bullshit. It was the doctor who gave me trouble until I said I had these strange pains in my back. You can't go wrong with them.

With the money I'd earned by my own hard work on the docks, plus what came in from health insurance, Claudia, the baby, and I had a good life. Instead of bread on bread with bread in between, we had potatoes with gravy, cauliflower, and steak. But Claudia spent money like it was water, so pretty soon we were back to counting pennies again.

One day I gave her the last twenty-five guilders to get a pack of cigarettes and a thimble. Those twenty-five guilders had to last us for quite some time. For at least two days, I figured; maybe even two weeks. When she got back a few hours later all she had left was twelve cents. She'd bought material to make clothes for the baby. It was bad enough that the baby already had more than enough dresses to clothe half an orphanage. What made it worse was that when the coffee pot fell over, Claudia mopped it all up with the stuff she'd just bought. So soon enough, there we were broke once again.

I didn't care. I could always pick up money when worst came to worst. In the meantime what I was after were the sweet juices of marriage. I wanted to find out all I could about that blissful feeling of living together with a woman. I took to it like a bear to honey. Claudia was some woman—big, broad, beautiful. Well-stacked, as they say. Not too much or too little of anything and everything right where it should be. A kind of star. Walking down the street beside her, I felt very proud as everybody turned around to stare at us. I felt at home next to her. And lying next to her body was great.

166

Anastasia was throwing a party for her birthday. Claudia and I were invited. The party was held in the bar where all the bus and truck drivers hung out. Everybody was there. Anastasia and all her court jesters. A grotesque bunch with their party hats and fake noses and tooters, all seated around a long table.

A busload of English tourists (buy one hundred-guilder suit from the Pant-King and get free: 1 return trip ticket + 1 rain hat) left their nearby table when our merry crew blew huge clouds of sneezing powder their way. But the British didn't abandon the bar immediately. Under the influence of crates of beer they intrepidly bellowed out British battle songs. When the chorus could no longer be heard over the explosions of sneezing, even the carrot-top chorus leader with the streaming red eyes gave up. The group took off, dragging along with them their Dutch driver who was crowing away, "En hee is a cholly koot fallo" at the top of his lungs.

It was a nice, folksy birthday party. Lots of old-fashioned fun, with stockings and panties being hoisted like flags. We had a good time and that's what counted. We were out on the town for once. Sitting at home all day in a cell filled with the smell of dirty diapers and a stinking stove gets on the nerves after a while.

Our baby-sitter was named Olivier. The young son and heir of a famous wine merchant. Olivier wanted to lead a Bohemian life of his own. Who was I to say no? So he looked after the baby while drawing up detailed plans for all sorts of unimportant protest marches: against A-bombs, or H-bombs, or any kind of bomb you can think of; against racial discrimination; even against other protest marches as far as I know. That was the way he spent the money Papa paid him to keep his nose out of his wines. Olivier was the guy behind most of those posters and pamphlets and newspaper ads summoning Youth to protest against some government or other, urging them to march to some embassy and either sit down or smash windows.

Since he picked up the bills, Olivier always led the parades. Our fart-faced literary friend Soggy Noodle was also sure to be up front except when he saw a uniform. Then the Noodle was suddenly very hard to find—way back with the stragglers somewhere, or up on the sidewalk lost in the crowd.

I joined in a march once. For Negroes, I think—the Washington March was going on then. They wanted J.C.'s name in the papers and besides I love Negro girls. The march got off to a great start. I held high one end of a banner reading:

FOR RACIAL EQUALITY

But after five minutes my arm hurt and after ten it was numb and then I lost all interest in any kind of racial equality. I'd already done what I was there for (reporters and photographers had seen me in the march), so I tapped an army-surplus coated broad ahead of me on the shoulder—a broad well known for her affection for at least the male half of that mistreated race—and said, "Hold this for me a second, will you? Got to tie my shoe." And in no time at all, there I was at the end of the line.

I was still shuffling along inconspicuously when we got to the Square where I saw a familiar-looking bar and disappeared behind the leather curtains to fill up on quite a few beers drawn cool and delicious straight from the keg.

The only time I really felt like protesting was when I was living in Paris and saw on the front pages of the Parisian papers that Caryl Chessman had been executed in spite of all efforts to prevent it. Reading those articles, I was stunned.

A bunch of artists and intellectuals at a meeting at the Coupole decided to march to the American Embassy to protest this shocking miscarriage of justice. The idea was, among other things, to smash some windows at the Embassy. I went along—brave, undaunted, and with a clear-set goal. But by the time we got there, I thought: how dumb could I get, and what do the people working in the embassy have to do with a decision made in some court in America anyway? So I threw away the stone I held ready for action.

It was when the procession had reached its peak and Holland's One and Only Cabaret Star was dancing around on the fake-Persian tablecloth with his prick hanging out that my Second Great Love (Claudia was my First) caught my eye. A lean freckled lass from the sticks; a country girl with thick blonde hair, blue eyes, and a turned-up nose.

She had come to the big city as a nurse to get over her Great Despair. Day after day she bravely steered her bike through the jammed city streets wearing her nurse's uniform. She was so proud of her nurse's cross, she'd show it to anyone. She came into the place where the big protest show was being held to get a look at—me, because I was *her* Great Love too.

As soon as I saw her something blossomed. It was Love without Words. It was Roses and Moonlight with violins playing. Day and night she wanted to be with me, but, alas, I didn't quite go for her suggestion that I leap off a roof near her hospital or throw myself under a garbage truck so she could take care of me in Ward B, and thus I weakened our relationship.

It turned into a brief but deep-rooted love and some of those roots still go on growing in my heart. Every time I saw her, something melted inside me, whether it was on the street or in the Lucky Star, where we'd seen each other the first time and where she smiled such a smile at me that I floated right up to seventh heaven and by mistake said "Hello darling" to Koos the bartender.

We ran into each other almost every day, and I was faced with having to come to a decision that would affect the rest of my life. Stay with Claudia and share my sorrow and misery with her, or start up a new future with Lucia? In a moment of great confidence she'd told me she "wanted to be somebody," that she'd had enough of nursing now that she'd got her cross. "Be a model," I advised her. Pretty, slim girls were in demand now that the type with a stack of blonde hair and a pair of thick sultry lips was going out of fashion.

"And," I said, "don't put on a lot of weight. Thin is in now."

Every time I saw her a warm feeling spread down from my throat to my stomach and prickles stabbed through my heart. This was love and I sang:

> *little lucie frisian lucie*
> *lucie from the low low land*
> *blonde of hair and blue of eyes*
> *hop on and we'll take all our rides*
> *together hand in hand*

A little verse I tossed off in a rush. I played the old tune "Juicy Lucie" for weeks until early one morning a Negro banged on our door and came to pick up the record player and the *West Side Story* record because they were his. He was Claudia's sister's ex-fiancé, just back from Italy, where he'd been dancing as one of Elizabeth Taylor's slaves in *Cleopatra*.

167

One evening Barry got into a fight with the doorman at a night club. The three of us had gone out together. We'd had some beers at the Lucky Star where, my heart suddenly thumping like mad, I'd seen Lucia. She was standing at the bar surrounded by a pack of prim little snots (the future stars of the Dutch stage) and kept looking over at me with a sweet wondering look in her eyes. She couldn't understand why I stayed on with Claudia.

After Claudia and I left for Spain, I got a letter saying Lucia had married one of those sad-assed lads who speak such exquisite Dutch—an effeminate ballet dancer who, if you looked at him through dirty glasses from far enough off, looked like me and who later went on the stage because his two other brothers were actors too, and because he enunciated his words so beautifully. Also, with all three of those brothers taking speech lessons, they must have gotten a special reduction.

Before making up my mind to share my life for a while anyway with Claudia, I was terrifically mixed up. Lucia was a sensible, sweet kid, lots of fun, with plenty of guts and a good sense of humor, but she was also a climber who wanted to be the *the* Belle of the Ball, while Claudia—warm, feeling, and motherly—represented to me the peace and security of a home. In the end, it worked out very well: I was happy, Lucia was happy, we were close in our thoughts though far from each other on the map. I knew exactly what she wanted, thought, felt, saw, and was, and she knew the same with me. Our ways parted, for the time being.

Barry was stoned and the doorman of that pimp's place was really working him over. There wasn't anything fair about it. Barry plastered and slack, the doorman a big, well-trained slugger with his Charles Atlas muscles bulging all over him and punching hard.

I tried to pull him off Barry, but he wouldn't let go. I had just lifted my booted foot to give him one final skull-cracker that would get him off Barry fast when I saw Claudia looking at me. I just managed to keep my foot back (it would have been a real pleasure to knock his insides out through his ass) and then stand there watching him pound Barry to pieces.

My hands were itching and I would have loved to bury a knife in the bastard's thick neck, but like a coward I stayed out of it. Because I could already see visions of the bulls running in, the arrests, the night in a cell. I had a woman to sleep with now. Doing nothing was my first deed in Adjusting to Society.

168

I painted in a studio that belonged to a painter friend and his painter wife. It was in an old house across the canal from ANNE FRANK, INCORPORATED. I tried hard to sell my works.

. Usually, though, Art Lovers regarded me with deep suspicion. Why? Because I didn't look like a Real Artist. An artist without a beard or even a mustache? With ordinary shoes and no corduroy suit? How could he possibly be a Real Artist? So I had a rough time. But I kept on. After all, I was a genius.

For the big-money art collectors (generally notorious black marketeers in the last World War) or for museum directors (well-mannered little gents who never touch anything stronger than orange juice, who graduated from college with honors and who got to be directors because their families pull weight where it counts, and who tap a punching bag a couple of times after getting home from High Mass on Sunday so they can call themselves boxers which makes a big hit with museum personnel), for these types the last thing they can recognize an artist by is his work.

Dutch art stopped living when the fifties began. It ended with Karel Appel in 1950. What they still call art in Holland now is just the work of scavengers and imitators. Nice guys that come in two sorts: the old Bohemian with the greasy mop and grubby beard, and the new generation sort in natty suits and the sleeked down, nicely trimmed hair.

You can find and inspect the first sort in the artistic cafés where they sit around pouting and nursing their grievances about the Government, the Royal Family, the beer, the Catholic People's Party, the Government's Financial Support for Artists, the museums, the museum directors, the high price of living, taxes, children's allowances, the proletariat, landlords, the housing shortage, the decreasing standards of the artistic climate, America, Jan Cremer, Capitalism, the New Thing, the Beatles, commercial radio, the paint manufacturers, the police, the price of gin, and Other Artists.

Every third sentence begins with, "Now back during the war when I . . ." and for a glass of gin they're eager to tell you about how they refused to cooperate with the German's *Kulturkammer*. Those simple but not too bright artists who did collaborate are still considered to be suffering from some unidentified plague. Their creations can't possibly be good. It can't be Art because they were on the "wrong side" in the war. There's a chance that when they're dead and buried it'll turn out to be Real Art after all. For most Dutchmen the war was one gigantic Happening that lasted for five years. Twenty-five years later and it's still the Big Topic.

The older artist (pronounced *arteest*) gulps noisily when he drinks, walks around in a wrinkled corduroy suit with a few well-placed paint stains (plaster stains for sculptors), wears goat's-wool socks and sandals or goes barefoot. You can spot the barefoot artist by his two bare feet or by the distinct Camembert odor emanating from under the table or from between his toes.

I have been fortunate enough to have had the opportunity to make the acquaintance of various types of artists in my career. The Bohemian type smacks his lips when he eats (usually red herring or mackerel but preferably red herrings) and when he's finished shakes the crumbs out of his mangy beard, farts, says "Sorry!" and burps. They have an incomprehensible charm for certain young girls. Above all, their dissertations about Vincent van Gogh, Rembrandt, Freud, and Peruvian art assure them a place in the limelight. In music their favorites are Bach and hurdy-gurdy tunes. A true Artist can distinguish from a distance and name all the street organs of Amsterdam.

A real Artist can fall to his knees at the sight of a pretty girl and convince her she's got the most beautiful face he ever saw in his life. A portrait must be made immediately. For Art's Sake. With clasped hands perhaps the Artist will even burst into tears and praise Fate for permitting him to discover the reincarnation of Mona Lisa.

Thus is the innocent girl lured up to the studio—a dingy room, usually in an even dingier working-class neighborhood, in an attic, preferably with bare ceiling beams, a rope tied in a noose hanging from one of them. The Artist puts water on the kerosense stove for tea and the little girl takes off her coat.

Hanging on the walls are: (1) a palette artistically daubed with paint, (2) a picture of Lumumba, (3) a newspaper clipping with a picture of an accident or a war scene, (4) posters from exhibitions of Etruscan art and the Rembrandt Exhibition at the National Museum, (5) a copy of Van Gogh's *A Boat near a Bridge,* and (6) a few of the Artist's own Works of Art, along with a few nude Playgirls of the Month cut out of old *Playboy*. Above the bed is a copy of Rubens' *Two Women at a Waterfall* or some other lewd scene. The bed is unmade.

The easel is in the center of the room, an unfinished work still on it in which, without much effort, you can make out two apples, a pitcher, and a teapot. He calls it "The Unfinished." While the tea steeps, he whips out a few portfolios of old work. The rest is hanging in the museum—to the left of the staircase near the entrance. A smelly greasy cat called Cleopatra or Mimi meows whenever the Artist stamps his bare foot on the dusty floor.

While enjoying a cup of tea, the Artist explains to the girl, gracefully seated on the bed, how hard life is for a serious Artist. He chooses as examples: (1) Toulouse Lautrec, you know, that dwarf with the crooked legs, (2) Modigliani, who suffered his whole life from the clap, (3) Good Old Vincent van Gogh with the ear, who had such a hard time of it with the ladies.

The prospective model takes delicate sips of her tea while the Artist himself gulps down a glassful of gin ("Not for you, Child. No sense in getting addicted"), while the Artist goes on for a while about the radio and TV set he doesn't have because they're products of Western Decadence, and remarks that this is the first time in his career he has ever felt a true sense of communication. The aspiring model is soon devoid of her stockings and panties and is lying stretched out on the pastel-gray aromatic sheets panting to the strokes of the Artist's Special Brush. The girl, impressed and influenced by our Artist, who happens to be a talented craftsman with the Special Brush (Catholics and Artists have the highest birthrate), returns to the studio at regular intervals. Thus many a portrait is painted.

In the beginning the girl may feel a bit ashamed walking down the street with the Artist (amidst shouts of "Hey, need a buck for a barber?" or "Hey, how'd you get off the cross?" with the Artist nonchalantly mumbling "Squares"), but after a while she turns into a full-fledged painter's woman. She wears brightly colored heavy woolen stockings and a purple velvet dress, wears her hair loose and stops washing around the eyes. Her bra is spotted from the many caresses of the Artist's paint-stained hands. She doesn't wear panties because, after a drink or two, the Artist wants to "get right in."

Their next best form of amusement is going to The Circle—a meeting place for Artists, Art-makers, Art-lice, and Art-pimps—where they can get beer, gin, or scrambled eggs at a reasonable price and at the same time rub elbows with the other Greats of the National Art World: Novelists, Poets, Composers, Comedians, Pianists, Typists, and Bookkeepers.

Then of course there's the Young Artist. A separate sort deserving our attention. Usually the Young Artist comes from a Rich or Intellectual Family.

"Daddy, I don't know what I want to be!"

"Well boy, why don't you become an Artist!"

So, with a chunk of dough from Dad to start with—off to Paris, the cradle of the Arts, to look around the Louvre. Via some of Dad's old friends from the war, Sonny gets letters of recommendation for a juicy scholarship. Chances for fame are even better if the old man made the supreme sacrifice of himself—in the war. Then you have a name to uphold.

Because so many great Artists in history had hot pants for whores (just think of Van Gogh's woman or Little Nellie and Julius Hertenszoon, famed for his Veluwe landscapes painted by the light of candles on his simple straw hat at night), the Young Artist pockets his monthly scholarship check and sets off for the red-light district where the above-mentioned check soon dwindles to nothing. "For a hundred, I've got a special French trick for you. For another hundred you can do it three times." A telephone call to Dad, whose bank transfers some extra money "for supplies," anything, as long as Sonny doesn't come home.

The Young Artist sets out to learn his trade. He buys himself a bookcase of art books plus all the catalogues and prospectuses of Contemporary Modern Artists known to the International Art Market. His work consists primarily of a thorough study of the Modern Masters and, after a while, he's able to make reasonable facsimiles of a particular style or master, either Dutch or foreign.

He buys himself an exhibition. The day before it opens he invites the critics to an excellent dinner where the whisky flows like water and there are nice fat cigars to top it off. The next day the critics speak and write in glowing terms in their papers about his original style. An official representing a Museum of Modern Art promptly purchases a number of paintings by the Young Artist. He is referred to as a "talented Young Artist" and is invited for dinner with the museum director at his home.

If the Young Artist is a gifted conversationalist who can chat for hours about art and drop a reasonable number of modern masters' names, and if he happens to have a cute little wife who can hold her own on the subject of art, then his knowledge and sensitivity will be exalted far and wide. His creative ability isn't what counts. What does count is, is he good for a cozy chat? Is he nice to the director's wife?

169

The Dutch art world is a scrambling pack of parasites, bandits, conscientious objectors (to work), charlatans, plagiarists, bores, and part-time lushes. With few exceptions. And now, go to it, boys! See who can get to the top first! What a crew—they always want to "break through, to overthrow, to demolish history, to do something new, something great," but all they do is talk about it. Action, actually doing anything, is too exhausting. And also, of course, there's a place for the artist in our welfare democracy; the Welfare Department has a special division just for these people. Because, after all, artists are human too.

Though the unemployed worker (Common Man variety) has to

brave the wind and the snow every Friday morning between nine and nine-thirty, hold out his hand for his weekly check, and listen to all kinds of bullshit, the artist gets his check in the mail, and plenty of it. Most of them can live like kings on it and even afford a big house and a car and the annual month-long vacation on the French Riviera or an exotic Greek isle. And their checks follow after them wherever they go.

The Old Artist has his story to tell and it's always the same one. About "When I was working with Karel Appel up in a loft and all our paintings went for a song and whatever we did get we spent on booze," etc. The Young Artist talks about "Willem Frederik, who hugged me like a long-lost brother over at The Circle," or about Picasso, who said, "Drop in if you're ever in the neighborhood; you can stay as long as you like," or about Salvador Dali, whom the Young Artist and his wife met on the beach during their vacation on the French Riviera and who fell madly in love with Trudy and wanted to take her off with him.

The Young Artist with more than three exhibitions to his name, and one or more paintings sold to museums, considers himself *arrivé* and looks down on the Bohemian Artist. American Art Collectors line up in front of his house waving thousand dollar bills, begging for "just a little one."

The Young Artist is ninety per cent ass and ten per cent talent, and every night before he and his wife leave for The Circle for a game of bridge or a nice chat about art, they rehearse a whole repertoire of cute exclamations and resounding laughs just in case a Master or a Museum Director known for his "clever remarks" or "hilarious jokes" shows up.

170

The Circle, meeting place for Arty Vermin and Kindred Killers, is near the Square. Two bare rooms with old brown wooden chairs and benches along the walls, a billiard table in the middle, and a decaying jukebox that plays only "nice swinging jazz records" (since that's what these artists go for—"jazz, Man, jazz") plus a few Fats Domino and Paul Anka singles dated 1958, slipped in by mistake.

The Circle looks like the waiting room in a train station in a medium-sized industrial town in East Germany. You can play shuffleboard and once a year the artists give an Evening with Dancing and, for the winners of the sack race, shuffleboard, and checker tournaments, a prize: a bottle of Sweet Red Wine (price one guilder fifty cents, no deposit, no return). I once watched astonished to see the whole cream of Holland's Cultural Life hopping around The Circle in potato sacks.

Besides which, if you're an artist's child, you can come to the Santa

Claus party. Then on Friday evening there's the Ball where the artists and their hangers-on all get together to sulk or giggle or maybe even fight. The fighting never gets any further than a soft slap on one ear, after which both parties burst into tears.

The only difference between this and the Salvation Army canteen is that at The Circle you can drink beer or even stronger stuff—a privilege the artists take grateful advantage of. Everybody drowns their *Weltschmerz*, from the periodic lushes to the secret drunks. The artists call this "atmosphere."

Up the stairs and you're in the so-called TV lounge, a dark little room with big leather easy chairs and an inviting sofa arranged in a semicircle around a pint-size TV set. Many a happy marriage has met its end in this peekaboo room, better known as the Passion Pit. Many is the time Old Artists, peacefully enjoying an opera or some such thing on the screen, were startled out of their doze by the shrill yelps of artists' wives getting their lube jobs from some Young Artist in the pale blue light of the boob-tube. One friend and colleague of mine takes pleasure in announcing that he personally used the above-mentioned room to plow a voluptuous lady journalist from an independent weekly whose name must remain unmentioned here. Simon, the Soggy Noodle, often came to the room to proclaim his belief in "love love love" to everyone unfortunate enough to be within hearing distance.

The managing board of The Circle consists of a number of power-hungry pseudo-intellectuals willing to fight to the death to hold on to their positions on the board. The eternal managers, as they are called, are headed up by a bureaucrat who in everyday life is a bookkeeper in charge of the delivery division of a leading department store. A number of members have been expelled for not cleaning off their shoes on the doormat, for cheating at shuffleboard, for saying dirty words, or for bringing in guests after two o'clock.

The Soggy Noodle was once expelled for a few months because he smoked a forbidden Black Grass cigarette. Nobody would have noticed it if he hadn't put on such an interesting show. How can I be conspicuously inconspicuous? That's what good old Simon was aiming at—he who will perhaps go down in history as the first Black Grass Martyr. The day Simon smoked his stick he first of all announced it an hour beforehand, then he held his breath for four minutes, his pale poet's face turning vermilion, then he let out a very loud peep. For whoever had somehow missed out on the fact that our Simon was doing something Forbidden, he repeated the whole act. Until everyone was convinced he was stark raving mad. As for him, he thought they were gazing at him in admiration.

The regular patrons of The Circle, besides the above-mentioned Noodle, consist of Nifty Needlenose, a young egghead and man of letters whose fame is largely due to his nose (and, I must admit, it's a rare specimen, that nose). Usually in the company of his faithful comrade, the Mealy Meatball, winner of various checker tournaments, notorious for his hasty departures before or during a great number of checker tournaments as a form of protest against police brutality or against the noisy ticking of the game-timers or against the victory of the other player.

Besides that Fast Forgotten Fashion Fad of the Fifties, Baby Face Fantaaastic—the sweetest little boy with a pair of tremendous eye-glasses any oculist would have bragged himself to death about having prescribed—the culture from south of our border was sometimes embodied in the person of none other than the Flemish Sugar Plum (famous for his books and plays: *Sugar from the Thames, The Most Unforgettable Sugar I Ever Met, Black Sugar,* and *Sugar at Tiffany's*). It seems he once worked in some sort of sugar factory toward the end of his sensitive adolescence. At any rate, one day when he came home bawling his mother slapped his face and he got some kind of complex, which drives him to write about sugar every time.

The Circle is also a refuge and popular gathering place for drama lovers and performers, ballet lovers and performers, photographers and their models—a refuge where you can have a cozy chat or play a game of billiards while enjoying a cup of dirty dish water and a chunk of French stink cheese with stale French bread. The Dutch really know how to put away cheese! Judging by the comments of our Stars of Stage and Screen, we are unparalleled gorgers and gobblers of potatoes and cheese. Just a bunch of wholesome healthy Dutch farmboys.

This den of iniquity, where culture is prostituted in the lewdest way, where vice reigns supreme, this rot spot in a supposedly civilized society, this Sodom and Gomorrah of the Low Lands, this love-nest for the lackeys who pay lip service to the Gods of Dutch capitalism—who has to work his ass off to pay for all this? The Working Man? Exactly! Of course my Former Fellow Artists will say, "Cremer has no conscience! He'll stoop to anything! He's unscrupulous!" But then I'd say, "Brothers, Former Fellow Artists, which of us has a conscience? You all maybe, or me?" That's what I'd say!

171

Nine o'clock Sunday morning. I wake up. Not a smoke in the house. I crumpled up the empty pack, got up, shot into a pair of pants and a sweater. The cigarette machine was just down the street. I clambered barefoot down the stairs.

"I'll get some cigarettes. Be right back," I said to Claudia, still in bed. The cigarette machine was ten steps from my door, and I ran. The pavement was freezing cold. When I ran back, the downstairs door had blown shut. I swore. I'd left the keys upstairs. Our room didn't have a bell to ring and the rest didn't work. Our one neighbor lived on the second floor in back and was pretty near deaf anyway and Claudia couldn't hear me.

I tried screaming through the mail slot. A few pious citizens on their way to church on this chilly gray Sunday morning looked at me, surprised. Nothing attracts attention like a guy with a sleepy unwashed face doing suspicious-looking things in front of a house that doesn't even look livable. Every time somebody passed, I quasi-nonchalantly rang the bell. When they were gone, I went back to swearing and screaming through the mail slot. Hopeless.

My only chance was that Claudia would start to worry and come downstairs. I waited for hours, pacing back and forth, always keeping close to the door. Because if she did come down and then didn't see me, she'd close the door again. Between the rooftops of the other houses I could see a tiny piece of our window way up there in back. Every once in a while I could see Claudia walking around. I threw pebbles at the window and hit every house except ours. When Claudia looked out the window, I screamed and waved at her.

There I was in my bare feet on the cold sidewalk and I'd damn well had enough of it. Besides which everybody who passed by thought it was a great joke. Cars stopped or slowed down to get a good look at me, no shoes on in the middle of the winter, thinking I must be some kind of health-fiend or escaped lunatic.

A patrol car stopped. But the cops didn't get out. Probably just checking up via their handy radio transmitter to see if there were any reports of escaped nuts or convicts. And me there, nonchalance itself, strolling along whistling, my hands clasped loosely behind my back. Or gazing into the junk shop window.

"Whatcha doin' there, mister?" asked one of the cops. I told him. He looked skeptical. After I'd told my story ten different heartbreaking ways, he and his pal finally got out of the car and tried a pass-key. No good. The only thing left to do was bash the door in. But that was going too far. Besides, it would mean trouble with the landlord.

In the meantime, a crowd had collected, attracted by the magic blue uniforms. I'd been on the street for at least four full hours and from sheer nerves I'd smoked up the whole pack. Then the door suddenly opened and Claudia struggled to steer the baby carriage outside. Surprised, she looked at all that commotion on her doorstep. I almost collapsed on the spot. A while back I'd thought up a few nice things to say when the door opened, but now I was more dead than alive.

"Why didn't you come down and open the door?" I stammered.

"Yes," she said pensively, "I thought you were gone a long time. "Yes," she concluded, "and I should have thought of it because I know the bell doesn't work."

172

To make some money, I set up "JAN CREMER'S ART-AT-YOUR-HOME, INC." An organization (me) sponsored by an anonymous Great Art Mogul (me) who commissioned Famous Artists (me) to go do their Art Thing at the homes of prospective customers. With a few connections in the business and art world, who were paid a handsome percentage for praising my talents among the Art-Loving Middle Class, I got myself a few customers. For one hundred fifty guilders + warm meal + unlimited supply of alcoholic beverages—since that's an essential part of the whole Art Thing—the desired Work of Art would be produced in the peace and quiet of the buyer's own home. The buyer could even pick out the colors and decide what the picture should be about, more or less.

On the particular evening in question my organization had tipped off a famous surgeon that Jan Cremer, the radio and TV celebrity himself, had an evening free and could still be booked. With an empty stomach I went that autumn evening to a quiet expensive street in the south of Amsterdam where I was welcomed most cordially and treated very regally by the surgeon and his wife. A very beautiful Scandinavian Grace Kelly type—big, blonde, blue eyes, and elegantly dressed—while the surgeon looked like a bookkeeper in a hick-town bank.

One of the few things I will never understand is why so many fantastic women marry such ugly little guys. It's not so hard to figure out when there's money involved, but lots of times there isn't. Or is that what they call Love?

First I sat down to a sumptuous meal, chicken in curry sauce with rice—asparagus soup before and fruit salad after—all washed down with good red wine. Judging by the dust on the bottle, a vintage wine. After the espresso coffee laced with cognac served in tiny cups, I started in on my stories. The middle class is always dying to know what the Artist's life is really like. And they want first-hand information. Of course there are books about it, but they never have the inside stories. That Doctor and his Mrs. didn't know how lucky they were to have me sitting there. They could have me any way they wanted me.

While enjoying their Johnny Walker, I described Life Among the Artists—a life full of orgies, bacchanalia, and sultry bedtime stories. The surgeon, a man with a neat part in his short-trimmed hair and a silly pair of thick glasses, licked his lips as he listened to my stories sprinkled with a generous assortment of cunts, cocks, bare tits, and tail.

His beautiful wife became more and more excited, wiggling and squirming her well-formed ass on her chair. When she crossed her legs my stories got even spicier. In the meantime I got down to work. After all I was there to make a Work of Art and not for chitchat. That was another department.

She wanted me to paint "something sexy," but he said he'd leave it up to me as long as it was "something different." I painted a big brightly colored bird with big eyes, jagged teeth, and outspread claws. "Symbolic," I explained to the awe-struck surgeon and his wife.

The surgeon was suddenly called away for an emergency operation. He apologized, said he hoped to see me again soon, and paid me right away because he was wildly enthusiastic about my painting. Me too. In fact, I thought it was a pity to give away such a great thing for such a measly price.

When I had washed my hands in the bathroom, the woman of the house came to bring me a clean towel. Rubbing her warm breasts against my back, she gave me a naughty look in the mirror. We had a nice chat about art and stuff. She loosened up, now that she was alone. She said she wasn't so happy with her life, though she had everything her little heart desired, and that what she really wanted was to live with some poet or writer in a garret with a candle in a Chianti bottle. "A free life," she called it. Before long we were panting and grabbing at each other on a magnificent plush sofa, and I pushed her tweed skirt up over her beautiful well-rounded thighs. Art demands sacrifices, let's face it.

With my well-trained artist's fingers I opened her ripe vaginal lips, kneaded her well-shaped clitoris, and plunged into her perfumed cunt. She moaned and cooed underneath and pinched me. When I had finished giving her my patented treatment with the Special Brush, she sighed, "Darling, darling, you do it like no one ever did it before." I thought, yeah, Baby, there are experts and sexperts.

173

oh netherlands oh netherlands
my small cold stinking netherlands
oh what a balls oh what a balls

Jan Cremer *Arty Vermin and Kindred Killers*

> *you are my rotten netherlands*
> *how I love you and love you true*
>
> *my once and always fatherland*
> *just ram it up yours will you please*
> *I love you so I love you true*
> *my stiff fartheaded netherlands*
>
> *here far away now*
> *here I lie*
> *a woman lying*
> *under me*
>
> *and if I think red white and blue*
> *it's thanks to you*
> *my fatherland*

174

I'd been back in Holland for a few months. Too long for me. Nothing was happening. Every since the trouble with the Spaniards in the fifteenth century, Holland has been very quiet—in fact, fast asleep. The only feat of grandeur in Dutch history is Hugo the Great's escape in a packing crate. Other countries have the Count of Monte Cristo, who made a spectacular escape, or Napoleon slipping off Elba, or Lenin breaking out in Siberia. Escapes with a lot of shooting and stabbing, bombs and grenades. But what do the Dutch have? The simple Hugo who had himself lugged out of his heavily guarded castle in a simple packing crate. Heinrich Heine, the German philosopher, said more than a hundred years ago, "When the world comes to its end, I'll go to Holland. There everything happens fifty years later." Holland is pure slapstick. It's all so tragicomic you can't whimper; you have to laugh.

I yearned for the sun again, milk and honey. Life was getting too boring. I longed for action and couldn't stand the stink of the kerosene stove or the simple Dutch grub.

"I don't get you," said Claudia one evening, surprised, as she set our pot on the floor. "Tuesday you said, 'Good, sauerkraut. Just what I wanted.' Wednesday you said, 'Aha. I see you've still got some of that delicious sauerkraut left! Great!' Thursday you said, 'Good old sauerkraut again.' Friday you said, 'Nothing like a good plate of sauerkraut, is there, honey?' Yesterday you finished it off in no time. And now suddenly it's that dirty filthy stinking rotten sauerkraut! What's the matter with you? Don't you love me anymore? Of course I'm going to make sauerkraut since you're so wild about it."

Holland irritated me and I wanted to leave. With Claudia. But she couldn't leave because her husband wouldn't let her have her daughter. "First prove you're able to take care of her," he said. The longer I stayed in that tiny room the more irritable I got. The walls were closing in on me and the only way I could stand it was to drown my sorrows in drink in one of the nearby bars.

Claudia's husband was patiently waiting for things to go wrong. He suddenly refused to get a divorce and made her life hell under the pretense that he was doing it all for her own good. One day when we didn't even have enough money to buy kerosense for the stove and the druggist on the corner didn't want to give us any more credit, we took the baby to a "good friend" of Claudia's, a woman with a huge wart on her forehead and two children, who had our best interests at heart. To take care of the baby till we could lay hands on some money. It was just for an afternoon.

Claudia was going to try to find a part-time job as a salesgirl and also sell her leather coat; I schlepped my paintings around from one art dealer and gallery to another. Without any immediate results. When we came to pick up the baby at Claudia's friend's house that evening, it turned out she had called the father who, with the help of the Child Welfare Bureau, was granted custody of the child a few weeks later because it had been "abandoned, uncared for and helpless."

He saw the baby as a way of getting Claudia back. He got daily reports on our difficult situation in all its gory details from a so-called girlfriend of Claudia's, a dyke from Surinam, who dropped in after work every evening just to see how things were going. I threw her out one day when I heard her trying to turn Claudia against me. It took all the self-control I had to keep from literally throwing her down the stairs.

"We're going to Spain," I decided. "I know everybody there and I can get an exhibition right away and sell a lot, and till then I can get credit to keep us alive and buy all the supplies I'll need. I want you to come with me, but you'll have to decide that for yourself. I got hold of some money plus two one-way train tickets to Barcelona. One for you. Wednesday morning at eleven. If you come with me, you're to forget about your baby—for your own good. Let your husband's family take care of the kid. Fighting for the kid—hell, that's not for you. That's exactly what they want you to do and that's what they're trying to provoke you into doing. That's their only way of keeping you here. It's their last chance. All those scenes are just helping them get what they want. They want us to leave each other and you to go back to your pathetic little prick of a husband. Otherwise they wouldn't screw up the divorce either. You've got to make up your own mind. Me? I've had it here!

"I hate it here. I can't stand the people any more. I want to go back to Spain. Money isn't important there. Holland makes me all depressed. I'm crazy about you, you know that, and I want to take you with me. I want to be with you always. But you've got to decide for yourself. I can't and I won't tell you what to do. I don't want you to blame me later for taking you away from your house and your baby. Your mother, his mother, the whole damn pack is against us. They're all looking out for themselves.

"There just aren't any kindhearted people in this world, honey. Can't you see that? Stop kidding yourself. There are no friends. I am your only friend and you are my only friend. Let them all go to hell, the whole fuckless bunch of them. Goddamn it, I want to live my own life. If you want to stay here in this mess, it's OK with me. I love you, and at any rate we've had a great time together. I love you and that's why I won't force you if you don't want to come with me, no matter how hard it'll be for me. You have your life and I have mine.

"I'm definitely taking off next Wednesday. There's no point in putting it off any longer. I've been wanting to go away for a month. Every time there's some money I think, come on, let's move. But somehow we never got around to it. For me now, Holland is suicide. Next Wednesday I'm going to get on that train and by the end of the week I'll be in a house of my own on a nice warm island with no vultures around to spoil the landscape. If you and I part, we'll get over it. Don't you understand that that's exactly what your husband's family wants! They trapped you with that good friend of yours who felt it was her duty to call the baby's father and the Child Welfare Bureau. It's one big conspiracy. Those people, they don't want you to live your own life. If you stay, you give up, you capitulate. If you leave, they'll have all the more reason to say you abandoned your baby. They'll never leave you alone, not even if you stay. They live off this sort of thing. Somebody else's troubles. And in a month you'll leave again anyway. They'll hunt you down again and call you a slut and a bad mother. I don't know. You'll have to make your own decision."

"Jan," she said, "if you really love me, I want to stay with you forever. We'll go away together and start up a new life somewhere else. I'll miss the baby terribly and I really have to think about it a while before I go. I was brought up in children's homes myself. My mother didn't give a damn about me. But I love you and that's the most important thing. I want to have children by you and then later maybe when things have calmed down we can give this baby a home too. It was good, wasn't it, the three of us? Promise me," she whispered, "that I'll have your baby."

"Dearest Claudia," I said, "you are the only woman in the world I would want to have my baby."

And I meant it too!

175

The train left Amsterdam Central Station at eleven. The evening before, Claudia went to her sister in a town south of Amsterdam to pick up some clothes and make some last minute arrangements. She was going to get on the train when it stopped where her sister lived half an hour later. I desperately searched the platforms when the train stopped there. No Claudia. Didn't she want to come? Changed her mind? Had her sister talked her out of it?

When the train started moving again, I threw my suitcase out onto the platform and jumped after it, though I'd vowed I wouldn't get off that train or wait or let anything or anybody get in my way.

Two hours later Claudia appeared with a sleepy face and swollen eyes but as cheerful as if we had planned it that way.

"Sorry," she laughed, "I overslept."

the rain gods

176

Midsummer, 1961. Carthage. Port near Tunis. A broiling afternoon, so hot our sweaty boots sank into the sticky asphalt and left deep prints. Barry and I wandered aimlessly around the docks. Siesta time. Spicy aromas drifted out of the bars and taverns, packed with seamen, stevedores, whores. Against the sultry stillness of the air you could hear people smacking their lips and chewing and the click of silverware. A few customs officials were leaning uncomfortably against a pile of crates, their rifles grounded. A stifling heat in a tropical hot house. There was a storm in the air. In the sunlight everything trembled.

177

After a trip packed with obstacles and adventures plus plenty of laughs, howls, and screams, Barry and I wound up in Tunis with Silver Monster. I'd bought this magnificent, tough, silver Harley Davidson back in Holland for one hundred twenty bucks, dirt cheap. Of course everybody said I'd been swindled, said it wouldn't even get me out of the city. The Monster got us to eight countries and two continents and licked up more than six thousand miles with its well-notched tires, desert stretches, sandy roads, muddy trails, pebbled paths and highways: and at the end it was held together with bits of string, Scotch tape, Band-Aids, clothes hangers, and chewing gum—the sleeves of my shirts bandaged up the ravaged tires.

We didn't have much money left, just enough to live on for a while and enough for the cheapest way back to our Mediterranean island where we had a house, farm, food, a dog, and women. The trip had taken us about a month, a month of the good life. A nice ride puffing through the North African countryside, then at night a good meal in a little village, settlement or trucker's diner. We filled up on wine, smoked a joint or sucked away on the waterpipe offered to us on various occasions, which they had waiting for the customers in bars and restaurants. A month of fine eating and drinking, garnished with lots of adventure, sex, excitement, and thrills. A bare-ass dip in the ocean or a little lake, then away on the Monster, drying your shirt off in the wind. We hustled up food everywhere. No problems. I had my orange cast-iron frying pan in the side-car, famed far and wide because of my delicious one-pan master-pieces, and a whole bag of spices, herbs, and other ingredients. When we stopped at nightfall in a village and set up our tent, it didn't take long before the curious villagers came to watch us and we traded toilet articles and jewelry and trinkets (showered on us when we were taken for Rain Gods) for food, goat's meat, decanters of local wines, and loaves of bread.

We had been on Ibiza for a while and when I'd managed to scrape together some money, Barry and I crossed over to Spain. After spending a few days running like madmen dodging hopped-up bulls in the streets of Pamplona during the Fiesta de San Fermin, we decided it was time for a short vacation.

We rode down the Iberian peninsula and pushed on relentlessly under the fierce sun. After the ferry boat from Algeciras to Ceuta we were on African soil. We finally wound up in Carthage and spent days on end wandering around in search of a freighter with a captain who would take us on and let us work our way over to Barcelona or Alicante. There was no rush. We were having fun in the meantime. We had a room with bath in a little hotel near the waterfront, crawling with thieves, American junkies, whores, and sailors, right on top of a brothel.

Twilight was coming down on the mountain tops. The breeze, just starting to cool off, blew still warm through our hair. We took our time through the mountainous North African countryside. Every once in a while we'd pass a peddler with his heavily laden donkey and no kind of light. I almost rode right up on top of one once. Barry was sitting with his legs dangling out of the side-car, leaning back for a look at the gray-blue starlit sky, and was scared out of his wits when I jammed the brakes on to keep from piling up on that donkey. "Shit!" I swore. "They ought to light those things up or ram a bulb up their ass. The next time there's going to be a hell of a smashup."

We had left Annada, an Algerian port town, late in the afternoon. We stopped for a drink at a wood shack on the side of the road.

"I could have told you," said Barry. "But that's what you get if you stay on those waterpipes too long."

I was high as a kite. Out of Van Nelle's Strong Shag, we smoked ordinary hash or pot in North Africa, and we'd had quite a lot of sweet wine afterward too.

"Remember that fish soup we had in Gerona?" Barry laughed. "Man, I almost broke up when you nearly fell off the Monster!" When we first got to Spain, just after New Year's, we'd stopped in a roadside snack bar because our battery was dead and it was thundering, lightning, and pouring. We ordered a glass of wine, since wine's cheap there, and a bowl of fish soup. Delicious savory spicy soup. It was so good and cheap we each had five more bowls. When we finally got back on the road again —the storm had stopped and the battery was recharged—I started singing, "What Shall We Do with a Drunken Sailor" and "For He's a Jolly Good Fellow" at the top of my lungs, while fearlessly cutting in and out between huge trucks.

Barry, also feeling great, stood up in the side-car and tried to piss on the road. When I made a sharp turn, he nearly fell flat out on his face in the middle of the Spanish countryside. Suddenly I felt absolutely stoned. We were. That fish soup had sherry in it instead of water, so we must have put away a good three quarts of warm alcohol. The fresh air made it really start working, especially with all that bouncing around on the motor- cycle. We lay in the grass for two hours telling jokes until I could stand on my feet again and get Silver Monster started up by pedaling with a steady foot without falling.

"Somewhere in these mountains there must be a border," Barry said.

"What border?" I asked. I didn't have any idea any more where we were.

"Tunisian border," he said, "Let's stop in a village, put the tent up, and then tomorrow we'll go straight on to Tunis."

"Up yours," I said, "or wherever you want to stick that tent. This night isn't going to see *me* under that stinking canvas. I want to lay up, warm my ears in the saddle, knock off a piece, get me a warm crib somewhere. That tent gets on my nerves, man. I keep thinking a baboon is going to jump me or a rat gnaw my toes off. After that snake in Miliana trying to get a taste of my arm, I know all I want to know about camping out."

"If you'd just sat still," said Barry, "it wouldn't have gone after you like that. Even if it had bitten you, I would have cut it out for you."

"You can have that, Jack," I said. "That monster was staring me right in the face, and you're trying to tell me you would have just sat there? Man, I almost shit in my pants when I saw those eyes and that weird little tongue. Still," I said, "I wouldn't mind having a tongue like that. Might come in handy. Give all the ladies hot pants, a little licker like that with two tips. I get hot pants myself just thinking about it. If I don't get me a good lay tonight, I'm going to grab a boat in Tunis tomorrow. I don't call this a vacation. It's more like a chain gang. And damn it, I want to get to know Tunis. My father always said . . ."

". . . if you haven't had a piece of Tunis, you'll never get to know the city." Barry took the words right out of my mouth.

And the old man was right. What were we doing here of all places, I suddenly wondered, in this hideous sand pile with all those funny mountains and these brown-skinned jokers? I didn't like these A-rabs. They knife you in the ribs just for the hell of it and they can't even dance. Ha ha ha, I laughed, relaxed on the studded Texas-style saddle of my Silver Monster as I cruised along at a good speed, with one hand loosely steering through the countless sharp curves of the mountainous countryside.

"Both hands!" Barry yelled when I barely missed smashing up against a steep cliff. "Another like that and we'll be at the bottom of a gully like at Napmaquac."

"Forget it," I said. "If that fruit truck hadn't followed us into the gully, there wouldn't have been a thing to worry about—no police, nothing. That nut was sticking too close behind."

"Sure love to have a nice juicy orange right now," Barry said dreamily.

"Me too," I said, "with a beautiful broad to go with it. Then I'd skin the orange and start sucking the broad."

"Quiet," Barry said suddenly. "You hear that bird singing?"

"No, man, it's just the kettle from the broad in that farmhouse over there."

"You really think they've got whistling kettles out here in the middle of nowhere?" Barry asked innocently.

"No," I said, "but the chicks whistle through their cunts when the water boils. Ha ha ha."

In the distance we saw the border—two horizontal poles blocking the road, a few little shacks, the lanterns already lit on both sides of the road, in the middle of the mountains.

"It's just like those stupid bastards to have a border way up in the mountains," I said. "Sit down, be a good boy and keep your trap shut. Don't let them know where we come from."

I slowed down at the border and pulled up right at the feet of a customs inspector, a young guy with a Mafia mustache who glanced through our passports and gave the signal to lift the poles. And so on we rode into Tunisia. It was still nice and warm and the afternoon was just about over.

178

We rode across a flat stretch of land with pine trees lining the road, yellow sand, fields of sand and cactus. The sun disappeared beyond the horizon and the sky lit up with thousands of twinkling stars. I kept my eyes on the road and out of the corner of my eye I saw the Big Dipper, Mars, the Little Dipper, Taurus the Bull, a Sputnik chasing a UFO, and a TWA plane where I could tell dinner was being served because all the lights were on. What are they eating? I wondered. The usual two potatoes, twenty-four green peas, fillet of beef two inches wide and four inches long, coffee afterward with milk in a little paper cup and two lumps of sugar and a dried-out piece of cake.

"Bah," I said, disgusted. "Am I ever glad I'm not on that plane. That awful cake. Somebody's making a wad on that cake. What do you figure it costs, a piece of cake like that?"

"It depends," said Barry. "On what kind of cake it is."

"What do you mean, what *kind* of cake?" I said angrily.

"Well, cake is cake," said Barry nonchalantly.

"Oh yeah?" I said. "Cake is cake? You don't know what you're talking about. Those people there," and I pointed to the sky, "are eating the cheapest, most awful cake in existence. You go to the A&P and say you want a piece of cake like that and, man, even they don't have it. That's how bad it is. They'd be ashamed to sell cake like that. And meanwhile all those poor people up there are just eating away, eating their cake. Naturally, when they first see it, they think, Ah! Cake! But they're in for a surprise. They need thirteen cups of coffee to wash down a piece of cake like that. Figure it out for yourself. That's twelve cups and they each cost who knows how much—and you only get one cup for free on a flight like that.

"If you're lucky, maybe the stewardess pours you another cup free. Then you can thank your lucky stars and try to get your mouthful of sawdust all washed down with that second cup of coffee. Poor passengers," I lamented, "and if you think First Class gets the same lousy cake, you're crazy. Champagne and little crackers with caviar, that's what those fat slobs get. Still, a trip like that costs plenty. Must be pretty near four hundred guilders just from here to Amsterdam. And who has to pay? The Poor Working Man who has to visit his sick mother in Tunis. I think it's a scandal—scandalous exploitation. And especially with that cake. That's *too* much."

"Why don't you can that cake?" said Barry.

"Cake?" I asked. "What cake?"

All that cake-talk made me awfully thirsty and when we came to a well, we stopped.

"I'm dying of thirst," I said. "Got to have some of that free beer."

It was a well with a rod and rope you pull on, the kind you see lots of alongside the roads in North Africa—except in the desert, of course, but there you can always have a drink of water at Hertz Rent-a-Car as long as you buy some of their greasy gas. The gas the Oil Mob is making such a killing off, swindling the poor sheiks and Tuaregs out of their oil wells, using a little show of muscle here, a little bag of salt there. I'm thinking in particular of that world-renowned firm called Seashell.

A round well made of baked clay and surrounded by a kind of low stone wall you could lean over. Usually sticking up in the middle of a big puddle of mud. Today, however, the yellow sand was dry like sand ought to be. Some of the locals were standing in line with jugs on their heads, most of them old women, some of them still keeping the lower part of their face hidden. Because of bad breath. If I were selling mouth rinse, I could have unloaded a ton right there.

There was a terrible drought in North Africa. It hadn't rained for months and according to the news on the radio, the length of this drought had broken all the records. (Of course they could have been talking about the Olympics. My Arabic isn't all that good, except for the Napmaquacian dialect, but then of course that's a snap for Europeans.)

The people were under great strain and their nerves were on edge. First the election riots, then Independence Day, and now almost half a year without water. The fields were scorched, the vegetables and fruit dried up—which meant a windfall for the Dried Apricot Business.

There were protest marches in the cities. They blamed the government for not having stored up enough water. The whole country was in a pretty black mood; everybody was jumpy and aggressive. Water was rationed; you could only get it once a day. It's true of course that the average North African doesn't use much water, but still you can't make soup out of sand, so there was a long line of women and old men waiting for water.

I got at the end of the line. The line was inching ahead. There was an old guy at the well using a frying pan to give everybody their fair share of water. There was a little old woman standing in front of me, holding a heavy jug against her hip.

"Want me to hold your jug for you, granny?" I said chivalrously.

I thought that way I might at least get something to drink even though I was a foreigner. At first the old lady thought I was trying to steal her jug, but then I explained everything patiently in sign language. I put both hands to my heart (honest guy, good heart), then peered into the distance with one hand shading my eyes like a ferry boat captain scanning the waves (I come from far lands), then shrugged my shoulders and looked dumb (I'm a stranger and can't say a word), then made a little gesture with thumb and forefinger (just a little bit, please?), and then made a glass out of one hand and drank it empty. The old lady followed me, and when I was done, she smiled a deep warm toothless (except for one little ragged one) grin and nodded.

"Barry, throw me the cup," I yelled, and with a skillful flick of the wrist he flipped me the empty tin can all the way from where he sat in the side-car.

"Get me some too, will ya?" he yelled back.

I kept up a sign-chat with the old lady and by the time we both signed out I'd understood her to say that if it didn't rain soon and God didn't drench the fields it would be a catastrophe. The people just couldn't take it any more. The old lady herself was having troubles with her oldest son who was feuding with the local agronomist who'd been out on a date once with the girl her son had married. No, nothing happened—not what you think—nothing horizontal. Just some innocent star-gazing, a walk in the woods, a kiss, and a pinch here and there. But her son, a simple lad with all the innocence of youth, was mad anyway. In short, everybody was waiting for Heaven or Valhalla to break loose and help out. Rain.

The man who was portioning out the water at the well was another of those evil-looking types with a little mafia mustache. An old fart in a long baggy black robe and a white starched collar and a necklace loaded with beads, sort of a rosary.

As soon as he saw me, he started screaming, "Happerdepap, ellellellel gakarak," and waving his arms around like he was chasing away a whole battalion of alley cats. He gestured at me threateningly with his frying pan while screaming out more of the above.

"Cool it, dad," I said. "I'm with the lady."

And I nodded toward the old woman who beamed and nodded back to me with her big warm one-toothed grin. The man in black took a pan of water out of the big wooden pail suspended on top of the well and poured it into the old woman's jug, and then once more leered at me suspiciously out of the corner of his eye. When I came a step closer, the man poured the water back into the wooden pail and spread his arms out as if to protect the well against enemy invasion. He shook his head at me, silently scolding me, making it clear he meant business, as if it had never entered his head that I was planning to stay, that I would fight my way past him to the well, employing any means necessary, to get myself a gulp of that water.

In Algeria the wells were guarded by soldiers armed with machine guns, but that was because of the rebels, the Algerian Liberation Army, who kill off the population or at least give them something to worry about by throwing poisoned oranges or peppers into the water to make it undrinkable.

The waterman took another panful out of the pail and emptied it very fast. The next one even faster, and he spilled a few drops. The old woman swore at him.

"Oesjipappa," she said and I decided to remember that word. It probably meant something like "son of a bitch," "bastard," or "jerk." I slapped her on the shoulder to show my appreciation and said, "That's the girl, granny. That's telling him." She looked at me tenderly and smiled, a deep warm grin on her one-toothed mouth.

Mr. Waterman poured the fourth pan into the old woman's jug, but first he held it close up to my thirsty parched lips, invitingly, and then just as I was about to take a good-sized gulp, he pulled it away and laughed a satanic laugh. He proudly pointed with his finger and gestured with his hand: 'Look, watch carefully, the fifth one, the last one.' Then with a dramatic flourish he took the pan out of the pail, pretended he was going to drink it himself, looked at me with a wicked grin, and held it in front of my parched lips again. I thought, I've had enough of your game and grabbed the pan with both hands. He snatched it back, but not fast enough—at least I got a taste of it. He jerked at it so hard half the water spilled out over the edge of the well. He mumbled something under his breath and tried to take advantage of the confusion to pour what was left of the water into granny's jug. But I knew his game. I pointed to the half-empty pan. The guy cursed. The old woman said "Oesjipappa" again, but this time very shrilly, and pointed to the well. She wanted her full share and she was right. I also pointed vigorously to the well and to the old woman and said "Oesjipappa."

The people waiting in back of us buzzed their admiration and approval. I looked at the woman and on her toothless mouth with just that one little tooth sticking up in it there appeared a large grin of gratitude.

The man pouted, reluctantly took the pan out of the pail again and though he wanted to try the same trick again he thought better of it and glared at me. When he had emptied the last pan, I put my tin can under the jug and the old woman filled it up, giving me that deep warm grin she grinned with her toothless mouth with just that one little tooth sticking up in it. When the can was full, I took a few sips, while the old woman smiled and watched me with a deep warm grin on her toothless mouth with just that—that's right—one little tooth sticking up in it.

I walked away and waved goodbye to the woman. Barry said "no thanks" when I offered him the can of water. We still had a bottle of beer tucked away somewhere. Then I gunned the motor, yelled "Oesjipappa" at the man at the well, and poured the water out on the ground so it splashed up and back onto the guy's bare feet.

I stomped on the gas pedal and off we went in a cloud of dust and gas fumes right past the well. Mad as hell, the guy with the fake mustache sprang back, then, as soon as we passed him, started off after us. He sprinted like a man with a pantsful of hornets and he almost caught up with us too (Silver Monster ain't what it used to be), but then stumbled over his sandals and fell flat on his face.

We roared with laughter and rode on a few yards and then there he was, up again so fast the sand clouds were flying. He tried to run again but we had too big a lead on him so he just stood there boiling over and shaking his fists at us. We had to go back the other way to get back on the road, so I made a hairpin turn, gave the Monster all she had and we shot past him, leaving him all wrapped up in a cloud of dust behind us. He was leaping up and down like a maniac, I was yelling "Oesjipappa" at him, then he jerked the string of beads off over his head, squeezed it up into a ball, took a good pitcher's stance, warmed up and threw the bead-ball straight at us as hard as he could. Barry just managed to catch it. It was a long string with all kinds of little round beads and a big ebony cross with a silver Jesus on it, arms spread out, legs pressed together.

The old lady who'd been nice enough to give me a few gulps of her valuable water had been watching the scene and when we rode past her, she waved with her one free arm, the other curved up to the jug balanced on her head. I pulled up in front of her. She smiled sweetly and I took both her hands in mine while her toothless mouth with just that one little tooth went right on grinning. Then I put my hands back on the Monster and started off. While we moved off slowly, she said "Oesjipappa, oesjipappa," in a grateful tone of voice.

I couldn't keep from yelling it back to her over my shoulder, so I was shouting "Oesjipappa, oesjipappa!" and then Barry joined in with his "Oesjipappas" and the little woman was so thrilled she smiled her smile once again, clasped her hands and sang out in a high-voice "Oesjipappa! Oesjipappa! OESJIPAPPA!"

The jug on her head wobbled, wobbled farther even, then crashed down on the hardened sand and broke into big splinters, giving the thirsty ground a good drink at last.

As we rode along we kept passing men dressed just the same as the man at the well. Exactly the same, right down to the same cross on the chain. A little later, when we saw a big dark building with towers and a brightly lit neon cross with the international sign "Eat More God," we knew for sure. The man at the well had been a monk and was wearing a rosary. The next monk we came to was briskly mumbling away at his prayers. We stopped and when he had mumbled to his heart's content and thrown in a few Hail Marys, Barry solemnly presented him with the rosary that had been pitched after us.

"Oesjipappa," we said in a reverent tone.

"Oesjipappa," he said and gaped after us thoughtfully.

"You know," I said to Barry when we were a few miles off, "if you ask me, the whole bunch was off their rockers."

179

We came to a little turn. Abas Ben Bella was painted on a tree trunk right near the first houses. The name of the place. It was just a little town, one street lined with a few villas built in the old French style and some white-washed stone houses.

The sun was setting and the sweltering heat was at its worst. In spite of the cool wind my shirt stuck to my body, and I was sweating like a pig. Every once in a while I turned my head into the wind and shook off the drops of sweat and Barry kept wiping his face off with his Scotch-plaid handkerchief.

"You can tell we're headed inland," I said to Barry. "It feels like the tropics. Hot as an asshole in hell. Ecch!"

We had to inch our way through the village because a flock of goats and sheep blocked the whole road as they were herded back to the safety of their fold (usually the farmhouse living room) by their shepherd, the lonely boy with the flute and the faithful sheepdog.

Lazily leaning over the backs of their turned-around chairs, the villagers glared at us suspiciously while women stood in little clusters, chatting and gossiping. Sometimes they swore at us because, since the Silver Monster couldn't idle in its present sad state, I had to keep stopping, then lurching forward fast until I was right behind the flock still leisurely clopping along in front of us, leaving no room to pass, but leaving the villagers suffocated by huge clouds of dust and exhaust.

"About time we looked for a place to sleep. Then we can have some chow and turn in early." We couldn't sleep late. The heat started up at seven in the morning, the worst part was between two and four in the afternoon. Then when the sun set, it got a little cooler, but even then it was stuffy, sultry, sweltering, and, worst of all, humid, and you had to push through that stuff until about eleven o'clock at night.

"What's the next town?" I called to Barry.

He fumbled for the map, managed to get it out from under him and tried to open it up against the wind.

"A couple of little villages and Tunis is more than a hundred miles from here, so is Bizerta."

"That's one place we're going to steer clear of," I said. "Bizerta."

The whole town came tumbling down a while ago. Four thousand dead.

"What do you want to do?" I said to Barry. "If we keep on going to Tunis, that means at least six hours more because it's mountains, winding roads and hell's own corners all the way. At least we'll wind up in a bed though. No flies. And a good lay."

"Or we can stop at the next village. If there's a cheap hotel and a bar, we can pull in and go on tomorrow. If there isn't, we can sleep outside."

"What?" I said, shocked. "Without a broad?"

"Broad sky."

"Snuggled up against God's bosom. Is that what you mean?"

We were on a winding road of a fair-sized mountain and down in the valley to our left we could see a little village on a slope of parched yellow grass. To get there, we'd have to turn off the expressway to Tunis —packed earth for the most part with a stretch of asphalt here and there, then big stretches of hard sand.

"Might not be a bad idea," Barry thought. "The people around here haven't been spoiled yet by all the English and American tourists. We might be able to get a good cheap meal and a cheap room too. Otherwise we can always put up the tent outside the town."

"As long as there's a nice piece in a stone house, anything's all right with me. I'll even sleep in a cell if I have to. As long as I'm nice and cool tonight—between the lovely cold damp walls of a jail cell, the kind of walls that keep sweating all night long so I can cool my face off if it gets too hot."

That heat got me down. It was really broiling now because we were inland and there wasn't any sea breeze. When we finally got down off the mountain and onto level ground, we took the first road we thought might lead to the village we'd seen before.

I kept imagining delicious cold showers or a bathtub full of ice cubes and cold cans of beer, a naked broad with big swinging tits sitting on the edge of the tub, and me holding a Mickey Spillane in one hand and fingering her with the other. It was the only way I could keep my mind off the heat.

180

We looked down the wide goat trail and suddenly, far off, saw the village, a tiny village, a Tunisian Dogpatch. An open casbah. A square in the middle with a well, some white limestone houses, mud huts, a communal restaurant, billiard table, and meeting hall. They don't have any churches. The wide open space is their church. At noon every day they bow to the east, to Mecca, with a high priest yodeling his prayers from the top of the highest tower.

"Here we go!" I said to Barry.

We shoved our hair out of our eyes, and I rode into the village at a good clip, gunning the motor straight to the square. Our tail-pipe sputter shot through the whole village, ricocheting off the whitewashed houses like machine-gun fire.

All the houses on the square were white, gray now in the fading light. The entire population had come out to see us, about fifty men, women, and children. They had heard the drone of the motor from a long way, booming off the enormous mountainsides. It was a pretty square and I rode around it slowly, giving the Monster more gas than she could swallow to make a real bang-up entrance. Not a restaurant in sight. All the houses were built in Moorish style, all the doors closed, and in a few houses the lamps were already on. Dim kerosene lamps or gas lamps that cast a sallow light over the bare living room. The villagers didn't trust us and we weren't welcome.

"Well, I don't see any hotel," I said to Barry, "and I don't see any restaurants either. Only thing I see is that funny Arab beer sign on that house over there."

"The guy could have inherited it," Barry said logically. "And when we get inside, all we get served is a knife in the throat."

I would have given anything for something, anything, to drink—cold beer or if nothing else 7-Up or lemonade, lemon juice, with cubes of ice and sugar water. There wasn't much to see in the village. Maybe fourteen houses, with children, dogs, men, and women perched out in front of them.

The sky suddenly turned almost pitch black. I rode up to the middle of the square. To the well. I thought, anyway I'll drink all I can hold and fill up the can because I knew if we slept outdoors, I'd die of thirst. Men in white or brown caftans started drifting around us for a look at the motorcycle. (Silver Monster has always been a hit. In all the villages or towns we passed through, people were always filled with awe for the colossus. They would circle it and look at the panel and gauges for hours. When I started her up, they would all smile wistfully and many of the men saw the Monster as the object of their motorized dreams come to life.)

I stopped, slipped Silver Monster out of gear, gunned hard, and let her roar. Jerking the choke out a couple of times, I made her really bomb the town with two short sweet explosions. Then I let the motor die; at exactly the same time as Barry stepped out of the sidecar and I stepped off the saddle, a flash of lightning lit up the village, followed by thunder, rain, sleet and hail.

God's water started pouring down by the ton. The dust clouds the first few drops made were laid fast by the enormous waves of water that came crashing down. The people ducked for cover and we said, "Great," and let ourselves get soaked.

In three seconds we were drenched to our tanned skins and I screamed, "Get the goddamn top up, the engine covered, my pajamas, my toothpaste!" We flapped out the canvas, threw it over the Monster and looked for shelter because we were still standing out there in the middle of the square.

The people were overjoyed. Men and women danced around and burst out in laughter and yelled "Hip Hip Hurray" in Arabic. People came racing out with stone bowls to fill up on the heavenly water. Children jumped up and down in the fast-forming puddles.

We'd never seen anything like this primitive spontaneous reaction before. Suddenly everybody came running toward us laughing and shouting with joy. Happy faces all around us, everybody touching us, men running off to their houses and bringing back decanters of wine and black cigars, the women, young and old, kissing us whether we liked it or not. They hoisted us up on their shoulders and bounced us up and down. We didn't get it. What was going on?

We were carried through the laughing crowd into one of the houses and tossed down on a big bed covered with pillows and animal skins—a couple of kids still lying on it too. It was one of those enormous beds the whole family sleeps in, together with all the livestock and where the chickens lay eggs between the sheets. The kids were gleefully cleared out of the bed and there we were.

The whole village was shoving and crowding in at the door for a look. No windows in the house, so no crowding about the windows. Everybody was shaking hands with the host and hostess. We still couldn't figure out what was going on. We sat up, greeted the people politely, accepted their words of thanks. Our hands nearly fell off there were so many hands to shake. Men pinched our arms, women tugged our hair, pulled our heads all the way back and, by the light of the lamp, looked us deep in the eyes.

One of the men, who spoke a few words of French, enthusiastically explained that they would be grateful to us forever. We were the real thing—the Rain Kings. We gradually understood that these primitive villagers thought we were some kind of gods who'd come thundering down the mountain, and thus from a long way away—the Tunisian is notorious for sticking close to home—had landed in their village on our silver machine, then put their village under a spell, contacted our chief somewhere up above (the one in charge of water) by making certain terrific noises, at which point the god had graciously granted his sons their request. We were the living proof of all this—our eyes, the way we looked.

As a matter of fact we did look like young gods. We had wild platinum blond manes, bleached by the Mediterranean. We were tanned by the hot sun, the spatters of oil and the salty wind on the motorcycle. Teeth white as snow, standing out against our dark skin (toothpaste manufacturers couldn't wish for better ads). We wore worn-out dungaree suits, frayed at the elbows and knees, light blue American work shirts, and boots of untanned leather that we'd had molded onto our feet in a little Moroccan village for a song, plus our last pack of Van Nelle's Heavy Shag. Most of all it was our eyes. Barry and I had the light blue eyes of the north, and that's what did it. Set against our brown faces, our eyes were the blue of the warm oceans, so we were real gods.

It was getting pretty crowded. Hordes of people were standing around in the room, and it stank like hell. All those warm clothes they had been sweating in for months without being able to wash them because there wasn't any water, and now suddenly that delicious wet rain. The cool rain started the clothes steaming. Pretty soon the room was like a sauna in Helsinki. Mmm, I thought, that's just what I need now, a nice steam bath and a Finnish Flicka lashing away at my back. Women sat down next to us on the big musty couch and wiped us dry with their crocheted stoles or night caps. Our boots were being cuddled dry between the full breasts of big warm country wenches.

"Hey," I said, and nudged Barry. "That's something I never really thought about, that maybe I really *am* a god. I always knew that deep down there was a god hovering around somewhere. Give 'em their money's worth. Look holy, man."

"Right," Barry said, and folded his legs up under him so he looked like some statue or other. I could think of two statues he vaguely reminded me of; one was the See No Evil, Hear No Evil, Speak No Evil monkeys, and the other was a guy with a peanut head and a big belly sitting just like Barry.

"Hey Barry," I said. "How do you do that anyhow?"

"What?"

"What you're doing now. With your feet curled up. Is it hard?"

"No, it's easy," said Barry. "Like a tailor sits."

I copied him and there I was with my legs crossed and my feet tucked under, just like the guy with the peanut head I had in the back of my mind.

"Hey," I nudged Barry again, "what's this position called anyway?"

"The Buddha sit."

"Oh. That's the guy with the peanut head?"

181

Once we got into the swing of things, we really liked playing the god bit. We'd already toasted and downed many a cup of full-flavored wine. Our host turned out to be a kind of top dog in the village, a lawyer or something. Anyway it was an important family in the row of huts and they begged for the Honorable Honor of having the Rain Kings as their guests for the night. We said that though we were accustomed to luxury, we would make an exception for them and would spend the night in these humble quarters. They jumped up and down, jumped practically right out of their skins, and then the whole village started cheering and jumping out of their skins until there wasn't any more skin to jump out of.

There was going to be a big feast that very evening and a couple of goats were slaughtered. They were going to offer up the blood to us, the Rain Kings, but we said that wouldn't be necessary, that it was an old-fashioned custom, much too sticky and messy, and, besides, what if one of the gods tripped over the sacrificial bowl and sent the whole bloody mess flying in all directions? But we said we'd ask Our Fathers in the Clouds what they thought about it.

The Wise Old Man of the village (he alone had that title and used it to ensure his position as mayor, notary public, consul, and police force) would also be at the party and would sacrifice his lovely mistress to the gods.

"But," we said, "our eyes are blue as the oceans of water that our upper gods, as well as our upper upper gods, conjured up for this clod of earth here, and such eyes have eyes only for the Beauties of the village, the girls, the beautiful women."

The crowd was deeply ashamed of the ignorance they had displayed and they ran off to pull their daughters out of the haystacks where they were putting out for the boys from a neighboring village. And maybe the Rain Gods wanted to pass the time smoking a real Napmaquacian water-pipe until the Snacks, Tidbits, and Delicacies, and above all the Luscious Dessert we had set our ocean-blue eyes on were ready to be served.

(I still remember the two waterpipes we had up in the attic. My father brought them back from one of his trips to Turkey. I took some of the kids up there on Saturday afternoons and we had a Secret Ritual. We'd lift a couple of real cigarettes from our parents, put some water in the glass ball, put one of the tubes in our mouth, and then take the cigarettes and blow the smoke through the tube into the glass ball.)

We told our host that the gods would greatly appreciate this gesture. We were always willing to smoke a Peace Pipe with our Underdeveloped Brothers. We leaned back on the pillows, took in big breaths of the sweet smoke, and then puffed it back into the long pipes so that the water got cloudier and cloudier and started bubbling mysteriously. It was a mixture of marijuana, hashish, and elephant toenails, and everything got even cloudier than the water. With all the wine we'd already put away, we felt like real gods. If it hadn't been so hard to steer safely out the door, blocked by all our enthusiastic followers and disciples, I swear I could have flown faster than a jet and straight as an arrow up to the sky.

The women were busy with the food. Heavenly aromas came from the kitchen where about ten women were milling around. It smelled delicious. Freshly slaughtered goat's meat, a nice leg of lamb, or brains picked out of a baby lamb's head (nothing to it really, and the only reason it's so good is that it's so expensive at Dikker and Thijs in Amsterdam). Sometimes I thought I smelled turkey, a light aroma that tickled my nostrils, but I couldn't say for sure. And further contemplation of the matter was far beneath the dignity of a god.

They had cooked up a kind of punch, with spices, wine, and fruit, and while it was still warm it was poured into our open mouths, our heads bent all the way back. If you thought about it, we really had done a lot for these people. For a few months we'd turned the heating up full blast in Tunisia until one day we suddenly decided to do a good deed for humanity and so we irrigated their land again, watered their gardens, sprinkled their plants, drowned their mosquitoes, filled up their reservoirs, fed their animals, turned their grass green, washed off their streets, fortified their spirits, gave them hope for the future—and even pepped up their women who were lying around, stupefied by the continuous heat, uninterested, their legs spread, and who were now fresh as daisies again inside and out. Now all the passions could sprout again, and the weeds, too. Pretty soon it would be harvest time.

We thought, what would a real god be thinking of after all this? He'd have humanity make sacrifices to him. His wants and desires would be taken care of. He would be universally respected by the townspeople so he could paint the town red if he felt like it. In the first place there had to be some festivities. Nothing was too festive for us gods. We didn't ask for much. Just food and firewater, peace pipes and beauties. The folks had fixed themselves up a little (clean shirts, etc., instead of those long, hooded tablecoths that are hot as hell—but then those sweaty rags are what make folklore) and they brought us their gifts and offerings.

One of the first things set in front of us was a huge, a gigantic, an enormous turkey. We lost no time sinking our teeth into the sturdy legs we carved off with two sword-size knives. The bird was packed with raisins and apples, and while we picked at the snow-white meat clinging to the poor turkey's bones, we looked at the other gifts being showered upon us. Jewelry, earrings, the women throwing us kisses along with their jewelry. One of them tossed a cast-iron coffee grinder that landed on my foot instead of in my lap, so for hours I nursed my bruised foot by sitting on it. And what was I supposed to do with a cast-iron coffee grinder anyway? I always buy ground or instant.

Everybody brought something. Silver and gold trinkets, beads and teeth, wrought-iron slave bracelets, old coins, groceries, hunks of material, embroidered pillows, four pairs of leather slippers with pointed toes, caftans.

73

Everybody gave and then helped themselves to snacks they'd brought with them and pieces of goat's meat. Outside, two more goats were being barbecued.

Young girls were brought in—a pretty sad gang. A few pimply teen-agers and three older but nice-looking broads who all looked around thirty to me. All the women—and some weren't bad—came and sat down around us, behind us, in front of us, or at our feet. They pulled off our boots and caressed our feet. A fantastic feeling.

I took off my shirt and handed it to a dark big-breasted woman with an ugly face but terrific tits. She wasn't wearing a bra, and when she leaned over her breasts hung down and bulged out of her flimsy blouse. Her skirt didn't come down to her knees, not anywhere near. More like somewhere around her crotch. She had a great pair of legs; her whole body was beautifully built. Her nipples stuck out indignantly and you could see the pink through her black blouse. A fantastic body, just that horrible face. Not really an ugly face either, just one of those unpleasant discontented faces—like once a long time ago she was mistaken for a cobblestone and spent too much time getting walked on.

I took her hand and rubbed it across my back, something I love. Later I want to hire an African girl to do nothing but scratch my back all day, and a well-built naked black man to shake a bunch of ostrich feathers around to keep me cool. She was a champion back-scratcher. I had the feeling there was a gorgeous girl in back of me with her breasts tapping against my shoulder blades. But that face!

But her girlfriend, who was sitting at Barry's feet, was gorgeous. Nice fierce sharp face. A kind of Ursula Andress, but a browner edition, with protruding cheekbones, lovely jet black eyes, and a broad toothpaste smile. Well-built, a whopping pair up front, but terrible legs. Fat ele-phant's legs, like balloons or sausages, big at the bottom, thinning out at the top. A beautiful woman except for those legs!

It became quite a problem because the girls made it clear they were meant for us, the High Priests, and wanted to have Satan driven out of them by the Holy King-size Magic Wand. The rest of the broads were nothing special. Nice friendly women, but no stars. Only the two girl-friends were left. I felt her tits poking around against my back, but when I thought of that face, I was afraid to turn around. I had a picture of her in my mind that was indelible: this girl had always been first in line when they were handling out all the body parts from the neck on down; it was just when they got around to handing out noses, teeth, ears, and eyes in the Face Department, there she was way back at the end of the line. Her girlfriend led the pack by a mile in the Ugly Face Department.

"Which one do you want?" I asked Barry.

"Well, to tell the truth," he said, thoughtfully, "that one's got an ugly face but from the neck on down she sure looks appetizing. The other one's got a face like an angel but I don't go for those grand-piano legs."

"Which'll it be?" I asked. "Top or bottom? If you're hot on bottom, the one with the face is just the thing. You've no idea what a ball that can be if you do it right. And then there are those tits. Big and a little flabby, yea. Plenty of babies must have been at them, and man-size babies too. The other one—just the opposite. She's got class, you can tell that by her face. Noble blood in her veins. A baroness or a countess, that's pretty clear. And a pair of A-1 tits. Very aristocratic. Wears a nice respectable light blue bra. Great girl. But obviously didn't take care of her legs. Didn't walk enough, lay around too much, not enough pinching and squeezing going on down there."

We argued about who would get whom, and how we would do it, and finally I said, "Listen, here's what we do. We get the girls to lie down next to each other flat on their backs, except head to foot like they're ready to sixty-nine each other. Then we lie down *across* them so we've each got two women, the legs of one and the tits and face of the other. The so-called two-by-four position. So we'll have to have a test question to see who gets the good half and who gets the bad. If you lose and wind up with the ugly legs plus face, it won't be so bad because you'll know you were tricked into it. So here's the question: What's the difference between a saloon and an elephant's fart?"

Barry puzzled away at it, working hard, and when he finally gave up, I said, "Well, one's a bar-room, Barry, and the other's a barROOM! So that settles that and I get the two good pieces. But first we've got a lot of drinking and smoking and laughing to do, because, after all, we're gods and we'll only be doing what all the priests and monks have been doing since the beginning of history—getting while the getting is good, exploiting people, sponging, cheating them out of everything they have by telling them pretty stories or threatening them with all kinds of tortures. And, talking about monks and priests," I said, "remember our host said that the Wise Old Man of the village, who must be some kind of holy hermit living up in the mountains, was going to bring his mistress along for us? Hermits always keep the best pieces up there in their huts."

"Yeah," Barry said, "the old lechers. Hermits, sure, between one lay and the next. Well, maybe his mistress will take care of all our problems," Barry said cheerfully. "Maybe she'll be such a looker that one of us will get her and the other can have the two-by-four job all to himself.

"Let's see what turns up first," I said. "And, don't forget, there may be some beauties still going at it out in the cactus fields. You never can tell."

75

The crowd in the room kept coming up to offer us more to eat and drink, helping themselves to plenty at the same time too. They were all either tight or stoned. And outside it was still coming down in buckets. They started doing some Tunisian folk dances and suddenly one guy started bleating away on a bagpipe. I couldn't believe it at first. I thought it must be some mixed-up Scot, but he was a native all right, who'd met some Scot out working on the Burma Road and swapped his veteran's pension for a bagpipe. It hadn't taken him long to see he'd been gyped blind and he was no longer fond—simple man that he was—of the Scots.

All at once a reverent hush fell over the room and an old man came toward us through the crowd, his outstretched arms clearing the way in front of him, the people all timidly stepping aside. Our host went up to the old man and hugged him the way Makarios always gets hugged or Joe Valachi gets hugged in jail. Then, holding the old-timer by his heavily-ringed little finger, our host brought him up near us.

He was a real weirdo, the Wise Old Man. A short fat bubble of a guy with a wild barbaric hairdo. It was hard to tell, looking at all the hair around his neck, if it was pubic hair pushing up from below or whether his neck hair went all the way down to his balls. One big black mass of hair. A big black mustache curled up at the ends, a bit smaller than Salvador Dali's, but thicker, and a long beard, black and gray and white, and with some first-class curls in it, too. He was wearing a dirty monk's robe with a piece of rope tied around his bulging belly. Fat greasy fingers loaded down with rings. I even saw a Yale University ring on his little finger when he took my hand and carefully kissed it with his greasy lips.

From close up he was a wrinkled old guy with chapped skin and crow's feet around his watery eyes and I could see he powdered his pale, smoked-meat cheeks and was wearing rouge and a touch of lipstick, and his beard must have been dyed. When he bent over my shoulder for the famous French greeting, I could see the remains of couscous, chicken feathers, and tomato pits stuck all over his beard, which turned out not to be dyed after all. It was just black from huckleberry juice and other juices and maybe hot tar, too. His breath stank like a sick sewer.

He was the kind of a guy who sits on top of a flagpole crapping in his pants all day or lies under a Sacred Cow. Looked like a kind of Allen Ginsberg type, only sixty years older. The Rasputin type, I realized— the Rasputin of Tunisia. (I thought, nice name for a jazz tune, "Tunisian Rasputin.") The beastly type, the nonchalant monk fearlessly wallowing in sin, a well-rounded all-around man.

While we were greeting each other French style, he pinched my pecker and squeezed my balls so that I had to extract my foot from its warm place among the women sitting on the bed and give him the knee. His balls felt like glass marbles against my sensitive knee, and he doubled up and stepped back with a pained grimace. I know it's not fair to fight a ninety-two-year-old man, but he was asking for it. Because he was such an all-around man, he was sure to have a nice piece of ass with him, and maybe a few more stashed away up in his holy hut. A smart guy like that was sure to have plenty of tricks up his sleeve. Just one was enough for me, and one for Barry.

The crowd flocked around the old man, and our host and hostess took their positions on both sides of him proudly, like a wholesome artistic Dutch couple standing on each side of the M.C. at the opening of their first Joint Exhibition.

(The M.C. is usually the Soggy Noodle. About a third of the exhibitions held in Holland since 1950 were opened by our soggy man of letters, whether they were exhibitions of art, or rare books, or no-hands paintings —the brush held between clenched teeth—or even the opening of a snack bar. Simon's always willing and able to say whatever the artist's little heart desires—for a small fee, that is. He can also rave about it in glowing terms and he won't give up before his article gets printed in one of the daily or weekly papers, also for a small fee.)

In broken English the hermit offered us his "Beautiful Fahra," his long-time mistress, his favorite snow-white bosom. The crowd started murmuring. They were obviously aware of Fahra's beauty. That name alone! I saw visions of a beautiful sturdy North African pin-up girl with a tiger's smile. An Eartha Kitt type.

"You accept? Yes?" he asked in his heavy accent.

We answered enthusiastically, "Yes, Old Holy Man, we do," knowing it would show a lack of respect for him if we asked to see her first.

"She is nice chick," he said, and all the bystanders nodded in agreement, like a chorus of connoisseurs, men and women both. So we could tell she really must be something special.

"Nice chick and nobody ever screwed her yet but me. Everybody, they like to fuck her but nobody he dares. I kill with knife bloody cocksucker who tries."

We said, "Thanks very much, Old Holy Man. We are very proud to take your love for tonight and promise we'll screw her cunt against the white walls."

"Bring my Fahra in," he called out to the people near the door. "Make room for my Little Darling. Let her pass."

There was a lot of pushing and crowding around the door where everybody was looking for Fahra to come in. Speaking hurriedly, the hermit assured us, "She has fattest smallest cunt in whole country. Please keep secret because Oilsheik Ali Makhaf Makhaf try to kidnap, rape, and eat her pussy. He swallow her, he think he soon become biggest Oilman in the world and use my strength and wisdom out of eating my dear Fahra. Here she comes!" he said, proudly pointing to a guy in a floppy striped suit with a dirty little mustache who came in carrying a cage.

The Wise Old Man opened the cage and after a bit of a flutter and clucking and feathers flying he brought out a chicken. We were still staring at the door, waiting for some knockout playmate to walk in.

"Here she is!" crowed the old hermit, and he hoisted the chicken over his head and stared straight up its ass.

"You mean that's Fahra?" we stammered.

"Yes," he said benevolently, and handed me the chicken. It wasn't easy to catch hold of since it was flapping and squirming like mad. A nice fat chicken with a bright red comb, grayish-green eyes and snow-white feathers. Moved, the wise man stared at me as I held the chicken in my lap. "Yes," he said. "For last two years she has been my fiancée. Never so long have I lived with one girl in my whole life. Fuck her. I see she likes you very much. Fuck her. I see in her eyes, her beautiful eyes, she wants you to fuck her. I see, pal, she digs you the most."

I was in a tough spot. I didn't see how I could get out of it, either. He meant well and if I didn't accept his generous offer it would be a grave insult and the villagers would lose all their respect for me, since a god doesn't go around insulting people. On the other hand, though, I didn't really feel like Fahra. I thought she was going to be different. But there wasn't any way out. Everybody was eagerly waiting for the big scene to come. I flopped the chicken over into Barry's lap, where she fluttered down between his legs and looked ready to spend the rest of her life there. She made a big flap when Barry tried to set her down on the floor or give her back to me. She was getting flustered.

"I don't think your fiancée likes me," I said to the hermit, "and I'm sad because I can see she likes my brother and I don't want to break up true love."

The chicken gave me a dirty look, threw back her head with her bright little comb bobbing vigorously, and then looked up at Barry fondly. She cackled out a few short no-nonsense syllables and, from what I could make out of her chicken-Latin, it was something like, "Who do you think you are, looking at me like that? Don't try anything with me, because I'm a respectable chicken and no two-bit chippie. So what do you think you're up to?"

It must have been pretty close to that, because the hermit suddenly fell to his knees, flung up his fat little arms and started wailing, "Oh, my Little Fahra is angry. Her feelings are hurt and now she blames me."

The chicken strutted off Barry and across the bed, then whistled once and let fly with a piece of chicken shit that shot across the bedspread.

"Fahra seems to be a little sick. Maybe she's got the Curse," I said, and quickly handed him his chicken. He held her gently, holding her up for a look at her snow-white ass that again made that whistling sound, *Psssshhht,* and a white wet stream came spurting out into the hermit's eyes and his wild hair. He laughed. The stuff was dripping down his face, along his mustache, down his beard.

"My poor Little Baby is sick," he concluded. "Better I take her home." And after we'd both kissed Fahra good night on her snowy-white bosom, the hermit and Fahra took off.

A man wearing a shabby caftan, barefoot, and in need of a shave, came up, pulling a girl along behind him. A fantastic feast for the eyes. About twenty. A girl like Pier Angeli or Claudia Cardinale in a faded, patched dress, and bare feet. A magnificent creature. Beautiful legs, beautiful face, and, as far as we could see, everything else in good shape, too.

"Well, I'll be damned!" we said in unison. "What a piece! Where'd she come from?"

The man knelt down in front of us. He had a nice friendly face and he begged us to take his daughter along with us. The man who'd been translating for us came over and translated what the old man was saying. He had one foot in the grave and knew he didn't have much time left, and the only thing he was leaving behind was his daughter. She had to get out of this village. She had to go to the big city because she needed help. Maybe we could bring her to the medicine men in white jackets with the white veils covering their faces. (He had seen a picture of them once in a magazine somebody had tossed out of a truck on the big road. He had stretched out in the bushes for hours looking at the colored pages and had finally taken it home with him.)

Now that he was about to kick off, and since we were gods anyway, he begged us to take his most valuable possession on earth and make sure she was in good hands. Maybe all the gods together could put in a good word for her. If just once in her life she could hear Ali Ben Ali's bagpipe serenade or the chirping of many-colored butterflies. If she could just learn to say a few sentences, she'd be happy the rest of her life. The poor kid was deaf and dumb. A pity for a girl as pretty and well-built as she was. Well, but that's the way it goes in these backward villages. Some people die without ever once having left the village they were born in. The old man wept at our feet and begged us to buy Fatima.

"How much?" I said in a godlike tone of voice.

"A hundred pieces of silver. It'll be her dowry."

"A hundred? Twenty-five, and not a penny more."

"Seventy-five?" he said.

"Okay," I said, "forty-five and not another word about it. I don't like haggling."

"All right," he said sullenly. "If that's the way you want it, I'll make up the rest of the dowry myself."

When we'd solemnly sworn on the Koran that we would take her to the medicine men in the white jackets and veils, he suddenly clutched his heart and collapsed by the bed. The good man died of a massive heart attack. He had felt his end approaching and had directed his last steps toward the Rain Gods. All for his deaf-mute daughter. He must have been a loving father, I thought. Amen.

A veil of mourning fell upon the festivities. When everybody had managed to disentangle themselves, the veil vanished just like in the fairy tale of The Vanishing Veil. They carried the man's body out. I heard a lot of banging up on the roof and asked the guy who spoke French if it was the custom here to leave dead bodies on the roof. No, no, he exclaimed, the body was just put up there to give the vultures and other carnivorous birds a chance to nibble all the flesh off the bones. It didn't take long. In this hot sun, all that would be left of the body by sunset would be a few bleached bones. This had to be done because of the burial problem. The ground was so hard in the mountains, they couldn't dig graves. The bones were put into a plastic bag, a few stones tied onto the bag, then the bag was dropped in the well. The birds had picked the bones clean and the well was deep enough.

We gently lifted Fatima onto the bed. She sat down next to us, a bit scared and very timid. The other broads turned green with envy and looked down their noses at her. They were afraid of the competition, and they had reason to be. Fatima's beauty far surpassed the others'. Experienced travelers that we were, we'd seldom seen anything like her blossoming in the wilderness. Any wilderness. She gobbled down the meat the hostess offered her, biting pieces off with her sparkling white teeth. After all, she was now one of the crew, my rightful possession, and she had a right to her share of the feast.

Our interpreter asked us, on behalf of a humble Tunisian citizen, if we gods were willing to help a simple native solve a big problem.

"Shoot," I said. "Everything's for free tonight. Tomorrow's another day."

The native was a little guy dressed up in a black suit, his shirt collar flopping out sportingly over his lapels, his shoes all shined up, and his hair smoothed flat with a gob of goat fat—a guy who'd obviously climbed into his Sunday best before daring to face the Rain Gods. He had a pale face with sunken cheeks but a jazzy little mustache that looked like our great statesman Luns'—as if the rats had been at it. He whispered something in the interpreter's ear, and while his problem was being translated he looked a bit embarrassed and even tried to put on a fake look of being ashamed.

The problem was, he was married to a prolific cow who every nine months unloaded one or two new hungry mouths to feed. He had, at present count, seven singles plus three sets of twins, and he realized he couldn't go on taking care of a tribe as big as that. He had a good job as a valve man in a nearby oil processing plant, but every morning he still had to get up and go off to work on his motorbike and put in his day's work, and there wasn't any chance of a raise in sight. Not for years. He loved his wife and liked a good lay when he got home from work. So what should he do?

I couldn't very well recommend a TV set, since there wasn't any electricity in the village, and anyway Tunisia didn't have any TV, so that wouldn't go him much good. Suddenly I got it.

"Barry," I said, "you still got that rubber on you?" Barry fumbled around in his back pocket and finally brought out a tiny silver-wrapped packet.

"Here," I said to the man. "This ought to help you. Use these, lots of them. Here's one for a start."

I handed him the packet. He gratefully accepted it, then worked off the wrapper and when he saw the condom said, "Hmm," and stuck it in his mouth daintily. After tasting it and chewing on it awhile, he stuck up his thumb, said, "Ho Americano!" and walked off merrily chewing away.

Suddenly I was surprised to see the woman from the affair with the jug at the well earlier that day, the old woman who kept smiling at me with that deep warm grin with the toothless mouth with just one little tooth sticking up in it and who kept on saying "Oesjipappa." Only it wasn't. This one had a red kerchief on her head and the other one had a dark kerchief on, but they looked exactly alike. Exactly. When she noticed I was gazing at her, she smiled proudly with a deep warm grin, just like that other woman in that other village. But when she opened her toothless mouth with just one little tooth sticking up in it the difference was obvious: this one had her tooth on the right side and the other one had her tooth on the left. I asked the interpreter to ask her if she had a sister living in the neighborhood. He walked over to her and when he shouted yes, the old woman looked on with a grin, the warm deep kind, spontaneously coming forth from her mouth which was toothless, except for one, only one, little tooth, which was sticking up in it.

Outside it was still raining cats and dogs. When we did a job, we did it well. It splashed down on the walls, washed off all the dust and heat, and cleaned up the whole village. The party was gradually breaking up, people going off to their huts after wishing us good night. When all the others had gone, Fatima, Barry, and I were left. The Beautiful Face and the Ugly Face were the last to leave.

My host and hostess insisted we sleep in their house. They could sleep on the porch, a kind of wooden platform with a thatched roof that would keep them dry, or at any rate keep out most of the long and eagerly-awaited rain that was still coming down in buckets.

We got all our presents together, all the gifts and sacrificial offerings presented to the Rain Kings by the good-natured villagers. Earrings, strings of pearls, gold rings with stones, wrought-iron anklets, coins, and other things. There were even kerosene lamps and crocheted mats, just right for the mantlepiece at mother's up next to the clock. Strangely enough there was also a pair of strong black knitted goat's-wool socks. I remember the woman with the sad melancholy eyes who tossed them to us earlier in the evening. I saw right away that they would be good to wear in my winter boots. She was old, but she was still all there. When she'd caught our attention, she'd said the socks had belonged to her late husband, and that she always wore them in the winter. It can get mighty cold in Tunisia.

In her broken French she said, "My late husband, may Allah save his soul, wore those socks for sixty-three years and never had a single hole. And he never once took them off. He went to bed with those socks and got up with those socks. Of course, it took a while for me to get used to them," the woman said with a naughty smile. "Those hairy socks rubbing against my bare bottom. The itching made me giggle at first. But think of it, in all those years I only had to darn them twice—while he kept them on, of course. He was a strange bedfellow, the old one. Born wearing those socks, he wanted to go to Allah with those socks on, too. One of the times I had to darn them it wasn't his fault. A neighbor slashed him with his scythe while they were playing a game of checkers. I say that should be proof enough that this nonsense about Tunisian wool not being any good is just that—nonsense. They're just jealous, that's all. Jealous."

"Let's get some sleep," I said to Barry. "I'm bushed. I've got to stretch out. What are we going to do with the girl?"

She was sitting just a little way off from me on that gigantic bed that was big enough for ten people. She was following our every move and expression very carefully. She was still a savage and she'd had a rough life, of course, being deaf and dumb. And now, to add to all that, her father was dead. We'd take her to the institute for the deaf and dumb in Tunis; they'd know how to help her there. We still had a few drachmas left, enough to get us back to Ibiza anyway. In Tunis, we'd give her whatever we had left over and that would keep her going for a while; then she'd have to get help from the state somehow. The villagers had given us a lot of loot—jewels and all that—and naturally they'd be worth quite a bit, maybe even worth a lot. You never could tell what you might pick up in a remote place like this. There might even be great treasures there, if the so-called civilized world with its explorers that mean so well hadn't gotten there first and plundered the tombs and raped the entire female population. Museums of natural history are stuffed with that kind of booty.

I tried to win Fatima's confidence, looked at her sweetly and motioned for her to come a bit closer. She was scared and didn't know what was going to happen. She was all alone in the world. I felt sorry for the poor kid. We tried to explain she should lie down between us. Frightened, or not quite sure what we were trying to say, she just looked at us with her beautiful chestnut brown eyes. Looking at her took my breath away.

We blew out the oilburner and I opened the doors in front and back of the house and a nice breeze cooled the room off and cleared out the stove stink.

The bed was covered with carpets and cushions and the sheets were silk. That bed could handle anything—and it did, too. The host, now rotting out on the porch with his wife, usually slept in that bed. Together with—on workdays anyway—his concubine, his eldest daughter, his wife, and a blue Pomeranian, plus the sow, the favorite goat, the money box, and his three little kids. It was different on Sunday. Then he slept with his wife, his wife's brother, all his brothers-in-law, the blue Pomeranian, plus three aunts from the next village. They threw a cozy little goat-cheese party for the occasion and the three tiny tots were cruelly bundled out of their three little dreams and had to nestle in under the branches of the old pine tree for the night, while everybody else stripped down for the big bare-assed goat-cheese party.

I got in under the sheets and after a lot of arm-waving finally got the mosquito net spread out over me. There'd be millions of mosquitoes as soon as the rain stopped, and steering clear of them would be a real problem. Our host has assured us that as long as you stayed under the *klamboe* you were safe. He said he'd had an insect spray once but that was so long ago he didn't know if he still had it or not. I motioned to Fatima and she looked at me with eyes full of question marks and then crawled over a bit closer. I tried to win her confidence and had some luck anyway. She wasn't staring at me so strangely any more. But she was still afraid to get undressed. She crept in under the sheets like a tired kitten and curled up her legs just far enough so I could see she didn't

have anything on under her shabby dress. She was lying in the middle of
the bed now, between Barry and me. Just a bit closer to me, I thought.

"Don't try any tricks while I'm sleeping, huh?" I said to Barry, and
pulled the mosquito net farther up over me. I nodded comfortingly to
Fatima and wished her sweet dreams. Though she didn't understand me,
she knew what I meant. I shut my eyes. It was warm. Too warm. A
few minutes later, I shoved back the net and slipped out of bed very carefully, felt my way to the front door, and stood there awhile enjoying the
breeze.

When I'd cooled off, I got back in bed but not under all those carpets
and blankets. I lay there awake, my arms behind my head, thinking about
the crazy way things turned out. And not just that night either. My whole
life long.

182

Last night we were in Annaba playing twenty-one with a couple of sailors
and now all at once we're in another country, in the middle of a wilderness of sand and shriveled trees. In a pint-sized hick town where everybody thinks we're magicians and rain gods.

This morning, on our way, mussel soup. In a little restaurant on the
coast road just before the border. It was one of those little roadside places
with wood walls, a big kitchen stove and two huge propellers twirling on
the ceiling to cool off the customers.

When we came in I saw the row of pots and pans steaming invitingly
on the warm stove and took a peek. Typical Tunisian food. I also saw a
big bucket of mussels, fresh from the sea. The restaurant wasn't far from
the sea. You could look out the window and see the blue summer sea
glittering in the bright sunlight. The mussels were still black from the
cold dark depths they'd been heartessly hoisted out of into the warm sunlight. They were living creatures like anyone else and they hadn't asked
to be born either. They made my mouth water.

I asked the waiter if they were on the menu.

"No," he said. "They're not. Some guy who goes for that kind of
slippery stuff is going to pick them up here later on."

"Well," I said to the man, "I can see you've never eaten mussels.
They're the healthiest seafood there is and" (I winked) "a damn good
aphrodisaic too. Whenever I'm in love, I always stuff myself on mussels,"
I told him, because I really had to have some of those mussels and he was
the man who could fix me up with them.

"And," I laughed, "you can bet your bottom drachma I'll get what
I'm after, after I've finished off a few dishfuls of those things. Northern

France, around Lille, is famous for its mussels. Every year in September they've got this big Mussel Festival that lasts for days. You can imagine the screwing that goes on then!" I said to the man, and suddenly his ears pricked up and he was dying to hear more. "It's just one big love-in. The waiters have to step over their fucking customers if they want to serve new customers. And the children they make there every year! Just like that, right on the restaurant floor or out on the terrace flat out on the shells! By the end of May all the maternity wards in France are packed. People charter busses to come all the way to Lille.

"All the monasteries and convents in the region have their own Mussel Festivals too. There're a few cloisters for nuns and monasteries for friars so it works out just right. First the monks pack away as many mussels as they can eat, all of them together in their dining room. Trays and trays of the heavenly seafood. The sauces give off a fantastic aroma! It's the parsley that gives it its terrific tang. All that eating and drinking and smelling makes all those monks gradually recall that little thing between their legs whose true function they'd long since forgotten. All they used it for was to ring door-bells, or for a trumpet when the abbot felt like playing a solo on it. Then the monks storm down to the convent and suddenly the henyard is bristling with cocks!

"The nuns rejoice, recalling the function of that hairy slot between their legs. The Mother Superior probes them daily with a long thick pole wrapped in a goat hide to see if the evil fiend Satan is hiding inside. The pole is two yards long, and with the older nuns the Mother Superior has to stick more than half of it in because Satan might be hiding way back in some little nook or cranny. It hurts the new nuns in the beginning—the raw hide on the wood pole—but the more it hurts the surer they can be that Satan is being hunted out of them. If Satan still pesters them in their cells with his dirty stories, there's always a cat-o'-nine-tails around. Or the long camel whip they use on each other to banish Satan from their flesh. When all the nuns have come a few times getting rid of the Devil, they feel liberated at last. Such a blissful feeling. Enough to keep convents going forever.

"They all eat from the buckets of mussels set out for them. A gift from the simple fishermen for God's humble servants. The Carmelites loll in the confessional stalls or sprawl on the heavy tables, some of them half, others completely, undressed. After all, the Mussel Festival only comes once a year.

"The simple fishermen gather outside the walls of the convents and feast on the deep-sea mussels. They build big campfires and cook big iron potfuls of mussels. Tons of virile robust old salts fill up on the exquisite seafood.

"When they're all worked up to the boiling point, they make a mad dash for the open gates welcoming them into the convents. The nuns scream, screech, barely escape, get caught, and are flung onto the tables in the dining room. The tables are nice because it's cold in the grim little cells. Mussels or no mussels, it's no fun lying bare-assed on a chilly cement floor.

"A lot of musseling goes on, as the simple fisherfolk put it. And it is good musseling with the mussels. The festivities last until vespers and by then everybody's all musseled out.

"Then came the year when the Mother Superior was surprised at the enormous number of Arabs and Negroes who'd recently joined the ranks of the sailors and fishermen. Until she found out that for weeks the rabbi from the nearby synagogue had been doing a booming business selling tickets for the convents' Mussel Festival. A law was passed in the bishopric in question, affecting all the monks and nuns in the district. The law was blessed by the church and the Pope personally okayed it. He scribbled in the margin that he was terribly sorry he couldn't attend the Festival. He was fond of mussels and he'd heard so many stories from his daughter in one of the convents there.

"The Order of the Holy Cobweb endured these festivities, as they did all festivities, in complete silence—as, in fact, they endured everything. They had to because they were a very special order. They take an oath of silence. Hard Labor and Trap Shut. Otherwise, out you go. If you get more than fifty demerits for coughing or sneezing, you've had it. A dull life, but, the brothers remarked, if you hadn't opened your mouth for four years, you kind of got used to it and finally came to like it. There wasn't much left to talk about on this earth anyway. When they got to heaven though, Peter assigned them to jobs where they had to talk a lot—to pester them and to put them to the test, as if they hadn't had it hard enough already. Once a Cobweb always a Cobweb. Jobs like fish peddler, traveling salesman in the neon and silver halo trade, or tourist guide.

"There's the old story about one Cobweb who was hired by Our Lord as court jester. Every time he told a joke, Our Lord muttered he'd heard it before, usually centuries before. Anyway, Our Lord finally got fed up and said that if he couldn't come up with fresher material fast, he was through. The poor Cobweb was sent back down and accidentally dropped into a savage jungle where a band of parrots saved his life and fed and clothed him. They taught him how to talk again. By the time he'd finally learned all the jokes in the world and practiced till he could tell them all perfectly, Our Lord had already got TV.

"It was this same Cobweb who amended the by-laws of the Order to include the provision that every year on the last night of the Mussel Festival (the night everybody rushed to get in a last bit of musseling before it was too late), when the temptation was greatest, one of the monks of the Order could pronounce a complete sentence at the dinner table as some kind of compensation. Also to get them back into the swing of things so they'd be up to it when Our Lord pulled a stunt like making them talk.

"The new law went into effect two years ago and the brother who'd proposed the plan and got the by-law passed was given the honor of being the first to utter a sentence. The whole table stared at him expectantly, the monks' silent mouths hanging open. He pondered deeply and then, on the assumption that on this night, when the museling was going at full pitch, the last night of the Mussel Festival, he could hardly choose a better subject than museling, he uttered those historic words, preserved for all time in the books of the Order, 'I find the mussel soup a bit flat.' That was enough to last the Cobwebs a whole year. They retired to their cells while the walls talked about and pondered the deep significance of this single sentence.

"A year later when it was Mussel time again, it was Brother Tarantula's turn. This chubby, sparkling little monk, a true-blue mussel buff, took a deep breath, smiled happily, and carefully enunciated the solemn words, 'I find the mussel soup a bit too salty.' Then he proudly strode back to his seat.

"The Abbot made the annual speech at the next Mussel Festival and all their ears perked up because they didn't want to miss a single word. After all, he was the Abbot, and it was their food for thought for the whole year. Clearing his throat, the Abbot took a good look at everyone seated around the table, and said, 'All this bickering about mussel soup has got to—goddammit—stop!"

183

While I was telling these stories to the proprietor, a crowd had gathered around to listen to my discourse on the hard life and high times of the common mussel.

"Yes," he said, "now you mention it, I'd like a mussel or two myself." He bent over and whispered in my ear, "I've got a friend, a real knockout. Think I could mussel her up a bit?"

"Man," I said, "once a museler always a museler. You go show your fiancée they just don't make muselers like you any more. Of course, you've got to know the right recipe for the sauce—I mean the kind they make up in northern France. Because that's where the whole secret lies, in the sauce."

By now I was really aching for mussels and I said to the Algerian,

"Listen, it just so happens I know that recipe. It's called 'Moules Erotiques de Nicole Cano,' named after a real dish, the star of the Mussel Festival. And cook? I swiped the recipe from an old monk out there in France where it's all happening and that's what makes the mussels so erotic, remember? The sauce. Just don't ask me exactly how I got hold of it. I'll make a deal: I'll mix up some of that old 'Moules Erotique' for the three of us, only we don't pay and the wine's on the house."

"Cessibon," the innkeeper said and he rubbed his hands together in eager anticipation.

"Let's get started," I said. "Dump the mussels into the water!" But when he clumsily tried to tip the bucket and let a few mussels clatter onto the floor, I said, "Forget it. I'll do it. Just give me a nice big onion, a bottle of sharp white wine and a nice long celery stalk. And Barry," I yelled, "go get the spice bag from the side-car."

Barry came back just as I was slicing up the onion. Tears trickled out of my eyes. I rubbed them and they burned like hell, so I stepped outside. Fresh air ought to stop the burning, but not the Algerian air. I rubbed some cold beer over my eyes. That helped right away. I finished the bottle and set to work washing off the big stalk of celery in the bucket of water. I cut out the bad pieces and lopped off the top. Then I jerked off the thin skin and cut the stalk up in little square blocks. In the meantime the boss was watching to see if there was anything to sample yet. When there weren't any customers to wait on he stood around and got in our way.

"Boys, out of the kitchen!" I said, and Barry and our host sat down at one of the tables with a French-style red-and-white checked tablecloth and drank from a big bottle of white wine. Things quieted down. The customers paid their bills and on their way out stopped to watch approvingly as I cleaned out the mussels until there wasn't a grain of sand left.

The door opened and two broads came in, two voluptuous Algerian broads, obviously old friends of the boss since he ran up and embraced one, an ugly bitch whom he brought over to meet me—me, sweating like a pig, between the kitchen sink and the big hot stove and wondering why in hell I always felt obliged to show off my talents as a cook. Oh well, I thought, it's my hobby and it's more nourishing than saving stamps.

I grabbed a towel, dried my hands, and wiped the sweat off my forehead. This broad who came over to me—the proprietor's fiancée—was a guy with black hair, hands like coal shovels, and a nose Harry Mulisch must have overlooked when he was shopping around for his. His face was caked with powder and he missed looking like a woman by a long shot, but the proprietor didn't seem to notice. They gazed into each other's eyes and melted away, exchanging naughty-sounding remarks in their dialect, pinching each other's cheeks (and cheeks), and cooing with joy.

They watched me carefully as I flipped the mussels out of the strainer into a big iron pot. There was plenty for all of us, including the two "ladies." I poured three-quarters of the bottle of white wine into an earthenware pitcher, after taking a sip myself. It was good sharp tangy wine, remotely resembling retzina. I took down the cognac bottle—good French cognac, Rémy Martin—and added a dash of it to the pitcher. I asked the man in charge if he had some Burgundy vinegar stashed away some place, since that gives the sauce a good sharp sour flavor. Since he didn't know what Burgundy vinegar was, I used Algerian.

The other guy, the one who'd come in with the proprietor's fiancée, kept looking at me, and now and then I saw him talking to Barry. They seemed to be getting alone fine. The boss was oozing charm and kissing his fiancée smack in the middle of the nose, other facial areas being inaccessible due to the proportions of above-mentioned nose. I thought the other one looked pretty much like a woman and started wondering about Barry when I saw him moving in very close and cozy to give the guy a light. He was practically nosing his way into the guy's low-cut neckline.

I looked for garlic in the big vegetable bin, and when I found a clump I broke off four or five cloves, peeled and sliced them up very, very small. Then I chopped up a few stalks of parsley and let it all tickle my nose. Great smell.

All the burners were full up with pots or pans or kettles. I took a pair of iron tongs with a wooden handle so I wouldn't burn my hands, pushed a big soup tureen back across the hot iron, and hoisted my big pot with the mussels in wine up onto the empty burner. I'd already added the cognac, the onion, celery, and vinegar. I sprinkled it with the diced garlic and parsley, took a handful of salt and a fat pinch of pepper—not too much, of course—and then added a dash of olive oil plus a few spoonfuls of sharp French mustard.

While stirring it to get it all mixed in, I suddenly felt a hand on my shoulder. I turned around. First I thought it was the guy, but it turned out I was wrong; what I'd thought must be a guy in drag was a woman. And what a woman! Not so young any more, in her thirties, but still a feast for the eyeballs. A fresh sock-it-to-me face and straight black hair, shoulder length and sloppy. She was wearing a flimsy dark loose dress with a spectacular wide-open view. No bra on, you could see that through the thin dress, and the neck of her dress open practically down to her nipples.

I said, "Howdy doody to *you!*" and she said something in Arabic, something my ears couldn't follow but my balls understood like lightning.

"Oy, oy, oy, *what* a pair of boobies!"

She seemed to understand that without much trouble, and answered with a glowing, inviting smile. When I'd expressed my admiration a few more times by licking my lips and tracing the shape of her breasts in the air, she laughingly grabbed my hair and pulled to see if it was real. She laughed with her snow-white teeth (on the sides she had gold teeth, though) and her fiery jet-black eyes looked deeply into mine. Then she pulled my head down and bit me on the neck, very hard.

I screamed "Aaaaahhh. . . !" but mainly because of the unobstructed view I had of her natural charms, which were tremendous. Brown with pink tips, breasts that had been fingered often and well. They hung nicely, which added to their charm.

"Oy," I said, "mustn't forget the chow."

I poked up the fire in the stove and put the lid on the pot with the mussels. It had to stew for a while now. I heaved a sigh, wiped my hands and my forehead, and sat down with Barry, the boss, and his fiancée. And the double-barreled knockout sat down, too.

"That's the biggest cockcatcher in the neighborhood," Barry said. "He was just telling me," and he pointed to the restaurant owner who was engaged in an animated conversation. Probably telling his pal all about musseling it up at the annual Mussel Festival.

"Once she put out for three days and four nights without a break. The whole town rushed out to score a screw. She says she took on fifty-two different comers; he says it must have been at least sixty. She lost count. She's lovely to look at and she's yours for the asking. You can tell she wants you."

I thought about all the stories I'd just been telling, and thought if I stay here and ride that hump it'll take me about a week. Because I want to see who's going to come out on top, her or me after three days and four nights, just the two of us. I'll make mincemeat out of her.

The woman was still smiling at me, and just that look on her face made my mouth water. She'd obviously followed the gist of the conversation. She was sitting next to me and she lifted one beautiful brown leg up across my knees under the table. I stroked it here and there, and she grabbed hold of my hand and led it up with both her hands, over her knees, over her thighs, and then on in between. What I felt then sent a shock streaking across my chest and then a hard jolt farther below.

"Looking for something?" Barry asked, since I was sitting with my head against the edge of the table, practically falling off my chair. The boss and the others all laughed and winked at each other.

I said, "Barry, it can't go on like this. In a minute I'll fuck her right here under the table." And I pointed to the floor.

The woman tapped me on the arm and smiled and nodded toward a separate little room with a curtain for a door. She took my hand and tickled my palm. She wanted to get up and go right then. I was seeing nipple-shaped stars and long-tailed comets—until suddenly I remembered my "Moules Erotiques."

I jumped up, rushed over to the stove, picked up the steaming pot, and, getting a good grip on both handles, using the towel as a pot-holder, I brought the pot over to the table which our host had already set for the five of us. The dusky sexbomb served the food. The mussels had popped open from the heat and bulged out of their shells like lovely well-formed yellow-orange baby cunts. They tasted fantastic. We dipped them in the smooth yellowish sauce that was so sharp it tickled your tongue.

"Great, great, great," Barry said, "I don't know why you don't write a cookbook. Man, you could become Master of the Royal Kitchen. Just look at that broad putting them away. She looks like she's ready to come any minute."

As a matter of fact, the three Algerians did seem enraptured with delight. They grunted approvingly, and I didn't need three guesses to tell what they were going to do as soon as the meal was over. The meal was absolutely out of this world, and all that for a few minutes' work. It hadn't cost me a cent. Any way you look at it, it was a good deal—for connoisseurs only.

Every time I severed an organeish mussel from its base on its shell and slowly dipped it in the delicious sauce and brought it quickly up to my mouth so as not to feel that yearning one second longer than necessary, then first salaciously sucked the sauce out of the soft little body, then the sauce clinging to the outside, and then went on to take a tiny bite, as if torturing it just a bit, then finally swallowed the whole animal down—each time I did this it melted on my tongue and I could feel it gliding on down to my stomach. That's what I call erotic food!

All the other customers in the place stopped eating or talking and turned to gaze at us. One steady customer worked up his nerve, came over to our table and, after requesting our permission, hunted through the empty shells until he found a left-over mussel. He nibbled at it carefully and slowly, and then nearly fainted on the spot. His eyes glazed over with joy. He tossed some coins on the table and, sticking his finger in the pot on his way out through the bead-string door, licked off the sauce and let out a mighty "Whoopee!"

"His poor wife," the innkeeper mumbled.

He got up and put on his espresso machine. With a little bit of Kirschwasser, a pinch of cocoa, and some sugar to top it off, he made us all a boiling pot of espresso Café Kirsch. Then we settled back in our chairs. The woman had her skirt up way past her knees now, and I expected to see her full-fleshed coffee bean pop into view any second now.

Everybody was in a good mood. When I felt that slow heavy feeling coming on, I said to Barry, "Come on. Let's move. I want to be on the wide open road again, out in the fresh air. Before I know it, I'll be cuddled up in a warm cozy nest and I'll have to go back to the doctor for another shot. Man was made for better things than just to come down with a dose."

It made me proud to see I was able to resist temptation, although my little one-eyed brother would have liked nothing better than to bury himself for a while in a native Algerian flesh-hut.

184

Slowly I dozed off again. Just the thought of that tawny bitch in that Algerian roadside dive! Boy, did they ever lap up my "Moules Erotiques de Nicole Cano"! I smiled wistfully when I thought about it and regretted I hadn't taken her on.

I'm a genius—let's face it—when it comes to pots and pans. Not earlier, though. On the contrary. When I was seventeen and had just been kicked off a coaster and had sworn never to go back to sea, I got so drunk I staggered on board another ship. A Panamanian ship this time—the *Orang*. With a Turkish captain, Greek first mate, Chinese cook, and the rest of the crew Spaniards and Germans.

The ship's radioman talked me into it one afternoon when I was in Rotterdam to pick up my back pay and stopped in at a sailors' bar. There he was, a friend from my Navy days the year before.

"You've got to come, man," he said, and he described the boat he'd just been signed on to as if it was the greatest ocean steamer ever built.

Annabel was waiting for me, and though I'd promised her I'd be back on the first train out after I picked up my pay, I felt adventure pulsing in my blood and wanted to go to sea again. After all, I'm the great-grandson of Ramblin' Jack, the famous eighteenth-century British pirate captain.

I sent Annabel my back pay by money order, since I had plenty to eat and drink for the time being and wouldn't need it, and if we called in at a port I could always get an advance. In my tanked-up, half-stoned state, I'd said yes to Steven, who didn't feel at home as the only Dutchman among all the rabble and vermin that made up the crew of the S.S. *Orang*. He told me that "on board, the radioman is top dog, the only one the captain and the officers can't push around. So it's a perfect set-up."

When we finally stumbled onto the pier where the *Orang* was anchored, I got the shock of my life. A terrible old tub with a bad case of steel cancer. You could push your thumb against the steel plates and bore a hole all the way through. Rusty, rotten, and not a speck of paint. Just yellow and brown lubricating oil and splotches of red lead on the sides. One enormous SOS that could just barely stay afloat. Too late to go home, to Annabel's soft warm body—beautiful Annabel—instead of this carcass stinking of sour oil.

I got a cabin next to Steven's. A tiny two-by-two cabin, but at least I didn't have to share it with anybody. What a hell-hole! Unbelievable! The cabins were a mess and the heads caked with shit, as if everybody had shit around the hole instead of in it. The cook's galley stank of cod-liver oil, but that was just the cook's body odor. A toothless fat greasy Chink, about thirty-two years old (though he might have been 189—you can never tell with these Chinese).

I had signed on as cook's mate.

"Congratulations!" I roared at the Captain in a carefree moment. He was a chubbier version of Captain Walrus, with a big drooping mustache that ended up in a thin little curlicue, and he was juiced up like a proper drunken sailor. "You've just hired the best cook in the business!" I said.

By the time we were out past the New Waterway on the wide open sea ("Think it's too far to swim back?"), the Chinese cook was in the land of Fu Manchu by way of the Opium Express. If the cook wasn't high as a jet-propelled kite, staring at the far-off horizon, he was half blind from the booze. So he didn't get around to teaching me how to cook for an international crew of rabble and vermin, which would have come in handy if I ever wanted to apply for a job on shore. Soda-jerk, maybe, or top dog in a frankfurter stand.

185

I was close to broke—but alone, so I managed. I ate at Heck's on Klaver Straat every day. I scraped together a couple of guilders and got there around four since that's when they started serving their special: pea soup, a fried egg, a meatball with French fries, string beans and peas, pudding (chocolate), coffee or milk, and a doughnut. If you came at four you got the best meatballs and the freshest French fries. If you came a little later there weren't any more French fries and it cost too much to make more, so give the lad a boiled potato. If you came even later all you got was a plop of instant potatoes, mashed, just add water, made by Scholten & Company, Groningen. If you came even later: "See that dish over there? Take a good look. There must be some spuds left."

One chilly afternoon I was hungry and had one guilder fifty, just enough for the special and a glass of beer. Carefully balancing my tray of deliciously appetizing warm food, I looked around for a seat. There was a huddle of little old men and even littler old ladies who came every-day—the homeless. If I'm sitting in a restaurant having supper, whether it's fancy or cheap, and a little old man with white hair, a pair of state-supply glasses, a shabby brown jacket, a shiny little drop dangling from his nose, and ear plugs peers inside and sees me sitting there eating, I feel like a certified turd. Sometimes I think I'm just too good for this world.

It was crowded. I looked in the pink mirror, a special mirror with a rosy glow that flatters everybody who looks in it. Even Herman of The Munsters would look in great shape in that mirror. A fraud!

I sat down at one of the tables, back to back with an old man in a faded coat who was talking to a woman sitting across from him. From what I could make of the conversation it seemed the old guy in the old suit with a paper dicky and a bow tie held on by a piece of elastic was the father of the woman—a strong healthy working-class woman in her forties. The problem, as I got it, was that the father didn't like sticking around the house and so was never there when the Unemployment Insurance Inspector came to have a chat with him. And now he was due for his old age pension but there wouldn't be any pension if he was never at home, and so on and so on and so.

I listened with half an ear to the woman's booming voice and the old man's mumbles. He lit up a Virginia cigarette—judging by the smell it was a Bond Street—and inhaled deeply into his squeaky lungs. He'd finished his supper and was having another cup of coffee. The conversation went on. The woman sat sideways on her chair, eyeing her father as if he were an old vase or a secondhand Singer sewing machine, completely uninterested, now and then barking, "Quit complaining, Pa."

I tried to control my still half-frozen muscles, at least enough to cut my huge meatball in half. I'd already finished the French fries, the beans and peas, and the soup and I thought, Ah, great, saved the meatball for last. Now I'll sit back and enjoy it.

My fork skidded off the meatball and clanked hard against the metal plate. The ball took off and sailed across the table like a flying saucer right onto the grandpa's empty plate. I reached over, forked my meatball, and brought it back home to my dish. The old guy hadn't noticed a thing. But his daughter, always on the lookout for injustice, sure had.

"Hey hey hey!" she screeched like a fishwife. "What do you think you're doing? Stealing food from an old man, huh? You got some nerve! You give my father his meatball back or I'll call the police. Goddamn, you ever seen anything like it? Here's my poor father dying of hunger and this good-for-nothing beatnik too lazy to work steals his food right off his plate!"

By this time a crowd had gathered and I was getting all kinds of compliments.

"Yeah! Punched the old man right in the nose!"

"Not the same sort of people they used to have here. They ought to refuse to serve those kids. They're just looking for trouble."

"They ought to lock them up, cut off their hair and give 'em a good beating instead of a square meal."

"Sir," I said to the old man with a trusting smile, "you know as well as I do I didn't steal your meatball. If you'd be good enough to explain the situation to your wife, we can forget about the whole thing."

"Wife? What wife? That's my daughter. Where're your manners, snot nose?" he snapped.

"Father," the woman egged him on, "did that punk pinch your meatball or didn't he? Yes or no?"

The man said, "Yeah. Yeah, he did," like a fourth grader telling a fib.

"You see!" crowed the woman triumphantly.

That was going a little too far. What made it worse was that I was in one of my rare (luckily they're rare) bad moods and I was feeling pretty sunk anyway and so I wasn't too sure of myself. Ordinarily I would have slaughtered them all with a joke or a pun, but it's always like that—things like that happen when you're least ready for them.

I felt like a zero with everybody standing around staring at me like that. I noticed that the "unemployed persons" who always hung around the fruit-juice machine were starting to look very mean all of a sudden. (The guy who runs that machine must be an ex-unemployed, or maybe they're planning to crack the joint and need an insider.) First I turned pale and then my heart, when I saw all those eyes fixed on me, started pounding away a mile a minute. I've always had a guilt complex, God knows why. Whenever I see a squad car, I'm convinced they're after me. When I pass through customs I always act so guilty, it takes hours to pack my suitcases again. When a loudspeaker called out that a wallet with two and a half guilders was missing and it must be somewhere in the room, I used to blush so red my head felt on fire, and dive to the floor and start searching. I was the Hardened Criminal in everybody's eyes until the wallet was found.

The cook came out and before he could reach my table he was bombarded from all sides with all kinds of helpful advice.

"Throw him out!"

"Beat him up!"

"That punk over there, that rat-faced creep, he's dangerous! Always looking for trouble, trying to raise hell. Same damn thing every day."

The cook was wearing a neatly-starched white apron. "What's going on here?" he demanded.

"That dirty young, filthy young, dirty young . . . !"

"Father, leave it to me. You're getting too worked up. Here's what happened. Now listen. That good for nothing, trouble-making, long-haired hoodlum stole my father's meatball! I swear he did! I saw it with my own two eyes. Sitting here minding my own business and—now you see it, now you don't—no more meatball."

"Yeah," the old man echoed, "no more meatball. Should have tried that trick on me twenty years ago. I would have beat your brains out, buster. And if I have to, I'll take you on even now, you dirty young, filthy young, dirty young . . . !"

"Calm down, Father. Easy does it. Think of your heart," the woman hushed him.

"Calm! Nix on calm. . . . What kind of bullshit is that anyway? My hard-earned meatball swiped right off my plate and I'm supposed to calm down? To have to hear that from my own flesh and blood!"

"Well," said the cook-general-manager-boss, knifing me with a hard, sharp, critical glance, fully aware of the gravity of the situation—a fresh kid swiping a poor old man's humble meatball in his restaurant. ("In my restaurant! This is only the start. Tomorrow it'll be the whole damn meal and the day after that the cash register. No, we can't have any of that!")

"Buddy," he said, "give the man his meatball back and everybody'll be happy."

"No," I said, "because it's my meatball and I'm hungry."

"Gimme that meatball!" the old man screamed and he lunged for it. I moved fast and when I looked up again, all I saw was this arm in front of me clutching a fork.

"What happened?" somebody asked.

"Oh, the guy in the white coat—the boss or whatever he is—he almost stabbed the old man with a fork because he was complaining about a meatball he gave that boy."

"No wonder he's complaining. You ever tried the knishes here? Limp turds with a tough crust."

The whole business was starting to bore me stiff. "Okay, brother, if that's the way you want it," the cook-general-manager-boss said. "I'm going to call the cops and that's that. I'll give you one last chance. Give that meatball back or you're in for some real trouble."

The woman started up again. "I knew the streets were crawling with scum, but this time I just happened to see it with my own two eyes. Poor Father, poor Dad, poor. . . ." and she made a face like a martyr queen in a soap opera.

This is going too far, I thought. I could just see it—the police station, scenes, fingerprints, arrest, resisting arrest, escape, a criminal record dating back to a misunderstanding about a meatball (*une boule de hachis,* in case I became an internationally known criminal). And all that for a measly meatball—Today's Special—and though you could get seconds, all the vegetables and potatoes you wanted, you couldn't get a second meatball. Why didn't a French fry hop onto his dish? Let them all go to hell, I thought. I'm starved—especially since I practically had that meatball in my mouth, and now farewell, meatball. All I'd had was a bit of the gravy.

It was just like Aristotle's sword or Tantalus' heel or Damocles' torments—at any rate, bad. I decided to abandon my rightful claim to the meatball.

"Here!" I said, my voice cracking. Because I felt like a punk who'd filched food from a hobo, stolen an old guy's one good meal while I was still young and strong enough to go without eating for a day.

"Father. You've got your meatball back!" the daughter said triumphantly.

"And now for you," the manager glared at me.

186

Just like our teacher, Piet Prikkel, used to do: cane our asses if he thought we'd done something wrong. You had to lean over the first desk and look straight into the saintly face of a revolting little guy with freckles and pimples—the richest kid in school. Whenever the little monster came down with German measles or mumps, we each had to chip in ten cents for a grotesque gift basket of fruit. Ten cents meant a lot to us and for me it meant a choice between helping pay for that basket or not getting to see the weekly movie out in the park. I held onto my pennies as long as I could, but there was simply no way out and I had to hand them over to the teacher. And when Frits Bakker or any of the other kids from school got sick and stayed in bed ten times longer than Pimple Face, there was never a fruit basket or any kind of present at all. All they ever got was their homework.

187

The old guy muttered some more and the manager repeated, "And now for you," adding a twist to the knife in his eyes. "Don't ever show your face around here again. I'll let you go this time, but if I ever see you again you'll be sorry. Now get out of here."

I stood up and tried to say something but all that came out was some incoherent stuttering about how it all wasn't true and I was half way to the door with that whole gang of vicious eyes boring into my back when I suddenly heard the woman's voice.

"But Father, you didn't even have a meatball. You had goulash."

"I'll be darned," the old man mumbled. "You may be right, but I coulda sworn there was a meatball on my plate. Well, it's their own fault, those punks."

188

The Chinese cook had four fingers missing from his left hand. He'd lent a hand unloading once. He used his left-over thumb as a kind of cork. There was always a bottle of self-brewed alcohol hanging from that thumb. When he was sober, he'd pull the same trick three hundred times —stuff his fingerless hand down his throat as far as he could. It was funny in the beginning, later it got on my nerves. A peculiar guy.

When there was a storm at sea—the wind lashing in at eleven on the Beaufort scale—the ship creaked at the seams, squeaked at the rivets, and you could see inch-wide cracks in the sides. It was a floating sheet-iron coffin that shook, rattled, and pitched. The captain was seldom sober and the ship was surrounded by a constant mist of alcohol. He was an old seadog whose only interest in life was women. For all he cared you could flush all seven seas, he wouldn't mind. He tanked up on shore but never as much as when he was on board.

I was cook's mate which meant helping the Chinese cook out a bit. The first few days I bluffed my way through with all kinds of Dutch dishes: ham and eggs for lunch, or scrambled eggs, or sunny side up—and bread with everything. When everyone had gone back to work, I was supposed to wake up the cook for supper. He slept bolt upright in a tiny cabin that was more like a closet and stank of sweat, incense, cod-liver oil, and hashish. The cook was stoned all day. He wasn't really Chinese, more like a mongrel. At any rate he was stoned all day and every day.

I hated that ship. Nothing going on at night. The sailors were always arguing—arguments settled with fists, knives, glasses, and bottles. I've never seen so much hate between people from different countries in one place all at once in my life. The Germans, a quartet of six-foot gorillas, kept to themselves and had their own card games going—nobody else could play. The Spaniards never wasted a word on the Germans and didn't want anything to do with us either. The first mate was a Greek with pinkish hair, almost white, and white eyes—an albino. We didn't want anything to do with anybody else, so all in all it was a very convivial voyage.

The captain summoned me on the third day out. I sprinted up to his cabin and he lost no time offering me the cook's job because the men were grumbling. When Chang got better everything would return to normal, but right now Chopsticks was a little too hung up on his pipe and sometimes his mind took off for heaven to join his numerous noteworthy forefathers there.

My salary was doubled and I would collect double pay the whole trip (we were on our way to Tripoli and Libya), even after Chang got "back from his trip." I rolled up my sleeves and went to work.

Breakfast and lunch went fine. I did my best since I knew they'd pound me to pieces if the food wasn't good. I made fantastic ham and egg concoctions and gave them bread plus enough cold cuts to stuff an army. But I had to make warm meals at night. How do you learn to cook in two hours from a Greek cookbook for a bunch of clowns whose patriotic preferences have to be respected? Besides, I was just a simple Dutchman and couldn't read all the Spanish, English, German, or Italian labels on the food. So I picked the menu at random, usually going by the pictures on the cans (beef from Argentina always has a high-spirited horse on it).

I clued in Steven the telegraph operator beforehand: "Listen, it's going to be one hell of a mess tonight. Nobody ever tasted anything like it before. Delicious but a little on the spicy side. When I dish it up, you take the first bite and say 'Great! Stew Hollandaise!' Then they'll eat it too. Don't forget, you dragged me on this tub. I don't know the first thing about cooking, let alone for this pack of Panamanians."

Everybody was waiting impatiently for the meal to be served. I'd made an announcement at lunch: "Tonight, boys, you're going to get a feast fit for a king. A friendship feast—something very special. Actually, it's Indonesian but before the war it was once served to the Maharajah Coco Nut Tull Band who snapped it up for the army menu right away." So everybody was eagerly waiting to taste it.

I was known for my stunts, so they were all curious to see what I'd cooked up this time. It had to be good, otherwise they'd let me know fast. The trouble was—and I was very sorry about it—the goo I'd brewed wasn't edible. Even I couldn't get it down. It was a mushy blend of chopped spinach, pancakes with syrup, and raw potatoes with spaghetti sauce. And it tasted like it. I tried to make the best of it, but when I tasted a spoonful in the galley, I thought I was having hallucinations. Everything twinkled in front of my eyes and I had a sudden urge to play the violin.

Steven the Sparks kept munching away at his glop, apparently having the time of his life. He was badly over-acting his part, the ham.

The men chased me all over the ship and when they finally caught me they were worn out. Still, they managed to twist my arms and tried torturing me by wringing my wrists.

Sometimes they set out after me down the gangways with that evening's supper—hot potatoes that were too hard, burned vegetables, gravy made from bouillon cubes, etcetera, and then poured it down my shirt. Then they'd mash the hot potatoes and vegetables, pounding my chest as if it was a chopping block. The food I cooked that first month was crazy. I don't know how I got away with it. I think it was the big bluff that kept me alive, since cooking was the one thing I couldn't do and the longer it went on, the less the crew liked it.

I told the captain I'd been trained as a cook in the Navy, so he'd just better keep his nose out of the kitchen, but that being trained to cook for the Dutch Navy was no training for trying to feed Turks, Germans, and Greeks.

"Furthermore," I said, "Dutch cooking is much too subtle for this riff-raff. Last week, for instance, I made some 'Stew Hollandaise' and you must know what a dish *that* is—the terrific ingredients it calls for! Even the Royal Family can't afford it every day. And me, simple well-meaning cook that I am, I try to cook up a royal surprise and what do I get for my trouble? More trouble!" And so I bluffed my way through.

One day we set out from Edinburgh for Vladivostok, the outermost tip of Russia. The only port in between would be Hammerfest, the northernmost point on the globe, up by the Arctic Circle. We'd take on coal there, then call in at Archangel, a place I knew very well. The last times around, on the other ships, I had almost always been to Scandinavia and Russia. And Arabia.

We took on enough oil, water, and ship's stores for six weeks. Two weeks after we'd left Archangel, the first mate came down to the galley to tell me we were out of bread. I'd have to bake some right away and how many sacks of flour would I need? There was only one cookbook on board; it was in Greek. I started nonchalantly asking around because I couldn't show too much curiosity about how to bake bread, since when the first mate asked me if I could, I just laughed in his face and asked him what kind of wisecrack that was meant to be. Bread just happened to be my specialty!

Somewhere in the back of my mind I had the idea: bread, nothing to it. But I couldn't find a single man on board who really knew how to bake bread. One Spaniard even thought it grew on trees—bread trees.

There was an old Greek in the engine room who had a vague idea how it was done. Years ago when he'd had a girl who didn't want him to ship out, he'd worked as an apprentice in a Greek bakery.

When he'd described the whole procedure half a dozen times down to the smallest pinch of salt, I gave him my expert opinion. "Yeah," I said, "that's the old-fashioned way." I raced to the pantry, mixed up some flour, yeast, milk, and eggs and started kneading a good firm dough. I kneaded so long I finally had half the crew looking over my shoulder. Okay, maybe they didn't go for the stuff I put in front of their noses every day; it was foreign to them—no good. But bread! Why, even a child could see they were in for a treat. I smiled at the world in general and when I'd worked up the dough into long loaves (the kind you see in Italian films, usually sliced with a big knife by the mother who holds the bread tucked under her hairy armpit), I laid them out on steel trays in the lower half of the big oven. Within half an hour the delicious aroma of fresh-baked bread was drifting out of the oven along the gangways, down the decks, and far out to sea. I peeked in to look at the loaves every once in a while. The dough was baking all right, but it wasn't rising. An hour later it still hadn't started to rise; it was practically lunchtime and there had to be fresh bread on the table. Fresh bread I had promised, fresh bread they would get.

The loaves were thoroughly baked and had nice tough crusts, so I just set them down on the table—big flat disks of bread. What difference does it make what they look like? It's the taste that counts. When they'd all sat down after a lot of moaning and groaning, Steven kept his promise and yelled, "Oh look, bread!"

Everybody grabbed a loaf and tried cutting into that heavy-as-lead unfermented flatbread that was meant to be two feet long and at least a foot high. The first one to say something was a German, Heinz, a muscle-bound cretin who squirted an oilcan around in the engine room.

"Mensch," he said, "dzat ist not brot!"

"Not bread!" I said. "What do you mean? You been in Holland, haven't you?"

"Nein," he said.

"Well, you poor sap. This is *Dutch* bread!"

190

I'd dozed off. Suddenly I was wide awake. It took a few seconds to figure out where I was. I was lying in a bed the size of a small desert. Barry was there, too, and lying next to me was a girl I'd bought. Of course this buying business was just a crock—a tradition that had come down through the years—and besides I didn't have any proof I'd bought her. No receipt, nothing.

Still, it was a problem for me. Fatima was a very beautiful girl. She looked like the kind of girl that's been brought up by the wolves, a kind of female Romulus or Remus. She was a head shorter than me and had long wild jet-black hair. She wasn't skinny and she wasn't fat—just right. The natural look, jet-black eyes and a sharply carved, fine face. And always walked barefoot.

I could hear her breathing softly beside me. It must be horrible for a pretty girl to be born deaf and dumb. Especially in a backward little village like this. A girl like that should have the best medical care, live in a big city, marry a millionaire. Maybe something could be done about her handicap, but not here.

It's when you start making drastic changes in a community like this that the misery begins. The people are happy with their miserable existence until along comes some well-meaning soul from UNICEF or UNESCO and tells them they're living in squalor and ought to be ashamed of themselves for being so happy. All those missionaries and do-gooders jump in half cocked and all wrong. They should leave a people to their own sense of dignity.

I thought about leaving Fatima there in her village, with a sense of her own dignity. I wouldn't have to lug her all the way to the city then, from her old clay hut or stucco house to a big clinic with heavy traffic crashing by outside. I'd decide in the morning.

We could scarcely communicate with each other. Except for the fact that she was a beautiful girl who would look like a dream in the right kind of clothes, I didn't know much about her. Brought up in a poor land where handicapped children don't stand a chance, she'd managed maybe to teach herself a few things, or maybe her father had taught her. But he hadn't been the most attractive businessman in the world—trying to sell his daughter with his dying breath. Even if it had been a bargain, it seemed a pretty lousy business to me.

Just like in South America. There they kick their babies till they're lame or crooked, or disfigure or blind them so they'll make better beggars later on and bring in money from the tourist trade. Just the boys, of course. The girls have a horizontal future cut out for them. In most of the poor and prolific families, it's still common practice to have six out of seven kids begging on the streets.

Fatima had crawled out of the bed and was curled up sound asleep on the goat hide on the floor. What simplicity. Eastern women—at least they know their place. After intercourse, Japanese geishas and African girls always sleep on a mat next to the bed—so the man has room to stretch out. They know their place.

I was touched by her simplicity and gently tapped her on the shoulder. I explained in sign language that she should come and lie down next to me. She stood up, bashful. She wanted to dive into bed, clothes and all, but I made it clear she should take her dress off. I closed my eyes because I sensed she was embarrassed about undressing in front of me. I could see through my eyelashes that she was looking at me and when she was convinced I wasn't watching, she undressed.

She was gorgeous—the kind of girl you see on the covers of African or Moroccan records. Robust, well built, but you could read her short hard life on her face. Which was what made her face so striking. I followed her every fumbling move as she slipped out of her dress. Outside it was still dark, but in the dim light of approaching dawn I could see how beautifully proportioned her body was.

She didn't have anything on under her dress. She stepped over me into the bed, showing a fine lean ass, covering her well-shaped breasts with both hands. Like a tender fawn she snuggled up next to me and with a pounding heart waited for what was to come. I was her Master, so of course it was my duty to take her. She was bright enough to have got that point a long time ago. I certainly felt like screwing her but, good soul that I am, I didn't want to force her. Love is love. I had a warm feeling for Fatima. Fate had brought us together. I thought how nice it would be to have a real woman all to myself—one who could make a good cup of coffee, etc.

I embraced her trembling body and felt she was yearning for my love. I rubbed and caressed her quivering body to put her at ease. Then I bent over and carefully placed a kiss on her full Arab lips. When I opened my eyes I saw her looking up at me, wide-eyed with delight. Silent ecstasy! We couldn't talk. She'd never learned how to read lips.

I magnanimously decided not to fuck her. After all I was a Dutchman, and for centuries we'd upheld the tradition of raping anything brown or black in our former colonial empire and I wanted no part in it. I gently stroked her until she fell asleep. Then I turned over and tried to fall asleep too. It was warm, so I pushed back the sheets and mosquito net and lay there naked.

I'd just about dozed off again when I felt something scratching my butt. I thought—ah, Fatima. Of course. She wants the big Dutchman in her and this is her way of letting me know. I felt her big wet tongue licking its way across my butt—a lusty lick—and I thought with a lick like that you could make a fortune. I moaned softly, rolled over and opened my eyes. Fatima pretended to be fast asleep. I turned the other way—some very strange thoughts running through my mind—and found myself looking smack in the bearded snout of a skin-and-bones desert goat. A splendid specimen. I could see at a glance it came from a long line of thoroughbreds. It nudged me in the ribs invitingly. Must be trained for bed, I realized. Weird guy, our host.

I poked Barry, who was snoring with his mouth wide open, and said, "Barry, why don't you sleep out on the porch and take hot pants here along with you."

It took some time for this to sink in. He got up with a sigh. "And take this horny goat too. I want to be alone with my fiancée."

Barry hadn't quite got the point, but fortunately I cleared things up just in time. He was trying to drag Fatima out of bed and she was mutely but firmly resisting. Barry was used to having to drag uncooperative broads out of my bed, but I managed to stop him just before he was about to slap Fatima around.

"No!" I screamed. "Not her. That horny goat lying here next to me."

"Oh," said Barry drowsily. Ever since he took up boxing he sleeps so deep it's practically impossible to wake him up. He pulled the reluctant goat out of bed and I thought, poor thing. Every night it's got to climb in and tonight it's got to climb out.

When things had quieted down again, I took a good look at the face on the pillow by the dawn's early light. What unspoiled beauty! What innocence! An angel come down to earth. She made me think of how beautiful and soft it could be on earth. I saw peace on earth for all men. An early morning desert breeze blew in through the door. Cooled by the wet earth. There'd been light showers all through the night.

I grew sentimental. Why hadn't I met Fatima earlier? Why had I chased after hundreds of women like a dog in heat? Was this the Great Love of my Life? The only trouble was you couldn't really talk things over with her because she couldn't say anything. On the other hand, though, that had its advantages—in case we ever had a fight, for instance. There'd never be much screaming or yelling. And anyhow, silence is golden.

All sorts of pink clouds and lilac-colored lambs floated through my worn-out happy head. I could actually fall asleep. Wonderful. I could feel her peach fuzz skin against my bare thigh. Surely a simple lad deserves to feel peach fuzz skin rubbing up against his prick at least once, doesn't he?

Her gaze was loaded with passion. It was a melancholy and at the same time yearning gaze—the so-called tortured gaze familiar from many a pre-war German flick. What must she be thinking . . . ? She didn't know herself, poor darling. Happy and satisfied, we fell asleep.

Early next morning I woke up with the feeling that somebody was looking at me (intuition, a kind of sixth sense I picked up in the Legion) and opened my eyes. I saw Fatima's virginal gaze trained on me, unwavering, affectionate and attentive. Her healthy body lay alert next to mine.

A sweet creature, with a sweet little ass to match. She'd finally got a new idea of what men are. The night before the other broads had whispered in my ear that I was buying damaged goods, that Fatima had been repeatedly raped by the local soccer team.

After the evening practice games for the Africa Cup, the soccer players had sneaked up on the shy Fatima, who tried, too late, to run back and hide in her house. Unable to scream or say a word, she'd been raped time and again. Though she'd tasted the forbidden fruit, it still frightened her. She was a wounded creature and I felt I had to chasten her with the merciless wand. Hard as it was, I could restrain my flesh, resist the satanic temptation of the tigress beside me.

191

In the morning mist her skin had a Max Factor glow. A tropical hen clucked its way across the Tunisian morning countryside. The smell of the drenched pine trees, the desert air, and the aroma of fried eggs tickled my nostrils. We got up. I stretched and saw Fatima gazing at my magic flute with wondering eyes. She reached out for it and, in the best old Tunisian tradition, played a brief but melodious tune on it.

In high spirits I walked out to the porch where everything was still wrapped in a deep sleep. I had that no-fuck-but-happy-anyway feeling. Barry lay there knotted up with our hostess while the host lay close to the goat. Only the goat was awake; it greeted me with a cool stare. I kicked Barry and sang out:

> "*Arise arise*
> *The sun is climbing in the eastern skies*
> *So open up your bloody eyes!*"

We're shoving off today and taking Fatima with us. Hurry up. We don't have any time to lose. We'll have breakfast, then off non-stop for Tunis." The rain had stopped and I figured if we stuck around much longer they might want us to make some more.

An hour later we were sitting out on the porch, our bellies stuffed with fried eggs, warm bread, and tea, when the bus came banging into the village. The weekly bus. The whole village ran out to meet it. It stopped right in front of our house—a ramshackle wreck, its windows taped up, its top piled high with baskets full of chickens, bales, packages, and fresh vegetables.

The crowd stepped back when the door tumbled off its hinges onto the ground and the passengers stepped out. Relatives got a hearty welcome. Suddenly I saw the woman from the night before with the toothless mouth with just one little tooth sticking up in it whom I'd mistaken for the other woman with the same deep warm smile from the well. A shock of recognition went through my body. The woman from the well stepped out of the bus.

The two hugged each other, affectionately thumping each other on the back and then walked away from the crowd chatting cheerfully. Passing our house they suddenly stopped. I could see they were each telling the other about us, and when they saw us there they waved enthusiastically. Their toothless mouths opened in deep warm smiles, and now I saw that one had two teeth and the other none at all. All that thumping must have sent one of the teeth flying across to the other. There they were, two sweet little old ladies in the same dark clothes, the same kerchiefs over their heads, the same short fat legs, the same deep warm smiles on their faces, and both jubilantly shouting "Oesjipappa!"

192

We made Tunis late that afternoon. After a long fast ride on the Monster. On the way we only stopped a couple of times for coffee or drinks. Barry in back, Fatima in the side-car. The streets of Tunis were packed with cars and donkeys. We asked a passer-by if he knew where the Deaf Mute Clinic was. But how do you explain that in Tunisian? Nobody understood what we meant and Fatima couldn't very well ask them herself. After winding up first at a glee-club concert, then at an insane asylum, we finally got an address. After a lot of looking and asking directions, we found the street the clinic was on. A big building that looked like a hospital. A big gate with a holy statue in front of it.

We got off the Monster. We didn't have to carry Fatima's bags since she didn't have any. We went in through the big front door. Although I couldn't quite see her becoming a world-famous opera singer, I did think that with proper guidance she might turn out all right.

It was a huge hall with lots of people walking around. They kept smashing up against the green tiled wall or banging against the open doors. Little men came toward us with their arms stretched out like sleep walkers. They touched us, felt our faces, mumbled something, then shuffled away. A woman dove down the staircase and made a resounding thud when she hit the floor. She was still scrambling around trying to get up when a man with a cane tripped over her.

There was something very weird about the whole thing. Dozens of people, most of them with their eyes shut, walking around tapping the floor. What a racket. BAM! KLONK! POING! WHAP! To the accompaniment of many canes tapping. Lots of sunglasses, too. Lots of people tripping on their way down the staircase, managing to grab the banister just in time. A hefty brown Arab in a pair of shades bashed BOOM! right into me.

"Pardon me," I said. "Could you tell me what time it is?"

"Yes," he said and walked on.

Out of the middle of all that bustling, banging, and tapping a nurse in a blue-and-white uniform strutted up to us and asked if she could help. Seeing her, I was suddenly reminded of that girl from the sticks back home, Lucia, who'd always wanted to be a nurse and carried around a little picture of Florence Nightingale. Nursing others had always been her one goal in life. Didn't matter what or who she nursed. For a girl like that, I thought, nursing must be a fine profession.

I explained Fatima's predicament as well as I could. Not too well, naturally. When an old woman bumped into me the nurse smiled and said, "Please be patient with her. She hasn't been here long."

I had to shout everything out loud and clear against that background of banging, shouting, and tapping. In the office we paid the bill (we gave the nurse all the money we had, which would take care of her board for a few months and then they'd find Fatima a foster home with some fat sheik; after all we still had lots of jewelry and trinkets left that we could cash in on), then signed some papers and said goodbye.

Fatima hugged me passionately and clung to my hand. She didn't look very happy about being left there.

"Yes," said the nurse as she showed us to the door. "Of course, it will take a while for her to get used to it."

We left with Fatima's desperately frightened eyes staring after us and were soon out in the bright sunlight again. As I started up the Monster we waved goodbye and with a loud boom we were off to downtown Tunis.

(For months I worried about the whole affair but didn't know why. Suddenly I knew. We'd brought Fatima to a Clinic for the Blind instead of a place for deaf mutes. Fortunately, though, everything turned out all right in the end. Fatima became one of Tunisia's most famous and highest-paid fashion models and worked a few seasons as star mannequin for Pierre Cardin. I'm delighted everything worked out so well for her, thanks to me, and now whenever I'm in Paris I've got a fine pad with great company waiting for me.)

We took our jewelry to a pawn shop. And we came out glad to have got the few coins we got for the stuff. The gifts the kindhearted villagers had offered up to the Rain Gods turned out to be completely worthless. Rings and bracelets you get from buying three boxes of soap, or for saving up bottle caps or coupons or green stamps. Junk. The joke was on us. We'd been had.

107

the magic nana

193

We checked in at an obscure little hotel near the waterfront at Carthage, just outside of Tunis. A cheap room with fringed lampshades, two beds, a bidet, and a bathtub. It was a dim joint, full of junkies, hookers, and sailors. Plus a few gangsters.

It was a big brothel with a plush bar downstairs, where we could sit around and where the local whoring-class hung out. The madam of the house took to me right from the start. When I signed the register, her eyes followed my hand like a hawk.

She was a fat mama of around forty-five who must have been a knockout in her prime. Even now she wasn't bad to look at. A real madam, big and sturdy, a hard but pleasant face, a wide smile on her full lips, black hair combed straight back, dressed in black, a tiny whip dangling from her wrist.

While she watched my hand write my name, her huge bosom hung down across the register. I filled in Holland as my native country and when she read that, she clacked her tongue and said in almost perfect Dutch, "Lekker neuken, niet betalen." * Then she burst out in a sparkling laugh that shook her enormous front bumper all over the place.

She said we had to have some drinks on her later at the bar. She liked the Dutch. Lots of Shell employees and embassy people dropped in. At least once a week. Good boys, always paid their bills. Never any trouble about that. And good drinkers, never got out of line. The only thing she had against them was when they'd had a few too many, they started dancing on the tables in their long underwear. The ambassador especially was a great guy. Spent money like water and there were flowers and champagne for everybody. Every day was a holiday for the ambassador. Sometimes he brought the whole *corps diplomatique* along to show them the sights. And never any complaints from the girls, either.

Late that night, after we'd taken a shower and a nap, we headed downstairs to the Chamber of Pleasures. It was packed with swinging sisters around the bar with nice low necklines and lots of lipstick on. A hot shudder shot through me.

* "Good fucking, all for free."

I said to Barry, "You start at that end of the bar and I'll start here. We'll see who makes it to the middle first."

The fat mama saw us in the smoky room and sailed over to us with outstretched arms. She embraced me, giving me the so-called French hello, and led us to a table near her own private table.

"Hello there, dearies," her husky voice came from deep down in her throat, "my luscious lover boys. You feel like something good tonight? First a bottle of champagne on me. Okay?"

She cracked her little whip against the table and a girl whose dress showed more than it hid came over at once. Her boobs swung over the table while she took the madam's order.

"What kind of treat did you boys have in mind?" she asked in such a sexy voice I practically choked on the warm feeling filling my throat. She stroked my well-tanned arm. "Want something young and fresh, or spicy and experienced?"

"Well," we said, "actually we just came in for a glass of beer and maybe something meaty too, but we're poor boys," we said. "Lost all our money gambling."

She pinched my arm and said in a mischievous sultry voice, "For a good-looking fair-haired boy like you, there're plenty of ways to earn money, no?"

I got the point.

"When I need some," I said, "I'll let you know."

"Yahoo!" she howled. "You're the type I go for, honey. Nobody shoves you around, right?"

We drank champagne and since she had to go off to talk to her other clients, she sent a couple of girls over to keep us company. Two gorgeous go-go grinders. One was called Miss Penalty, the favorite goal for soccer players and other athletes. A slick chick with a shiny dress and a pair of sharp tits. Barry had a real prize on his lap, a big blonde bruiser with a pair of legs and tits that made your mouth water. She was Swedish, and she hung around Barry's neck while we were drinking and getting acquainted. The madam kept coming back to sip her champagne and see how we were making out. She looked straight at me like a hungry animal. We were all feeling very gay, broke as we were. We were going to try to find a ship to Spain, and from Spain back to our island.

Meanwhile this was a cozy hangout. The cathouse part was just a couple of rooms with connecting doors, all furnished with big armchairs, couches, tables, red velvet on the walls, red lamps, and a bar. An old-fashioned juke box served up the background music—Tunisian flute or Malando. The men were all belly dancing with the girls or off in corners talking with them. Every once in a while a couple returned and gave back the key to Mama.

I thought, okay, so I'll lay the fatso and then we'll have plenty to drink and maybe she'll even offer us some of her girls. When she sat down again I rubbed up against her fat warm thigh, a greeting she answered by roguishly wiggling her ass. So that was settled. The champagne made me reckless and I asked her, "Any chance of sampling a special tonight? I could use some tail."

"For you, lover," she said, "I've got something very special. A triangle."

Count me in, I thought. You can always count me in for a triangle.

"Listen," I said, "we're not exactly millionaires tonight. How much you ask for a triangle anyway?"

"Well," she said, very businesslike, "the union sets the price for the triangle. I can't cut the official price. It'll cost fifty American dollars, that's fifty-six Canadian dollars. We do everything in dollars here," she explained.

All we had was twenty dollars to get us back to Spain. Gasoline and all.

"That's too much," I said. "We don't even have half that much."

"Don't worry about it, sweetheart. I like you," she said. "You know that. And for men I like I make a special price. You can have the triangle for free. Take your friend along and make it a quartet if you want to. As long as you do the Flip with me tomorrow, after you've had time to rest up."

It didn't take me long to make up my mind. It was practically immoral, since getting a triangle for a Flip was like getting it for free.

"Hmm, that's an idea. But I don't want any rush job on the triangle," I said.

"Sweetheart," she sighed, "you can pick your partners yourself, and triangle or do whatever you want as long as you want to. Just as long as you do the Flip with me, because we were made for it, you and me."

I thought, okay, so what's one Flip more or less. She wasn't even that ugly—more a kind of cozy mama. And hot. And the hotter the better was the rule I went by.

"But there's got to be something in it for my friend too," I said.

"You don't think I'm going to look after your friend? You think I'd let him down, my own Flipper's best friend? Well, that just shows you don't know Alie yet. Alie believes in good service. First-class service."

I explained the set-up to Barry and it was fine with him. Naturally he wouldn't be getting a triangle, but on the other hand he wouldn't have to do a Flip either.

"Put her there," I said to Madam Alie. We shook on it.

"Who should I take? Who do you recommend?"

110

"What do you want—black, white, or a mixed triangle?"

"Depends. What do you have in black?"

"Well, we've got a real winner inside—Crimi Nel. Fantastic in any position. A sturdy piece with a strong saddle."

"Okay," I said, "I'll take her. That's one. I need two more."

"Then there's that one up at the bar. She's free now. Odessa. Bites a lot. Likes tools inside and any kind of rough stuff."

"Okay," I said, "that's Nel and Odessa. Both black. Fine so far but what's for contrast?"

"Look," she said in her professional tone, "if you really want to have yourself a super all-night triangle, I'd take her."

And she nodded toward the blonde on Barry's lap.

"That's Swedish Sally. Sally's got real class. So that's your triangle. You've got yourself a mixture and that's a lot better than three of the same. Take it from me," she confided, "variety is the spice of life."

"Yeah," I said, "but my friend's with Swedish Sally and I don't want any trouble about who's whose. To each his own is my motto."

"Oh," she assured me, "we'll fix that up. There's plenty of other little treats for your friend. Or he can take two and have a Dynamic Duo and I'll throw in a jar of Black Tiger for good measure."

"Just what I need," it struck me suddenly, "You have some kind of nice dick grease for me? If I'm going to do the triangle I want to make the most of it."

"Don't worry about a thing. You'll get your Black Tiger fast enough!" and she snapped her fingers in front of her big pursed lips.

She called the girls over while I clued Barry into what was going on.

"Sure," Barry said, "take her if you want her. I saw a better piece at the bar a minute ago."

In the meantime the madam had fixed everything up with the girls. They were going to come up to our room. I wanted to start triangling fast and said to Barry, "Listen, you get your doll to take you up to her room. All of us screwing around in one room—they don't do that in good society, man, you know that."

He got the message and Madam Alie took me up to my room to give me some last minute instructions. She brought along a bottle of resin wine, a present from her to me. She punched the bed with her fists and said, "Good and firm for a triangle, but too hard for the Flip. We can do that in my room."

She opened a little velvet-lined suitcase and let me take my pick of various accessories. I took a small jar of Black Tiger.

"Better take some leather straps, too," she said, "for the girls. And if you don't mind my giving you a piece of advice, take that leather ring with the teeth for Odessa. Anyhow I'll just tell the girls to help themselves to whatever they want. I want to make it as easy for you as I can," she winked.

I winked back and thought, I got all this just for a Flip? I better make it a super Flip tomorrow. I opened the window a crack and then got out of my clothes fast. Madam Alie rubbed some Black Tiger Balsam on my . . . , massaged it between her hands, and when it stiffened up like a tree trunk, she said in admiration, "I thought so—the Perfect Flipper! We'll see how far we can go with it tomorrow, honey. I'm counting on a good long trip."

That Black Tiger was great stuff. At first it felt cold. But after you rubbed it in, it started burning like fire. It penetrated straight into my groin and my . . . stood out three times as big and hard as usual. You could smash a bottle against it. They ought to patent something like this in America, I thought; in no time the supermarkets would be selling Black Tiger in Flip-top Family-sized Super Spray Cans, gift-wrapped for Father's Day, Mother's Day, and green cans for St. Patrick's Day. It was a wonder drug.

The door opened and Odessa came in, a big black Negress. She was tall, about my size; her hair was short and kinky and her skin was coal-black.

I put out the lamps except one very dim one. I shoved the two beds up together and then closed the curtains, because imagine what a shock little kids would get if they peeked through the window—or what an album a photographer could make!

Madam Alie was whispering something to Odessa, and when she'd left, Odessa stripped, smiling her full broad smile. She was broad hipped, had pearly white teeth and a pair of lovely pointed . . . the size of big balloons, with good sturdy nipples pointing straight at me.

While she was still sitting on the bidet washing herself carefully and squirting something up inside, the other two came in—Sally the Swedish Sex Kitten and Crimi Nel, a savage fierce-eyed Negress with long hair, wearing golden rings on her fingers and bangles on her wrists. Swedish Sally was wearing a negligee that showed off her huge breasts and the curves of her firm white buttocks. Nel was a jewel. When she'd wriggled out of her dress, there stood an exquisite nude Negress with a remarkable pair of . . . that hung almost down to her navel, with big dark red discs for nipples, as big as jam jar tops. A slim dark beauty.

The party started when we were all in bed. I lay on my back, my legs spread. The Swedish siren sat on my thighs facing me. She was wet with sweat. Her hair hung in moist ribbons over her white voluptuous flesh. With a lusty grin she started warming up and moistening my . . .

112

with her mouth, at the same time opening up and feeling her own . . . with her fingers. Then, panting hard, she moved up and with both hands inserted my big. . . . Blissful feeling!

Odessa did the same thing, but at my head. She spread her legs and lowered herself until I could feel her big . . . smack on my face. When I was a kid of about fifteen, I never used to do things like this. But once I'd learned Nothing in Love Is Dirty, as long as it's clean, I liked anything and everything. A bit of perversity is great, but too much gets dirty. When you come to think of it, too much of anything isn't good—except satisfaction.

In the meantime, Odessa and the Swede were cuddling up to each other and Nel lay flat across my stomach under Odessa and Swedish Sal. With my one free hand I explored and felt Nel's enormous . . . that were hanging half on me and half on the bed and with my other hand I . . . inside her. This was what you call a real triangle.

Thanks to Black Tiger we kept it up for hours. The three girls kept changing places—three fantastic pieces. The whole scene had a musky smell to it, tinged with the scent of expensive perfume, Maya soap, and eau de cologne. They weren't only big but broad too, so there wasn't much room, even on the two beds. A couple of times I nearly flopped over on the floor.

Hours and hours, a kaleidoscope of purple twats, big soft breasts, and sweet female flesh. With some of these communal orgasms I was almost crushed under the heavy masses of flesh. While one of them kneeled and . . . my . . . with her . . . the other one had her aromatic . . . on my face and the third one lay across me. Suddenly I could hardly breathe. And a couple of times it felt just like I was rubbing up against steel wool—that's how hard those stubbles of frizzy hair were.

Sometimes they cupped their tits in their hands and squeezed them out for me to nibble. Nel was the wildest. Her white teeth glowing in a savage grin, she did her best to really finish me off.

After we'd run through all the angles of the triangle a few more times, all four of us were pooped. They staggered out the door; I fell sound asleep.

The next few days were good days, though it took me a while to recover from the triangle. It had been a great one. Besides, I still had the Flip ahead of me.

Since we were practically flat broke now, we hung around the waterfront all day long hoping to find a ship we could work our way back to Spain on. Madam Alie had connections on the docks and told us a ship would be coming in in a week whose captain was a special friend of hers, a long-time client. He'd take us to Alicante. We just didn't feel like hanging around in Carthage any more though, pleasant as it was. We were set on moving on. And I wanted to get back to Holland some time in the not too distant future. See how things were doing in the old turnip fields. We raced up and down gangplanks all day long.

194

I remembered how in Rotterdam once, years ago, my artist friend Wipperoen and I decided we'd go to sea. Neither of us had money or any hopes of getting any. A sea voyage, we realized, was just what we needed.

There were always full-page ads in the daily and weekly papers for seamen. A golden future on the high seas awaited boys of from sixteen to twenty-six—as long as you were healthy and willing to work. True Dutch hearts, daring descendants of Jan de Wit. Michiel de Ruiter and Piet Hein smiled invitingly from "Go to sea, Come Home with a Dose" posters in the Municipal Employment Agency. We—simple artists, failures, with a grudge against Society—we wanted to go to sea.

Early one morning we set off on the silver Harley-Davidson for Rotterdam. The shipping companies were all next door to each other on one big square with a herring stand. We started at the first and made our way to the last without missing a single one in between. Nothing.

We thought we looked like real seamen. I was wearing a sloppy gray bargain-basement suit—the pants turned up a couple of times at the waist, otherwise the crotch would have been at my knees. I'd combed my long hair back neatly and plastered it down with brilliantine. Wipperoen looked a little too arty. He was wearing striped bell-bottom pants, a corduroy jacket, and had a big droopy mustache.

With the rolling gait of an old sea dog, which I'd taught Wipperoen beforehand, we strolled into the offices, stopped in front of the counter, and I rapped on the frosted glass window which shot up at once.

"Ahoy," I greeted the man as a seaman should, while Wipperoen stepped back with a cry of "Yoho!" After we'd been sent away from five or six recruiting offices, I said, "Look, it's all because you look so goddamn artistic. You should have shaved off your mustache."

"Yeah, sure," said Wipperoen, morosely. "And then no job and me back in Amsterdam looking like a schmuck and unable to paint a thing until my mustache grows back. Forget it. Anyway how could they tell I'm an artist if I take it off? I didn't go to art school all that time for nothing. As soon as we're on board, I'll shave."

"Okay, brother," I said, "if that's the way you want it. But for God's sake keep back out of sight. Soon as they see that walrus hair, bang, down

114

go the windows because they think we're a couple of escaped nuts or that it's some kind of initiation stunt. Let me do the talking. After all, I've had experience. And I've got my papers, too."

We walked into one of the last companies left, one that was always encouraging youth of Holland to go to sea. The clerk scrutinized us from behind his frosted glass window after we'd greeted him sailor style, and said, "Good morning, gentlemen. Can I help you?"

I was our spokesman.

"You got a berth for two tars aboard one of your sturdy ships?"

"You might try at Personnel," the clerk said cautiously. "Up those stairs over there on the left, then turn right."

With a scornful laugh I said. "Oh, you mean starboard stairs then around to portside?" And, shouting "Ahoy," we sprinted off from the window which the scared clerk had slammed shut as fast as he could. In the recruiting room a respectable-looking man sat behind a desk.

"Well, boys," he said in a jovial voice, "what can I do for you?"

We explained we wanted to ship out.

"Do you have any experience?" he asked.

"Naturally," I said, as if how could he ask such a question. "Take a look at this," and I tossed my seaman's papers on the table.

He leafed through the booklet and said, "There's work. But you'll have to start as ordinary seaman again."

"Ordinary seaman?" I asked incredulously. "But my papers show I'm an able-bodied seaman, don't they?"

"That's right, but actually I can't even sign you two on. You're too old. You're over eighteen."

It was the first time in my life anybody ever said I was too old. I thought, thanks a lot, mister. First too young for anything and then suddenly too old.

"You've got your seaman's papers too?" he asked Wipperoen.

I nodded to Wipperoen, who lied, "Lost 'em in Port Said."

"Oh," the man said, "you should have put in for new papers immediately."

"Yeah," said Wipperoen, "but I forgot to."

"So you've had experience," the man concluded. "What kind of experience?"

"Oh, bodily-able seamen," Wipperoen said nonchalantly, blushing a little.

"He means able-bodied seaman," I corrected.

"What have you been doing the last few years? I see you haven't been out for two years."

"Well," I said, "last summer I was a waiter in Scheveningen. Last

winter I had a job on the docks in Amsterdam. Had a girl to take care of—
you know how it is."

"And what about you?" he asked Wipperoen, who'd forgotten the
lines I'd gone over with him so carefully. If you said you worked on the
beach or with a circus or on the docks, they couldn't check up on you or
ask for letters of recommendation.

"I went to Art School, sir," Wipperoen stuttered.

"Did you?" the man asked, suddenly very suspicious. "And why
this sudden urge to go to sea?"

"Well, sir, I changed my mind. I've always wanted to be a seaman."

"Oh sure you did," the man said sarcastically. "Couldn't make a
living at your paint-splashing, eh? No," he said, "we can't afford to have
any of that around here. Sign you up, and first thing we know as soon as
you've passed the three-mile limit you won't do a lick of work. A little
sketch here, a painting there, and running after the women on board to sit
for a portrait. No," and he laughed a nasty laugh, "I know your type.
Too lazy to work; nothing but parasites, that's what you are. Living off
the taxes the worker sweats to pay and boozing it up every night and a
different woman every other day. Now and then a little daub with a brush,
yeah, and then off it goes to an exhibition. Yeah, and an article in the
papers. No, there's no place for you on *our* ships. Try somebody else
and come back in a few years when you've proved you really want to be
serious seamen. Good day," he said firmly and bent back over his deskful
of papers.

"That's what you get, damn it," I cursed at Wipperoen. "We were
all set and you had to come on with that artist bit. We'll try once more
and if it doesn't work out, forget it, man. I'll ship out alone. It's your own
damn fault."

We finally ended up at the Holland-America Line and we were hired.

"They'll take anything they can get," insiders had told us when we
stopped for lunch at a French-fry stand. "Ask for Mr. Fokkert. He's in
charge of catering."

After he'd listened to a wide variety of blatant lies, Mr. Fokkert, a
man with a pock-marked face, signed us up as laundry boys on the
Willem Ruys. We were supposed to be at Pier A, Monday at one, and
we'd be going on a world cruise. The pay was lousy, something only a
foreigner would be satisfied with. But, we thought (and we figured all the
angles very fast) we'd go around the globe, we'd be away half a year,
have a chance to see the world, plenty to eat and drink on board, and lots
of laughs, and all we had to do was pick out a nice piece from the
passengers and go on from there as passengers as our price for sleeping in
her cabin.

We'd heard so many stories from guys who'd worked on ocean liners and who came back for a week every three months tan from head to toe, money coming out of their ears, living it up like kings, and things would have to get badly screwed up if two boys like us, ready and willing and handsome, couldn't make a go of it. So we signed up.

We were in a great mood when we took off for downtown Rotterdam to celebrate our success with a few good beers.

"Just goes to show," I said to Wipperoen, "art doesn't mean a fucking thing any more. It's a lost cause nowadays, unless you lick some big shot's ass until he feels like buying, or get a scholarship."

All that long waiting, all those rejections, and all the bullshit we'd had to take before something finally came through made us feel pretty frisky. I stopped unsuspecting pedestrians on the street and babbled to them in an unintelligible Scandinavian dialect. In a fish shop I threw a mackerel at the window pane because it tasted soapy. In a week we'd be far out to sea.

In Amsterdam we said goodbye to all our girlfriends and acquaintances. We even took orders for souvenirs. Everybody was green with envy when we told them our itinerary. We were going to Hawaii (just think of those luscious Hawaiian chicks naked except for garlands of flowers dancing the hula hula to ukelele music!) and the Bahamas (just think, when you poor bastards are freezing your ass off tromping through the snow, we'll be basking under the palm trees with a couple of well-tanned chicks). In Hong Kong, a short visit to the little ladies in their beautiful lit-up boats converted into floating cathouses—gorgeous women, young and old, very sharp and juicy. At Tahiti, just enough time to paint a few women dressed in batik with the Special Brush brought along for the occasion like Gauguin did. They know how to make real women over there. My type—big, robust and well-built. Gauguin knew all about it too, the old lecher.

Eastern Asians are the people I like best. The women, I mean. I'm always astonished by their beauty, non-aggressiveness, lucidity, and mysticism. Japanese girls! Indescribable with their tiny tits and lovely carved-ivory faces. Sweet and humble. They know their place. They obey without a lot of backtalk. Emancipation is for the birds. The cheerfulness of Chinese girls! The mysticism they radiate, that mask concealing their emotions. I knew a few Chinese girls once, from a Chinese restaurant. Beautiful, out of this world, and so graceful! But hard to approach. I had a Javanese girlfriend once, but what a catastrophe that turned out to be! She'd always automatically walk about two yards behind me, as a sign of docility, so I had to keep screaming back over my shoulder at her, otherwise she couldn't hear me. People on the street thought I was either a madman or a heartless beast to scream at such a sweet girl.

"You know," I said to Wipperoen, "if we really have a ball at any of

117

the ports we call in at, we can just jump ship and stay there. Simple. Like Gauguin did, or Willem de Kooning, who also started out as an ordinary seaman and now he's top painter of America and the whole world."

We'd made up our minds, and all the attempts made by various girl-friends to make us stay were in vain. I broke off with Paula, broke my engagement to Kathy, and told Willeke we wouldn't be eloping to Scotland for at least half a year so she might as well not bother escaping from the orphanage or stealing a passport either. Hard blows for the poor girls. But a sailor's life demands sacrifices. Always has, always will.

Yes sir, I thought to myself, they won't find Number One down there, slaving away in that chain-gang laundry with all the dirty sheets and steam. I don't care if they do give me the sack at some tropical island or other. I'll settle down and start a new life there. Nice and cozy with a native girl in a grass hut chewing betel nuts and twanging the guitar and producing Little Cremers. After all the boys from the *Bounty* got off and settled down on Tahiti, too. We just had to be careful—make sure we didn't wind up broke in Vladivostok. If we played our cards right it should be a snap. I saw myself strolling around Bermuda in shorts or maybe even a loincloth if we were farther inland, smoking pot from a big pipe, playing cards in front of the hut, warm all day, and all of Western civilization could simply kiss my ass.

Of course, if I felt like having her, I could marry the tribal chief's daughter right off the bat, just because of my blue eyes. And if the good man had enough minerals and uranium, or coconuts and rubber, and if his daughter was an eyeful, then everything was settled. I could just see all the jealous looks I'd get when I arrived at Schiphol for a brief vacation with all my wives and children. Nice and brown, at the head of a whole caravan of warriors and servants. Of course I'd have to stay at the Hotel Mongolia or the Amstel. Life is a poker game, I thought, that ought to be played with discretion. I could see it now. I'd follow in the footsteps of Jan Cremer senior, repeat his numerous trips around the world and go down in history as Jan Cremer, known for his nomadic way of life.

Suddenly the only thing we cared about was setting off—traveling. We pawned everything we owned: records, radio, a record player. We gave away our books and winter clothes. Only an idiot takes winter clothing along when he's headed for the tropics. Besides which, we were going to come back with a fantastic collection, the latest in everything. Good tailor-made clothes are still dirt cheap in the tropics since the wages are so low.

We gave everything away and packed a few essentials in a duffle bag. Tears from our girlfriends, warm handshakes (sincere or insincere) from friends and acquaintances, sad pats on the shoulder. We consoled all those near and dear to us with promises of picture postcards every week. With all that "work on board" we wouldn't have much time for letters.

We'd even figured out how much we could earn by smuggling and bringing souvenirs back to Holland—Prick Salves, Spanish Fly, Fucking Rings, Feelthy Pictures, etc. Very lucrative field. I promised my mother a crocheted tablecloth from Venezuela and batik curtains from Indonesia, and I promised Katryn a monkey. An authentic spider monkey from Borneo. We decided to keep the motorcycle. It would be good to have it if we ever came back. We'd just leave it near the docks. If somebody stole it, tough luck.

Wistfully we took leave of our envious friends and, early in the morning with a minimum of luggage, set off for Rotterdam. Right outside of Amsterdam the chain came off. Four AAA patrol cars stopped to help. I had to join the AAA. The motorcycle was finally in working order again, but by the time we reported to Pier A we were two hours late. The ship was just about to up anchor and move out. We tore into the dockside office, our hands black, our hair disheveled, oil spots all over our clothes. We reported to the clerk who glanced at the list and said, "Sorry boys. We thought you weren't coming and put two reserves on board. Too late to switch now. Better luck next time!"

We lay low in Friesland for two months, working in a condensed milk plant to earn enough to live on.

195

We became Madam Alie Bies' special protégés. She was proud of us. In exchange for bed and board I would Flip her and Barry and I could work for her if we wanted to. It was a standing offer anyway. We soon made friends with all the joy-girls and had a good time. Joints, a bit of food, and at night good drinks.

News of my triangle's success leaked out and like so many things I'm the first to do, suddenly everybody wanted to triangle. Business boomed for Madam Alie.

One morning Barry came zooming ecstatically into the room where I was still sound asleep. The night before I'd been plastered and had had a hard time finding my own bed. Madam Alie had said she wanted her Flip once and for all. I was game for anything that night, except for the Flip! She could understand that. A Flip calls for special care and attention. That's why there're so few good Flippers in the world. Everybody thinks: a Flip? Nothing to it! A cinch! But that's a mistake that won't get you anywhere. The real Flipper doesn't even talk about it before he's Flipped. Only after. I wanted the Flip with Madam Alie to be a Flip to remember, so I explained all this to her.

"Or," I asked, "would you prefer a Flip Flop?"

"Honey," she said, "your worst Flip is still the best there is."

"No," I said, "a Flip is a Flip. And only the best is good enough for us. Patience, dearie."

That same evening this fantastic girl came over to our table. She didn't fall for me. I fell for her. She fell for Barry. A disappointment for me, naturally. What normal beauty could fall for Barry? She was doing it just to give me a hard time. She knew I wanted her. And she wanted me. We were made for each other. She knew and I knew. Typically feminine. Drag things out. Act crazy. Keep him at a distance. Never go straight for what you're after. Let my best friend make her but not the one she's after. I was so mad I got bombed out of my mind.

And now when Barry came merrily zooming into the room, I couldn't take it. He had really hooked onto a masterpiece. A French girl, intelligent, pretty, knew how to carry on a conversation instead of just mooing. A little too self-reliant for my taste, maybe. Too sure of herself. Who did she think she was anyway? Just a two-bit whore like all the rest.

"So," I sneered at Barry, "I'll bet you didn't make her though, did you?"

"Oh, didn't I?" he said. "A fantastic girl—nice, warm, and a real ball in bed. I'm in love."

"What could you possibly see in a piece like that. She's strictly for nothing—you can tell that as soon as you lay eyes on her."

"She's got class, man. Anyhow, you didn't seem to think she was so bad last night."

"Who me? Okay, I admit she's a nice girl, nicely built. Okay," I said disdainfully, "but still, big tits and nice legs aren't enough in this life. She's okay to look at, but to fall in love with? Never!"

I thought, no sense in putting her down too much. Take it easy, nice and friendly, find out what she's like, make sure Barry cools, and then step in and take over myself.

"You didn't really screw her, did you?" I said suddenly, shocked and worried.

"Depends on what you call screwing, man, but one thing I can tell you—there were fireworks going off all night long."

"Jesus Christ, better get a shot fast. Even if it is too late."

"What do you mean?" Barry asked, "She's clean, isn't she?"

" 'Clean?' he asks. Clean? Man, it's written all over her face. They should get her out of here fast. She's a walking plague. That's why she's so stuck up. She's got every disease in the book. 'Isn't she clean?' he asks. Ha!"

"But that's impossible," Barry said, "she's only twenty-two, and only got into the trade because she had to. No way out."

"Twenty-two—that's what you think. You ought to have your head examined. That dame won't live to see thirty again. And they all got into the trade because they had to. An unhappy love affair, they say. Or a bastard baby with no papa. Or the family kicked them out. Almost makes me cry. And you fall for it hook, line, and sinker! I thought I'd taught you a few things about life. You haven't been paying attention, that's pretty damn obvious."

"You've got it all ass-backward, man. She comes from a very good French family. Had a rough childhood, that's all—very strict, no sex. She's just doing this temporarily. Wants to earn a lot of money fast, then give it up and sit back and live off what she's laid aside."

"Yeah, just what I thought. It's that kind of girl that gives prostitution such a bad name. Amateurs! How does she screw? Dry run, huh? Lies there peeling a grape while you're working your ass off."

"That's what you think! She screws like a zebra! Fantastic!"

"I wouldn't know. I never fucked a zebra. What's it like? Boy, you've been had. And another thing, she sticks like glue; once she's got you stuck on her she never lets go. That's why I didn't try to make her myself last night. All I had to do was whistle, but the other girls clued me in on her. There's no getting away from her. You'll be here the rest of your life.

"Her family's a gang of the roughest guys in town. They've already sent two guys down in the old concrete kimono. Not a very pretty sight, especially one of them—the one she helped shove off the pier herself because he didn't want to pimp for her. She claimed she was raped. Right out on the street."

"Sounds pretty fishy to me. Her father's a famous lawyer."

"Famous lawyer, yeah. You believe it. Famous for crooked deals. Barred from practice on account of abortions. That's the kind of company you keep! You better watch out. The whole family's the kind you don't want to meet up with in a dark alley. They've all been sent up the river at least once and they've all got enough syph to supply an army. But," I said magnanimously, "go ahead. I'll visit you in the hospital. Or I'll send you a card or a tulip when they fish you up. It's a free country. Just don't say I didn't warn you."

196

One afternoon I suddenly realized it was the perfect moment to do the Flip. I was in exactly the right mood for it. The time had come. I was in top form. Flip form. There's a special way you've got to feel for each different position. For some reason this is never mentioned in most erotic manuals. There's one reliable and stimulating book you can buy in Burma; it describes the physical and spiritual condition you should be in before, during, and after the Bump Pump, the Flip, Turkish Delight, Prairie Wolf, the Wink, the Pigalle Peep, the Argentinian Knot, Minetta, Whiplashes, Sixty-nine, the Quartet, African Nights, le Position du Sucker du Cock, the Dynamic Duo, the Bazooka, and Inside Tortures. A useful textbook and reference book for demimondaines, monks, chicken-fuckers, pornographers, ad men, my publisher, nymphomaniacs, sex maniacs, blowhards, and diplomats. Written by a monk, Brother Tarantula, it was first published in Calcutta by Purple Pussy Cat, Inc. It can be purchased at any nonaccredited book store. A book that fascinated me, just like the *I Ching* captivates smokers, and *How to Draw and Paint* absorbs artists.

I knocked on Alie Bies' boudoir door and heard muffled exclamations. When I opened the door I saw her naked little black girl gliding swiftly out of bed and Madam Alie jerking her Chinese peignoir shut.

"Hi, Flippie! You look so cute with your long blond hair," she said. "You drop in to do the Flip?"

"No, but I'd like to do it soon. That is, if you still want to and feel up to it."

"Honey," she said, "for you I always feel up to it. I've been waiting for this for years. For my own Flipper. For me, you're a champion even before we start. There's nothing I'd like better than a good Flip with you and then some nice Whiplashes to top it off.

"You know what?" she said with a sudden burst of energy. "I'm getting a truckload of fresh virgins in from the country tonight. Nice young flesh. Hand picked by me on my last safari. They've already learned a thing or two at my Reception Center for Young Girls. Only the theoretical part though. They'll be getting in tonight, and naturally I've got to teach them how to put theory into practice. Usually I have trained personnel for the job, but their heart isn't really in their work. Who could instruct them better than a handsome Nordic god with wild hair and blue eyes— who knows his way around, who knows the subtle nuances, and who is just a little bit blasé. One with feeling, who doesn't get stiff every time you look at him. That's the best kind of education my little girls could ask for!

"Better yet," she continued, "what say we do the Flip right in front of the girls? Once they've seen it they'll never forget it, and they'll know what to do if a client asks for one. Don't worry," she said. "I won't make you do anything after we've had our Flip. You can just stretch out and relax and I'll teach the girls what to do. They're very sweet," she confided, "all those little thirteen-, fourteen-year-old darlings. Very eager to learn. I'm getting eight tonight. Four are staying on here and the rest go on to a colleague of mine in Tunis—The Blue Grape."

It sounded like a good idea. I had to kill the time somehow. Barry had his nose buried in prophetic works like the Koran, while I wandered around all day through the narrow streets of Carthage. Or I visited the girls when they were off duty. Now that Barry was "going steady" I was bored stiff.

"You know, Alie," I said, "that doesn't sound like a bad idea at all. I just sit up in my room doing nothing much every night anyway. All those mini-maidens sound like fun, and I'm sure we'll all have a great time. But listen, I'm young and sometimes I get these crazy whims. My hobby's cooking. If you'd just let me cook up a nice erotic dish tonight—a good sexy fish dish or something—it'll get us all in the right mood and be a special treat for the new girls. A kind of welcome dinner. I'll have a ball making it and it's useful, too—a perfect blend of business and pleasure. We'll ask Barry to help get everything ready. And a couple of the girls. Nel's nice. And we'll ask Odessa and Barry's girl. I think he'd like to take Frenchy along with him when he shoves off. So we'll all eat, drink, and be merry. Then comes the Flip, and after that I'll sit back and let somebody else take care of the entertainments."

"Swell idea, sweetie," Madam Alie said. "Why didn't you tell me you could cook? I would have let you cook all you want. I thought, the simple boy, he's crazy about couscous."

"To tell you the truth, Alie," I said, "I've had enough couscous to last me a lifetime."

I thought the meal was a great idea, if I did say so myself. Madam Alie would have the room cleaned up and the table set while Barry and I went out shopping. She gave us some money and we walked down to the market. It was just about closing time so everything was going for practically nothing.

"You know," I said to Barry, "what I'd like is a really big fish spread. Lots of proteins—keep you potent. What about a nice fish soup to begin with? Or should we start right off with a big fish platter? What did you think of that erotic stimulation dish I made in Ibiza? Of course I could always make 'Casanova's Temper' again—that's got lots of fish in it, too. But that led to disaster, remember? Too bad for the poor guy. Just married. After I left, first his wife was jumped by fourteen of the guests, then him. And I'd told them straight out what the after-effects of that meal would be. But they said, don't worry, they were going to be among friends. And everybody needs a friend, I guess. No, as a matter of fact, I think we ought to make 'Fisherman's Orgy.' That fits the requirements. Although 'Sandwich à la Colette' wouldn't be a bad idea either, and it certainly does work wonders."

"You remember what happened last week in that Algerian village when you had to make your 'Sandwich à la Colette'?" Barry said. "Full-scale tribal war. They fought to the death over those broads. All because of that fancy cooking of yours. You know, if you used that dish the right way, you could rise to power fast. You've got something in you. Consciously or unconsciously, you yearn for power. It shows in everything you do. Even in your cooking. It could be dangerous if you used it wrong. Just think if a whole army ate your 'Sandwich à la Colette'! No telling what would happen. I'd be awfully careful if I were you. Let's stick to 'Fisherman's Orgy.' It's fun to make, too."

We bought a king-size fish at the fish market, pure white meat. A saltwater fish I'd never seen before, some kind of North African sea fish. It looked like whiting and weighed almost four pounds, which was just right. I also bought a pound of tiny little fish, something like sprat. Two dozen oysters, good solid oysters. Two dozen shrimp. A few little crabs. And a lobster tail for flavor. Everything else was sure to be in the hotel kitchen, like onions, garlic, bay leaves, parsley, flour, and olive oil. I knew I'd find olive oil. Every morning when they fried eggs for the hotel guests, our room reeked of olive oil.

When we got back we set to work right away. I had fond memories of "Fisherman's Orgy." Madam Alie's kitchen was ideal. A big hot stove with plenty of room for all kinds of pots.

Barry went upstairs to get his renowned spice kit. I needed paprika, nutmeg, a bottle of Tabasco, and one hot Hungarian pepper. Barry pried open the oysters with a big kitchen knife and cut them in half by squeezing the knife in between the shells and twisting. I put the shrimp in a pot of warm water and put them on to boil.

I peeled three good-sized onions, chopped them up in tiny pieces, and fried them in a big steel pan into which I'd already poured some olive oil. When the onions started frying, I threw in a few shreds of sliced garlic and let it fry till the onions were golden brown. I tossed the sprat into a bowl of flour and shook it around so the fish were all covered with a layer of flour. I'd mixed a few spoonfuls of paprika and a spoonful of nutmeg into the flour, so now the fish were red with paprika. I threw it all into the pan with the fried onions. A heavenly aroma steamed out of the kitchen. I threw some paprika and a can of tomato paste in with the shrimp. That would get the bleach taste out of them.

All of a sudden Nel came in, naked under a thin silk dressing gown.

"Smells great," she said. "Can I have a taste?"

She bent over the big pan where the little fish were frying in the oil, her enormous breasts hanging down, pressing against the flimsy silk. When she bent over I could see the clear outline of her stiff nipples.

"Mmmm," she said, fishing a little sprat out of the pan. "Nice and hot."

"Now out of the kitchen," I said, "before I throw you out on your ass."

She laughed defiantly and when I made a move toward her, she swished open her dressing gown and held it open with both hands. I had an unobstructed view of a pair of magnificent boobs. For a second I was speechless and dizzy. Laughing, she disappeared.

There was a nice atmosphere in that house. I had the kitchen door open to clean out all the smoke from the onions and fish. Sometimes I saw hotel guests shuffle past or whorehoppers quickly look the other way when they had to pass by the kitchen on their way upstairs with the girls. The girls all greeted us warmly.

I took a big pot, the biggest I could find, poured in a thin layer of oil, and set it on the stove. When the oil started going up in bluish smoke, I flipped the pan with the sprat in it into the big pot. I sliced a few red peppers in long strips and arranged them along the edge of the pot. In the meantime, Barry had talked Madam Alie into giving us a bottle of sharp white wine, resin wine. She'd be down soon to see how things were going. I threw the bay leaves in with the shrimp, Barry handed me the wine, and I poured about a quarter of the bottle into the big pot. The shrimp were boiling. Barry peeled them one by one and made sure the juice they'd boiled in didn't go to waste.

Madam Alie came in and sniffed, enraptured. The young girls had arrived and had been shown up to their rooms. I threw the juice from the oysters Barry had split into the big pot. When it started bubbling, I poured more wine in. Then I took the big fish, also dipped in flour, and carefully laid it in the pot. I put the lid on the pot and got a bottle of beer out of the ice box. It tasted out of this world. All that cooking had made me terrifically thirsty.

Madam Alie followed my every move with awe and admiration. I poured the shrimp juice with the shrimp into the pot, emptied the bottle of wine into it, and carefully peeled the shells off the crabs and threw them in too. I cut the Hungarian pepper up in little pieces and took out all the pits, then threw it all in the pot which was bubbling beautifully, giving off a fantastic aroma. I sprinkled parsley, pepper, and salt onto the big fish, and when the whole pot was bubbling away like mad again, I flopped the big fish over with a knife.

I split it carefully into halves and took out the bones in the middle so the white steaming meat crumpled up into a soft mass completely submerged in wine sauce. It smelled delicious. After letting the whole thing stew for about half an hour, adding some cream to the fish, putting the oysters along the sides of the pot, sprinkling in Tabasco sauce and pepper, my favorite unequaled "Fisherman's Orgy" was ready to be served.

I rushed upstairs to put on a clean shirt while Barry carried the pot to Madam Alie's dining room. I put on a fresh pair of dungarees and a light blue American work shirt. Then off to Alie's boudoir. It was almost eight o'clock. Suppertime.

Madam Alie's luxuriously furnished boudoir was drenched in the delicious fragrance of my "Fisherman's Orgy." Seated on big sumptuous cushions or ottomans, on chairs at the table, or on thick pink rugs on the floor, we loaded our plates and emptied them fast. Madam, Barry, Odessa, Nel, Simona (the French girl), and the four new arrivals.

Pint-size boppers, but they already had a grown-up look in their eyes, and they certainly weren't innocent. They loved the meal and eyed me hungrily when they thought I wasn't looking. Thalia and Alhambra were the most grown up, about fourteen, but they already had breasts and nicely developed bodies. Then there was Flora and Rena, a little younger but both very shrewd.

After the meal Barry went upstairs to read a book and the girls went to work. I stayed behind with Madam and the newcomers. After that delicious creamy meal I felt very pleased with the world. The marvelous white fish drenched in good spices and wine sauce, the oysters and the shrimp gave me a great sense of satisfaction.

Madam Alie told the girls to make themselves comfortable on the soft pillows while we did the Flip. The question period would follow the performance. I got undressed and Madam stripped too. She dimmed the lights to a nice romantic pink glow. Soft music was playing on the radio—Arabian music, and now and then some English or American: Glenn Miller, Peggy Lee, or Les Paul & Mary Ford. The girls sat quiet as mice while we executed a long, fierce Flip.

Although Madam must have been well past forty, she still had what it takes, well built and well preserved. In her youth she must have been a knock-out. Her breasts were still enormous but they'd gone flabby, and her belly wasn't really up to the Flip any more.

When we'd Flipped wildly for a while, she suddenly moaned, "Deeper deeper deeper! I want more of that stick," kneading my . . . like mad with her hands. After she'd sucked my . . . hard and strong with her full lips, while my fingers whipped around in her . . . , she said, "Now in, lover, nice and deep in my. . . . Yeah," she said, "I like everything just as long as it's meat."

After we'd gone on like that for a while she suddenly turned around and I saw her enormous buttocks jut up before me like a colossal boulder.

"In my . . . , sweetie. Come on in," she begged. "Stick it in! Deeper! Deeper!"

I caught a glimpse of my sweaty face in the mirror next to the bed. I looked at my tense screwed-up face with all that disheveled hair, working bare-assed like a horse, ramming up against her enormous . . . I burst out laughing. The whole scene was suddenly so unbelievably funny I just couldn't stop laughing.

"Come on, sweetie," she whined, like a little kid when somebody's taken a lollipop out of her mouth. "Come on, dearie. Fuck me!"

197

For hours I was laid and laid and laid again by four little girls. Under Madam's expert guidance they learned the tricks of the trade. How to excite men by tickling and licking them. How they could work themselves up to a climax. How to go a night without sleep with short breaks. And how to use those breaks.

I was their willing human guinea pig. I stretched out and relaxed as one by one the little maidens sacrificed their virginity to me. I drifted off into sleep and they went on with their lessons undaunted. I had beautiful dreams.

A villa in Scotland with a chorus of bagpipes. A store stacked with cunts. Beautiful cunts, clean and healthy. Elegant ladies come in and take out their cunts from under their skirts. Beautiful chicks take their cunts out and lay them on the counter. On a rack behind the counter— thousands of cunts, lovely cunts, fleshy cunts and slim cunts, oblong and round, cleanshaven and rippling with curls, pink and light brown, polka dotted and striped. Thousands of cunts. A paradise for the connoisseur. The dream made me feel at peace with the world, and when I woke up the girls were still going strong. Finally when we were all a bit haggard we dropped off to sleep together on the bed. I dreamed of a Paradise where gorgeous girls walked around naked, girls with three breasts and an extra cunt tucked up right under the belly button.

198

One hot afternoon I was reading in bed in my room right over Madam Alie's boudoir. We'd had lunch with her. We'd called up a catering service and ordered that well-known Tunisian working man's lunch, the

"Baghavad Gita," which was so good I even asked for seconds. After dessert—crisp crackers with mushy strawberry jelly, the kind served daily in all Dutch orphanages and boarding schools—I felt kind of heavy and lazy.

I decided to browse through my favorite book, *Alone in the World,* which I hadn't opened since we left Ceuta; I usually read it about four times a year. Stuffed and satisfied, I went downstairs to where the Silver Monster was parked in the hall. I lifted the seat of the side-car, took out a package, unwrapped the canvas, and took the book back to my room. Going into room 03, I lay down in bed, opened the book, and was soon caught up in it all over again. I lay there flat out on the bed, wonderfully relaxed, while the sounds of men hard at work in the harbor of Carthage and the sea-salty breeze from the Tunisian Gulf drifted in through my window.

Noise at the door. Then in came Barry. Panting for breath and pointing to the wall, he stammered, "A gorgeous piece just moved in next door, in room 05! A girl you won't believe till you see her!"

And, in fact, his description did make her sound pretty nice. Tall, sturdy, shiny black hair. An Amazon.

"Yeah?" I said, uninterested. "There're lots of good-looking chicks in the world. You could spend a whole lifetime running after them. Why don't you follow my example instead, man? Stretch out and read a good book for a change."

I read on, fascinated. Still, thoughts of a gorgeous piece of ass kept running through my mind. Of course, there were enough good-looking broads in the world, but why would a beautiful chick with that much class stay in a dump like this? The joy-girls all lived in the back of the house. It kept bothering me. I couldn't concentrate on the book any more. I sighed and shut it. When it comes to reading literature, I don't want to miss a single line, and now that I couldn't keep my mind on it, the best thing was to skip it entirely.

Why would a good-looking girl come and live next door to me of all people, I wondered? Was it Fate?

I went downstairs and asked Madam Alie, who was standing near the cash register. "Who checked into 05, Alie?"

"That chick? A journalist from London. Her name's Nana. Born in Bulgaria. Don't ask me what she's here for, but she's going to be staying a few days. I think maybe she wants to take pictures because she came in with a lot of complicated looking cameras hanging around her neck. She's your type. Good-looking. Very emancipated, though! You can see right off nobody's going to push that girl around. She might be something for you. Worth a look anyway."

The description intrigued me. I decided to keep a sharp lookout for her. Before going back into my room I stamped on the floor out in the hall. She didn't come out to look. I figured, living that close together, I'd bump into her sometime. Inside, I put my ear to the wall but didn't hear any strange sounds.

Around noon Barry saw her on the stairs. Fantastic, but very stuck up, he said, because she didn't even look at him. "Doesn't mean a thing, Barry," I said. "No broad in her right mind ever does."

But now I wanted to see her myself once. I was curious. When I went downstairs to the bar that evening, I saw her going into her room, but only a profile. Well stacked, broad shouldered, glorious long black hair. Light blue denim jacket, dark blue leather mini-skirt, fine legs sheathed in knee-high tan leather boots. An odd outfit for the middle of summer in Tunisia, but very classy, very exciting. She intrigued me. I wanted to see her face. If it matched what went with it, it would be beautiful, and I knew it would. A photographer from some weekly or monthly out shooting a travel story and now running low near the end of her trip, she's spending the last few days in a cheap hotel.

It was stuffy and crowded in the Chamber of Pleasures. Lots of cigar smoke and mumbled deals being made. I sat down next to Barry, who was chatting at one of the tables with Thalia and Flora, the girls from the night before.

I had a double shot of brandy and asked the girls, "How's it going, kiddies? Getting used to the place?" Turning to Barry, I said, "I just saw her going into her room. Great, but I still haven't seen her face. Can hardly wait." I put down the brandy in one gulp.

The place was packed. All the tables were taken. Madam must be raking in a fortune, I thought. The cash register didn't stop clanging for a second. Gorgeous chicks sat on old guys' laps, stroking their Tunisian whiskers, or retired to one of the curtained-off compartments.

In the midst of the crowd Madam Alie was bustling around, praising her wares. She was doing a terrific business. Whenever she passed our table, she always dropped a wisecrack or a friendly remark. As friendly as they come, Madam Alie, with a heart of gold—if you were on her good side, anyway. And because of the Flip I was. I'd done better Flips in my time, with more acrobatics and surprise effects. But for Madam Alie it was a Flip like she hadn't Flipped in at least ten years. So I was in with her. And didn't I know it! Drinks on the house, plus the pad for free, while we waited for her skipper friend who'd take us back on his freighter to Spain.

A good life. The girls dug us, which didn't go down very well with the gigolos and pimps employed by the house. Ever since we'd blown in, Madam Alie was snapping at them constantly, and the girls weren't very sweet to them either. The reputation of a good Triangler and Flipper works wonders. The pimp platoon acted friendly enough, but you couldn't ever really trust them. Irish Appie was the ringleader—a down-and-out man of letters from Dublin, whom Madam Alie had fished out of the gutter, in return for which he'd stayed on to work for her.

We got under their skin after awhile. It was bad enough to see Madam Alie giving us whatever we wanted, but what really hurt was that we were fucking the geese who should have been busy laying golden eggs for them. And for free. They sulked and muttered about the Triangle, the Dynamic Duo, the New Revelation, and all the food and alcohol we put away. Suddenly all the girls in the house wanted baby-faced blonds. A handsome guy with a haircut—healthy, tanned, and blue-eyed. Instead of those seedy couscous kooks with their greasy drooping mustaches. Pimps Incorporated had had it. They weren't going to take it any longer. Their protégés and wives were demanding they bleach their hair, shave their mustaches, burn all their baggy suits, and wear something sharp like those two Dutch Masters.

A formal complaint to the Union? Out of the question. Too risky. Could always be used as evidence against them. If Madam Alie found out about it, they'd be trying to swim underwater with a dagger in their ribs within half an hour. Besides which, most of them couldn't read or write, and nobody trusted anybody else when they got down to talking about who was going to sign the letter. They arrived at the decision that they would all be on the lookout for the perfect moment of revenge. Though we never went out at night, and were always in the hotel or down in the bar, it would come. The tide had to turn sometime. Only it wouldn't be any snap to get us in Madam Alie's house. She more or less ruled the entire Tunisian underworld.

The pimps kept up a steady fire of vicious, envious glances from their strategic positions at the bar or behind their tables. We kept our cool, we weren't looking for trouble. They were a bunch of weasels, small-time pimps, pickpockets and miscellaneous doormats for Madam Alie to wipe her feet on. And we were the deluxe duet who'd drifted in, and now suddenly everybody was taking orders from us, the bosses of the kitchen, who invited the girls for supper, who drank nothing but brandy and champagne, and spoke a foreign language too. That really burned them, because half the time we were talking about them and cracking up with hilarious laughter and they never got the joke. It couldn't go on like that.

Naturally I sensed what was going on. Right away. Other people can call what I've got paranoia, but it's saved my life on plenty of occasions. I explained what I felt to Barry. He'd sensed it too. We decided to watch out, take care, and be ready for anything.

Suddenly Barry nudged me, "Hey, look at who's heading for the bar!"

It was the girl from the room next door. Instead of her blue denim jacket, she was wearing a dark blue leather jacket that matched her skirt. She still had her tan knee-boots on. She coolly made her way through the crowd to an empty stool at the bar. All the men around her, drinking or talking, gazed at her for a minute and then made some remark. I saw her order something and turn down all offers.

She was sitting pretty far off from me. I was at the table next to the jukebox. From where I sat, her face looked fine. Wide jaws, prominent cheekbones. A clear pale complexion that contrasted with her dark hair. She spun around on her stool, crossed her well-shaped legs, and stared into the dim red lights of the crowded smoky room.

A shock jolted through my body when I saw her come in. I was too shy, though, to go over to her at the bar. I didn't want to force myself on her. The minute I saw her I realized this wasn't any ordinary woman. No flashy smile or excess friendliness. A manly kind of woman.

Sliding off the stool with her booted legs, she slipped through the crowd and walked past me to the juke box, threw in a coin, and picked a few records without even a glance at the clients who came up to help her select.

She had a hard but attractive, high-cheekboned face, outlined black on white in the juke-box neon light. She was a beautiful robust woman, a courtesan—the kind with a whip who treats her lovers like slaves. If she had lovers. Could be a lesbian prowling through this cathouse looking for some pussy.

After Barry and I had stared at the fierce beauty for what seemed like hours, I jumped up from behind the table so I'd accidentally bump into her in the aisle. I could brush up against her and turn it into a joke. She nearly walked right through me. There was something about her. I didn't dare cross her path on her way back to the bar. For approximately a second she looked me straight in the eye. A fierce gaze. Too short to be taken as a sign. I felt uncomfortable. Situations with women I don't have in my power always make me jumpy. I returned to the table and started talking to Barry about something else.

Madam Alie came over and said, "Some trouble with the law. I'll be right back, boys. If you need me, I'll be up in my suite." And she threw us a kiss and left the room.

Barry and I went on drinking and laughing over some of the crazy things that had happened on our travels. I kept one eye on the bar where the leather-clad beauty still sat smoking and drinking. She's got guts, I

131

thought, to stay at a notorious hotel in a foreign country and spend her evenings in a cathouse bar. That was asking for trouble. Maybe she didn't know what kind of place this was. Though she certainly didn't look like she was born yesterday. Probably a part-time hooker out to earn some fast cash. But she was at the wrong address. Here the whole operation was organized, ruled with an iron fist.

Taking over while Madam was away, Irish Appie—a slimy Irishman with cauliflower ears, a bright red bashed-in booze-veined nose, a dimmed-out Irish literary light—suddenly appeared next to the girl. I saw him make some witty crack to her which his whole rat pack heehawed at. The guy had a lot of nerve now that Madam was gone. I saw him put his big meaty hand on the girl's shoulder and could tell something was going to happen. The girl didn't look in any mood for swapping wisecracks with Irish Appie.

She just stared straight ahead of her into the mirror back of the bar. Then suddenly I saw her flick out a lightning blow to Appie's Irish chest. A hard chop that streaked up his throat and chin sending his bulky body spinning until he landed flat on his back.

The girl turned to offer her apologies with a menacing grin, then calmly went back to sipping her Tom Collins or gin fizz. I could have sworn it was a karate chop—*a coup de savate*—though the more I thought about it, the less likely it seemed. Karate chops from a broad like that?

The incident wasn't over, even though the bystanders joked with Irish Appie now, trying to cool him off by talking about canaries and little robin redbreasts, knowing Appie had a soft spot for those particular birds. No luck though. He'd been humiliated. Pushing his way through the crowd, he stopped and stood right behind the girl. Though it wasn't any of my business, I said to Barry, "Come on. We're not going to let that Irish fart massacre that girl."

We marched up to the bar. Irish Appie felt a gentle tap on his shoulder and turned to look. I was standing in front of Appie, Barry to his right. I wanted to say, "Anything wrong, pigface?" but there wasn't any need.

With hate in his eyes, he snapped, "What do *you* want? I'd keep out of this if I were you."

"Well, fortunately I'm not you," I snapped back, "so you know what I think you should do with your advice? Jam it."

"You're looking for trouble," he yelled. "You're just asking to get your ass whipped. You've been asking for it so long that's just what you're going to get, too!"

His ringed fist swung fast but I ducked faster. But while he was still out knocking on thin air, up came his knee and I hadn't been looking for that. Oof went my crotch, and I doubled up with pain. I twisted away from another punch. He was after my head this time, but I took it on my shoulder and the sharp pain shot through my collarbone.

Though I was writhing in pain, I didn't panic. I saw Barry jump him, but Appie was big and shook him off, slammed him down and kicked him when he lay stretched out on the floor. The customers backed off, forming a circle around us, very careful not to slop their drinks.

From my waist down I hurt like hell, and I hadn't got my breath back yet. Still, Appie was careless now, flailing around instead of planning his punches, and I got out from under most of them. Then, for a second, I saw him off guard and he took my kickoff right in the balls. He crumpled and I scored off his face this time. A dull thud and Irish Appie was bleeding like a pig, the blood spurting out over the rug.

Back in shape again, I booted him in the ear, leaving a river of blood behind. He was screaming with pain, struggling to get up again, to wipe the blood out of his eyes so he could find me, so I decided not to wait till he was up and chopped for his throat. Something went wrong. He flung me across the room into the crowd where I picked up a few more punches in the head, kicks in the back, etc.

I was still trying to get up when thonk, Appie's big black-shoed foot sailed into my face. I grabbed his foot and gave it a full turn. With a howl, Irish Appie came down on his side. I aimed the arch of my shoe for the hollow just under his chin and slammed it home hard.

Suddenly the whole Pimp Platoon was on top of me. Barry and I were fighting like crazy. We couldn't get out of the room because the crowd had closed in and wouldn't let us through. We were getting kneed in the back and bottles were crashing all around us.

I'd just about had it. I was bushed from dodging too many knives and broken bottles. Barry was swinging at everyone around him like a cornered animal. He'd picked up a faceful of bruises and kept going back to his flat-out position on the floor. My shirt was in shreds; my bare back had got clawed up and stamped on while I was trying to dodge whatever I could.

About ten men were working the two of us over. I was scared of their knives. They were the kind of guys who could stab me in the back or ram a broken bottle in my face without batting an eyelash. Bent over double I took one blow and kick after the other, trying at least to save my crotch and my eyes for later. I thought about falling in a heap on the floor hoping they'd let up after a few more kicks. But that's risky. For all I knew they'd go right on kicking until they'd killed me.

133

Suddenly I got a breath of air. People were being pulled and torn off my back one by one. I heard more screaming. Help must have arrived. Maybe Madam Alie had come back. That gave me a new burst of courage and I stood up and stretched out. With the last bit of energy I had left, I shook the last of the skunks, rats, and vermin off like a lion.

Suddenly I saw the beauty in the leather suit in the middle of a wild boxing match. Chopping and booting, she was mowing the guys down with the sides of her hands and the tips of her booted toes. I saw her slam into one guy who had pulled a knife. Her boot smacked him square in the face leaving behind one big bloody blotch.

I grabbed a stool, held its legs out and charged straight for the throats and faces of the pimps around me.

"Barry!" I called. "Barry, everything okay?"

"Yeah," came the answer from somewhere behind me.

"Keep up the good work," I yelled, while I made myself some elbow room by driving back the crowd with my stool. One of them tried diving under the stool for my legs. I kneed him so hard in the head I had to walk around with my knee bandaged up for weeks.

All at once I was back to back with the girl in the leather suit. I kept her behind me and shoved back the crowd while shouldering her over toward the bar where she'd be safer.

Hearing all that racket and smashing glass, Madam Alie came storming downstairs. She bellowed out orders to her pick-up gorilla pack, who clubbed the platoon of pimps out the door and into the street where, if they didn't clear out fast enough, they caught hell for a long time. A couple of girls who'd joined in with their pimps got mauled too.

It took a few minutes for peace and quiet to be restored. Chairs and stools were set up again, broken glass swept away, tablecloths put back on the tables. I looked in the mirror. I had a few bad bruises, no permanent scars—just a few deep scratches on my neck and back, tracks left by sharp shoes. Barry had a black eye and they'd ripped skin off along with his shirt.

I looked incredulously at the girl at the bar. She sat there cool as a cucumber and apparently untouched. She smoothed back her long black hair, buttoned her jacket, and smiled at me in the mirror. Madam Alie forged ahead through the crowd and came up to us wailing away.

"Did they hurt you, sweetheart?"

"No, ma'am."

We laughed.

"I'll get them," she said threateningly. "As a matter of fact, it sounds like they're already getting it!"

I heard yells, whips cracking, and the dull thudding of clubs, glad it wasn't I out there getting the treatment Madam Alie's trained goons were handing out. I went over to the girl.

"You all right?"

"Sure," she said with a nonchalant smile. "I'm an expert at karate and Ching Fu. I've made this kind of scene before. There's something about people fighting I don't much care for. It must be the smell of sweat."

She sipped her drink. She set down her empty glass.

"You care for another?" I asked. "My name's Jan Cremer."

"Nana's my name," she answered, friendly but still pretty cool. "I buy my own drinks. You'll have something too?"

"Sure," I said and ordered a glass of chilled beer.

Barry and I were the heroes of the day. And Nana the heroine, of course. The regular clients were all talking about how the three of us had stood up against about fourteen men. They'd never seen anything like Nana in action.

Simona, the French girl, gently led Barry upstairs. I noticed I was standing there half naked. My shirt had been literally stripped off my back. I apologized to Nana and said, "I'll be right back. You'll still be here? See you in a minute."

"Good," she said, less cool and more friendly this time.

After washing the cuts on my body and the blood off my face, I put on a shirt, the last shirt I had. I'd had four when we started out from Ibiza. One was now wrapped around Silver Monster's tires, the other had bandaged Barry's leg after I'd gone through a barbed-wire fence on the Monster. And now still another was in shreds downstairs.

After sprinkling my hair with aftershave lotion, I shot downstairs and back to Nana at the bar. I finished off the beer and we sat there talking. She was beautiful and intelligent. Friendly, but not too.

I felt a warm passion growing inside. She was a rare specimen. A broad who wasn't going to spread after half an hour of romantic bullshit. She would require a prolonged, serious seduction. A terrific woman. Tough face. Vivid light-green eyes. Not a bland face like a model's but a face full of character, a mouthful of sparkling teeth framed by fleshy thick lips. Broad shoulders, broad hips. Lean silver-braceleted wrists, strong hands. A Slavic type. A Balkan woman.

She told me she was an English journalist. Born and bred in Bulgaria, but had lived in London for years. She'd been traveling for months, working on a series of articles about "prostitution in Europe and North Africa"—a subject she specialized in. She also wrote reports for all sorts of big research institutions and scientific publishing firms. Sexual reform leagues bought some of her articles. In Holland, for example, the Dutch Association for Sexual Excess was a steady purchaser of her articles, which she illustrated herself. She was also a professional photographer. Her work took her all over the world. She'd just been in Tibet where she'd spent a year in a convent. She was writing books about her travels that she planned to publish some day.

An adventurous girl, I thought. A bit like me. She was almost as tall as I was. My female counterpart. I told her all about my adventures and plans, and she listened intently. The more I told her the more interested she grew. At first, she said, she'd thought we were beatniks, loafers, who wandered the world living like parasites, never doing a thing. I told her of my ambitions and explained how Barry and I had landed in Madam Alie's whorehouse. She'd come there, she said, because various people had recommended it to her as a good place to do research.

"If you want," I said, "I'll introduce you to Madam Alie. That may make your work easier."

"Tomorrow," she suggested. "I'm going to bed now."

She paid the bill. She insisted on that.

I said good night, but didn't get up. I knew I couldn't make her right away. Maybe not at all. So why go upstairs for nothing, just to say good night at her door? That wasn't what I was after. I don't run after women, ever. Although I was madly in love with her. All of a sudden. Nana's hard self-confident indifferent attitude intrigued me so much I was sure Fate must have brought us together. Figuratively and literally.

Tense and preoccupied I fell asleep, eager to see the Bulgarian beauty again as soon as possible. I dreamed about the fight and about her, and I felt practically sure we were going to get together. Why else would the Ideal Woman—a strong, beautiful, tough, healthy, proud, independent, and fearless woman with long hair and sea-green eyes—register at a cathouse in Carthage, move into the next room, and help me out of a fight?

I was so in love I had a hard time falling asleep. I tossed and turned in the warm bed. I thought of how nice it would be to lie next to Nana. It was as if I'd known her for years. Her face, her body, everything about her seemed familiar. I knew it. For years I'd dreamed of her as my Mysterious Dream Woman. Feverishly I wondered if she was feeling and thinking the same thoughts and feelings on the other side of the wall.

199

Every time I saw her in the next few days it was like a shock going through me. She looked great, dressed in her blue leather suit and boots, or in a short thin silver silk dress that looked as if she had been poured into it and showed off her hips and her butt and her breasts. She didn't wear anything under the silver dress. When she walked, her breasts swung out against the thin material and the silk switched wildly around her legs and thighs. It took my breath away.

I'd made up my mind to seduce her—with all the powers at my command and in a very special way. She had to become My Woman. I couldn't afford to make any mistakes. She was my counterpart. Her name wasn't Nana for nothing. She was a Nana right out of Émile Zola's *The Belly of Paris.*

At my request Madam Alie granted her numerous interviews with the girls and with herself, and let her take pictures at sex sessions and orgies. And also told her a few things about me.

Slowly, but surely, Nana and I relaxed with each other. We respected each other's feelings. I had years to spare, if I could only make her mine. When she asked me if I would do the famous Triangle with her looking on, I felt sort of ashamed. What did she think I was? My love for her was real. I knew this Panther Woman had been made for me.

She talked me over though. After we'd talked about it for a while, she convinced me her curiosity was strictly professional. So one afternoon I did a triangle in my room with Odessa, Nel, and the little novice Flora. Swedish Sally, who'd been in the original line-up, couldn't make it.

The triangle started off kind of stiff, but once we got used to the flash bulbs and the clicking of Nana's various cameras, we started to swing. Nana closed the windows and pulled the drapes shut to darken the room. Using flash bulbs, she took countless pictures with her Pentax and Canon miniatures.

While the four of us worked away at our triangle, Nana was always moving in with her light meter, then backing off and clicking her cameras. "Don't pay any attention to me," she said, "I'm just doing my work. Though it does look terrific! I've never seen a triangle like this before. They've got one in Tibet, but that's with a donkey."

When we were bushed from triangling and posing (Nana also made a few time exposures and we had to freeze in the most uncomfortable positions for a long time each time; twice I got a cramp in my leg, once in my tongue), the satisfied girls kissed me goodbye and went back to their rooms.

I lay back on my bed under a sheet and answered the questions Nana asked me from a journalistic point of view. We went into great detail about the triangle and the Flip. She had heard I was good at it.

It was the most peculiar publicity I'd ever had in my whole career. Long articles about the triangle and "A Visit to a Brothel"—illustrated by photographs in which I was clearly visible in spite of those little black patches over my eyes—appeared in illustrated weeklies all over Poland, Bulgaria, and Tijuana. But what difference did it make? Publicity is publicity. As long as you're in the news that's all that matters. Like Oscar Wilde said, "Better to be attacked by the press than not mentioned at all." Besides, I'm used to publicity. There isn't a single part of my body that hasn't been photographed and published.

200

A bond grew between us that became stronger every day. In the beginning Madam Alie wasn't too happy that I only had eyes for the Bulgarian journalist. The promise of a new Flip cleared that problem up.

We spent our days walking around Carthage. Just the way she walked, the switch of her hips, made all the men whistle. She had the sexiest legs in the world. And knew it. She never wore make-up. Her beautiful face didn't need it. Sometimes though she put on pearly-silver lipstick and electric-blue eyeshadow that made her bright sea-green eyes even brighter.

My love for her was overpowering. I wanted to possess every square inch of her. Though I'd never been to bed with her, I could imagine what it was like. Divine. Though I'd never seen her naked, I could also imagine what that was like. I could read her body like an open book.

When I knocked on her door one morning a few days after we met, I heard her voice say, "Who's there?"

"I Jan Cremer," I said, and she opened the door.

I stepped into the room and saw her magnificent naked body getting back under the sheet.

"Just keeping warm," she said.

She was a Nature Woman. Magnificent. I watched while she dressed. Her body was coarse but well-shaped. Broad hips, fleshy buttocks. Long heavenly legs. A pair of firm breasts, not too big, just big enough to handle a little. Her nipples were big flat light-brown disks, the tips dark brown. Across her breasts and belly, thin stripes of white outlined a bikini.

I'd never seen such a beautiful woman before. Her broad body was typically Slavic and the luxuriant hair around her massive Mount Venus made it all the more inviting. She radiated sun and energy. She had the kind of body you see in Swedish nudist magazines. She looked like a bronze by Rodin.

Without any embarrassment she washed in my presence. A warm

feeling spread up from my crotch as she bent over the basin. Her ass stuck out and swung as she brushed her teeth. I longed for her love. I couldn't stand it any more. I'd been a good boy long enough. I walked over and embraced her big body. Her flesh felt firm. She put down her toothbrush and pressed her butt up against my pelvis. I cupped her breasts in my hands. She leaned back, her eyes closed, and passively enjoyed my caresses. Then she turned in my grip and we kissed each other passionately.

201

She bit my tongue with her strong pearly teeth and tried to suck it clear out of my mouth. We bit and sucked and licked each other. And both our hearts were drumming hard as we licked and touched.

"What took you so long?" she sighed. "I've been waiting for you for days—every minute of the day and night I've been waiting for you to hold me in your arms. The first time I saw you a fire blazed up inside me. You're the only person who can put out that fire of desire. It blazes for you. Let's not leave this room today. Let's be together. This moment may never come again. You are the love of my life. For years I've been rushing to catch up with myself and you. I knew you existed. I've known you were there, somewhere, for years. Now at last I can touch your flesh. Let's stay in each other as long as we can. After that our paths will part and we will go our ways alone again. For a little while, or perhaps a long time. Wherever we may go, we'll meet again. Each time our being together will be longer and richer. Until finally we will never part. Like a pair of wild animals we'll find our den. In a city or a wood, on a boat or an island. All we will have will be each other. Take me. I am yours. Yours only. Possess me. Only you will ever really possess me. Take me please. For the first time in my life I am begging a man to possess me. You are the man. Take me."

I hugged her even tighter and drew her down onto the bed. She tore off my clothes while we kissed. When we came together I was the happiest man in the world. I dove into her. Deeper and deeper. It was as if I was dreaming. Sinking deeper and deeper into a paradise. Her flesh felt delicious. It smelled of salt air and sun. When I had possessed her all over, and she me, we fell into a deep happy sleep. For the first time in my life I fell asleep happy. With Nana. My woman.

We woke up late that afternoon and got dressed. Her face had changed. She looked like an angel. Her hard features had softened. She was a completely different person. She seemed lighter and glad, and we no longer had any secrets from each other. It had taken a long time, but I had finally met my love.

202

Nana, my Nana, I want to feel you up and peel you up, sweep you up, creep you up, suck you up, fuck you up, eat you up, meat you up, lick you up, prick you up, brush you up, and slush you up, chew you up, coo you up, ring you up and ding you up, knock you up, lock you up, rock you up and cock you up, sniff you up, stiff you up, lay you down and play you down, fight you down and night you down, screw you down, tattoo you down, strip you down and dip you down, lip you down, slip you down, drum you down, come you down, run you down and fun you down, tunnel you down, funnel you down, tongue you up and bung you up, wake you up, break you up, laugh you up and giraffe you up, swill you down, drill you down, dream you up and cream you.

In short, my dear sweet soft beautiful fine hot Nana—I love you and only you.

203

Nana and I spent a few sublime days together. After feasting on erotic dishes that I cooked in the hotel kitchen, we feasted on each other in bed again. We got out of bed only when we had to to keep alive. And always reluctantly.

One afternoon I'd fallen asleep in her bed and when I woke up Nana was gone. I was terrified. Had she left me? There hadn't been any quarrel. Seeing her suitcases calmed me down. I took a bath and washed my hair. Then I lay down to dry off on the sheets (permeated with the smell of our love) and looked through the suitcase full of photographs Nana had taken on her trip. Hundreds of nudes. Positions, orgies, bacchanals, sodomites, necrophiliacs, harems, women torturing women, women tied down to beds with donkeys on top of them; women tied up and slashed with knives. Horrible instruments of torture. Fourteen people squirming all over and under each other. Pictures of decorated and tattooed cunts.

I took piles of pictures out of the suitcase and, when I'd examined them, put them back neatly. Suddenly a little black jade box caught my eye, with "Magic Nana" written on it in tiny pearls. A strange thought flashed through my mind. "Magic Nana?" Was my Nana the Magic Nana?

Before I had time to think about it the key was turning in the door and Nana came in. I had put all the pictures back and I was lying on the bed.

In the reddish glow of the setting sun and approaching twilight Nana looked like a goddess. She was the most beautiful creation I had ever laid eyes on. She'd gone out shopping. While she put the bottles of beer in the bathtub and turned on the cold water, I thought with her I really hit the bull's-eye. Although it would soon have to come to an end.

She walked through the room, looking at me sweet and hungrylike. Her swaying bosom sent a stiff message down through my body and up shot a little tent in the sheet. She slipped her leather jacket off her broad bony shoulders and stood before me naked from the waist up, except for a big black leather bra that cupped only the lower half of her breasts. Her enormous nipples eyed me provocatively. The bra was dotted with tiny precious stones. A true work of art. I'd never seen this brassiere before. It sparkled in the orange light of the setting sun.

With a soft laugh, she unzipped her leather skirt and slipped it off. Dressed only in a leather garter belt holding up a pair of black silk stockings that sheathed her magnificent legs above her light-colored boots, she stood by the bed. The garter belt was broad at the waist and decorated like her bra with all kinds of precious stones. There were big roses embroidered on it and silver stars and nails. A very impressive belt. I'd never seen it on her before. She wasn't wearing panties, so her enormous Mount Venus with its wild clump of hair jutted out robustly.

She stood at the foot of the bed and extended one booted foot to me. I slowly removed the boot from her fine calf, and when she gave me her other leg I got a clear look at her superb full-grown twat. She sat down beside me on the bed, undid the black stockings from the garter belt, and stripped them off her legs. The leather straps dangled against her white flesh. Then she stretched out on top of me. I felt the cool leather rub against my warm body and while we made love the strangest thoughts ran through my mind.

"Take me from down under," she whispered beseechingly in my ear. I followed her hands. She pivoted until her crotch lay over my face and her mouth was over mine. It was wonderful to have each other like that.

We went on for hours. During a short intermission (I was lying on my back, her well-developed quim right in front of my face, looking like a full deep red flesh-tulip of enormous proportions) I thanked my lucky stars and made up an ode to her snatch.

> *Here I lie a simple guy*
> *staring a twat straight in the eye*

Jan Cremer *The Magic Nana*

> *I may be flat broke but so what*
> *I'm warmed by the mustache of her twat*

No·masterpiece, but then it took days for Cyrano de Bergerac to come up with his poems and odes.

204

It was as if her magnificent flesh-gate, which opened its portals wider at each touch, had been especially created by angels or by god. I crawled back to her face after spending hours lingering around her gate. Enormously firm lips down there. The muscles could lock up my hand inside. The clitoris was like a stubby dill pickle that had been sucked at too long and stuck up fiercely between the fortified flesh-flaps.

A thin strip of leather had been sewed in along her vaginal lips so that they possessed immense strength and couldn't slacken.

"You still don't know who I am?" she asked, after I'd carefully studied her reinforced vagina. She stood up and took a big heavy bull whip out of the suitcase, a whip used to drive cattle, or by a TV magician to flick the cigarette out of his lady assistant's mouth.

I had a suspicion then. With an expert flick of the wrist she inserted the handle between her legs, gripping it between the lips of her cunt. She pointed to a painting hanging by a nail to the wall, about three yards off. A Tunisian desert landscape with camels.

The tail of the whip hung down to the floor between her legs. She folded her arms and stood there, all her muscles tense, her feet planted squarely on the floor. Suddenly she yelled, "Pooshta! Pooshta!" and, giving her hips a jerk that traveled on through to her buttocks, she thrust out her Mount Venus. The heavy whip rose from the ground, and with a resounding crack, down came the painting from the wall. She looked at me in triumph, took the whip out from between her legs and flung it on the floor. "Now do you know?" she asked.

I stuttered, still incredulous, "Nana! Magic Nana! Are you Magic Nana? *The* Magic Nana?"

"Yes, sweetheart," she said. "I am Magic Nana. But from now on I'm working for you. I'm yours."

"Then," I stammered, "then you're Superwoman. Magic Nana, alias Piccadilly Lilly, alias Tiger Lilly! You're Superwoman, the woman every man is searching for, the idol of millions. Millions of people searching, pursuing you, and you keep appearing in different disguises. Only Piccadilly Lilly, alias Tiger Lilly, can do that trick with the whip. Tiger Lilly with the Iron Twat! But if you're Magic Nana and Piccadilly Lilly, alias Tiger Lilly, why aren't you wearing the dreaded Golden Serpent?"

"Here, sweetheart, sweetest darling in the world," she said, "I was waiting for you to find out for yourself. Well, and now you know. Put my Golden Serpent back on for me; the Serpent that will guard my Blissful Opening again against all intruders from now on. Until you return. You, and you only, will ever be able to remove the Golden Serpent."

She gave me a little hollow golden ring shaped like a serpent, with little vicious razor-sharp teeth set along the inner edge. I crawled down her body and, turning it carefully so as not to touch its sharp teeth, the barbed hooks or the razor-sharp edge, inserted the Serpent. I kissed her Venus-berg and now I knew for sure.

My woman was Nana, nicknamed Magic Nana, the most dreaded and desired woman in the world, known as Piccadilly Lilly, alias Tiger Lilly. She was The Famous Flamous. I had been permitted to insert her Golden Serpent, which she'd removed especially for me. We would meet again in this life and always be happy together. Our paths would part again and again, but each minute of the day we would each know what the other one was thinking and feeling. Happy, we fell asleep.

Early the next morning I woke up and felt in terror and despair the empty pillow beside me. Nana was gone. Her bags, everything was gone. There was a note on the chair my pants hung from. "Search for me, follow me, and you shall find me. Until we meet again. Wherever and whenever that may be! My dearest! Nana."

205

Two days later Madam Alie's friend the skipper arrived. He would take us to Alicante where we could catch a boat to Ibiza. We could make Silver Monster fast to the rail on the afterdeck. We said goodbye to everything and everyone, and promised to write and send lots of picture postcards.

"If you ever come this way again, you can always stay," Madam Alie said. "My house is your house," she winked mischievously, "but then there'll have to be some more good Flipping."

We left with Madam Alie, Nel, Odessa, Flora, Thalia, Simona, Alhambra, and all the other girls who'd showed us such a good time waving goodby from the pier. Wistfully we left the city behind and watched it sink below the horizon. I told Barry about what had happened with Nana and he could understand how I felt.

"Let's go back to Holland soon. See how things are going there. Maybe I'll find another Great Love."

I knew I wouldn't be seeing Nana again for a couple of years, if ever. Our love had been brief and beautiful. Very beautiful. Too beautiful. Everything that's beautiful in this world is dangerous. Think of the Pantra Dacynium mushroom. The most beautiful and at the same time the most poisonous. Woman, the most beautiful and the most dangerous. Birth, the most beautiful and the most dangerous.

I would search for Nana. At any rate I would always think of her feverishly. Restlessly and maddeningly I would keep on searching for my Great Love.

claudia's mother

206

Claudia and I were on our way to Spain. On our way to my dream island of milk and honey. I'd been waiting for hours when finally she arrived at the station with her expensive pigskin suitcases. The next train to Paris, where we had to change for the train on to the Spanish border, wouldn't be getting in for hours. Things began to look up once we'd crossed into Belgium. At last we were out of Holland. Away from all those well-meaning people trying to run our lives for us. I felt I'd been right to get us out of there and I was mad at her for being so late. I didn't say a word to Claudia until we'd passed the Dutch border.

We got into Paris late that night. An hour between rains. Time for a cup of coffee in the Restaurant de Flandre, across the street from the Gare du Nord.

We had agreed that I would take care of the money. Claudia spent money even faster than I did, so we'd have to be satisfied with just looking at all the appetizing food in front of us—mussels and delicious sandwiches. We had just enough money for two tickets on the boat from Barcelona to Ibiza, plus a meal the next day in Barcelona and one night in a cheap hotel. Poor but happy, we started sipping our two cups of coffee.

"I want a sandwich," Claudia kept whining.

After watching the other customers guzzling down crates of beer, I finally gave in. I had a beer, Claudia got her sandwich. Before we got up to go, I'd had six beers and a dish of mussels in a fine sauce and Claudia had put away two sandwiches with French cheese, a dish of onion soup with more cheese, and a few cups of hot chocolate besides. Then I had a cognac and Claudia two Cointreaus.

The waiter, who'd heard us talking, asked if we were Dutch. We said, yes, we were. Maybe we knew Anton Geesink?

"Anton Geesink!" I shouted enthusiastically. "Why, he's my kid brother! He's right here now for the Judo World Championship Match!" I remembered having read about it in the paper while I was waiting for Claudia at the station.

"How's it going with Anton?" the waiter asked. "Think he'll win?"

I laughed scornfully. "Is he going to win? Man, Anton'll pin that whole stadium of yours on the mat!" I smiled at Claudia, then threw a sardonic glance at the waiter. "Is Anton going to win, he asks! Hahaha!"

After that we got a round of drinks on the house.

When it was time to head back to the station, I said to Claudia, "Time to use Helpful Hint Number 3 from Jan Cremer's Travelers' Handbook. We can't pay for this unless we want to sleep on the street in Barcelona tomorrow, right? Okay. So I'll start a fight with you. You walk out mad. I run out after you. Run to platform seventeen and wait for me there. If they catch up with us, we can always pay."

Suddenly I started screaming at her. "Who the hell do you think *you* are? Look, you ordered it! Now eat that pie or you'll get the whole fucking mess thrown right in your face!"

A little bit unsure of how to carry it off, Claudia stood up, but when I hissed, "Get out of here fast," she did. And fast. The people around who'd heard us arguing, stared sympathetically as Claudia shot out the door. I sat for a minute, looking shocked, then stood up hesitantly, leaving an empty pack of Gauloises on the table. Then I took off after her. We met at the platform. We picked out a comfortable compartment. Three minutes later the train pulled out of the station.

After a long hard trip taking turns sitting on each other's laps and sweating like pigs in that crowded compartment (the windows fogged up from our breath, the stink of hot feet, and too many mouths snoring or coughing), the train pulled into Perpignan. We saw the first palm trees then and passengers getting off or on. Workingmen, with the fresh smell of cheap soap, sat down all around us and started eating their fat red sausages.

We got to Barcelona about noon and checked into a cheap hotel near the Plaza Real. A clean hotel I'd stayed at before. My manly instincts had been thoroughly roused by the long trip and the mussels, and after a satisfying session of lovemaking we got up from a blood-stained bed.

"Godamighty!" I yelled. "Why didn't you tell me you had the rag on? We'll have to pay for this, you know. I mean this isn't Sicily where they sprinkle the sheets with chicken blood the night of the wedding. They'll think we're nuts."

She washed the sheets out in cold water (never use soap on blood). "I can't very well stop it up with a cork," she grumbled.

"Forget it, baby. Love is love."

After taking a shower together we fell asleep exhausted. We slept late since we hadn't got much rest on the train. I was happy with Claudia. Finally I had a warm body to lie by and feel at home next to. Peace descended like a dark woolen curtain.

207

The Spanish fleet refused to sail, Dutch histories say, because the wind was blowing. No wonder they surrendered Zeeland to us way back when. We had to report to the pier every evening. Both times, no sailing. It was costing us money. Every night the hotel. Only first-class passengers could sleep on board. We were deck class. Two folding chairs on the top deck under an awning.

I still had an expensive watch and a gold Dunhill lighter. I pawned them at the market place so Claudia and I could go to the movies, a sob story with Marcello Menstruation and Melina Mercurochrome; have a simple meal; have a cup of coffee at a sidewalk café the next morning; look at a replica of the ship C. Columbus sailed to America in; take a sightseeing tour of the harbor of Barcelona; have our pictures taken twice by a photographer with an old-fashioned box camera on the Ramblas; buy a bag of sugar-coated peanuts; and trade our tickets in for the cheapest two-person cabin.

That evening we left on the *Ciudad de Alicante*. Claudia and I slept in iron double-decker beds way up in the bow of the ship down in the depths near the anchor-chain locker. At the crack of dawn we were jolted awake by the rattling of the anchor chains. The chains that held up the top bunk where we lay curled up together (if the ship crashed into any thing, at least we'd be flattened out in the iron together) stretched, snapped, and down came our bunk on the bunk underneath. Boom! It was all hands on deck and we went up for a look.

Spread out before us was Ibiza, in a blaze of autumn sun. The white city of the Moors. The whitewashed houses. The yellow wall of the former fort. The quay with the sidewalk cafés. Everything sparkled in the cool autumn sun. The quay was deserted. A few familiar figures strolled into view. It was off season. In the summer the whole island swarmed with vacationers waiting for the boat. All of a sudden, paranoia. Why were all those uniformed cops looking at me?

We marched down the gangplank and over to the Kiosko, a coffeehouse. I'd expected the owner of the gallery to meet us. I'd written him a long detailed letter from Holland. It was a famous gallery where painters like Tapiès, Saura, and Millares had had exhibitions. During my last stay I'd broken all previous sales records for art exhibitions on that arty island. I Jan Cremer came, saw, and conquered. He wanted me to sign a contract and stay on as his artist-in-residence, but he wasn't prepared to pay much. I told him I'd have to think it over. I thought it over in Holland and decided a little money was better than none. Now that I had Claudia with me I was completely dependent.

We had coffee with milk. Customs officials and longshoremen kept coming in puffing out clouds of steam. It was cold outside.

Jill came in. An old girlfriend of mine. A fantastically beautiful chick from New Zealand. We were good friends. Jill was a deepsea diver, and she and a couple of Australian guys had a boat. In the summer season she gave deepsea diving lessons to the tourists. For a steep fixed price you could dive off her boat into the sea with an aqualung and goggles. A fortunate learner might sometimes bring up mussels, sea shells, or a mossy-green amphora, an old vase, used thousands of years ago by the Egyptians and the Moors. What the fortunate finder didn't know was that Jill and her boys had tossed crates of brand new amphoras made in a factory near Barcelona into the sea the summer before.

She was a terrific chick. Long straight blonde hair and a Colgate smile. I'd been in love with her for a while and she with me, or so I thought. She lived near my place in the Peña, a region of narrow winding streets and storybook houses, the casbah of Ibiza. I had to pass her house every night on my way home and sometimes I stopped in for a nightcap.

Late one night I saw the lights on when I passed her house. I could hear strange noises through the open windows. It sounded like a fight. I heard her yelling, "You dirty bastard. You shit. You get the hell out of here!" With plenty of sobs in between.

No time to stand there thinking. Fast action was called for. Obviously. A damsel was in distress—the fair sex calling for help! I crashed through the door and rushed up the stairs to her room. She lay there looking at me in surprise. Some American summer fisher was working away on top of her.

"Sorry," I said, "I just came by to borrow some sugar and I thought . . ." And started back down the stairs, embarrassed and ashamed. Some women are funny that way. I once had a girlfriend, a girl in her thirties, worked in Helena Rubenstein's beauty parlor. She couldn't have an orgasm unless she was biting on something. Every week I had to go to the doctor or a hospital to get stitched up. Love is love.

We went around to the gallery later that morning. I got the key to my old studio in the Peña, a tiny square room with a view of the harbor. The room was too small to live and work in at the same time, but at least we weren't homeless. It took some doing to talk money out of the gallery owner, a six-foot eight-inch German long past eighty but very energetic. Long blond hair, blue eyes. He still did two handstands a day.

His knowledge of art didn't go further than the exclamation, "*Quel compositio!*" ("What a composition!"), but as far as getting things down on paper went, he knew everything. In two minutes I was the proud possessor of yet another impossibly complicated contract. He bought my paintings for a song and within a few days made three hundred per cent profit on them. Business is business.

At any rate we had some pocket money now and we could pay somebody to help us out. We picked Guiliano, an ugly little guy but very handy and shrewd, a jack-of-all-trades who found a nice little house for us within a few days. Eight miles outside the city of Ibiza. A cold bare little farmhouse with damp walls and cracks for windows. In the middle of the countryside, it was remote from everything, and every night before we went to bed we locked all the doors and barred all the shutters.

I gradually got back most of the things I'd left behind. The record player I'd lent to a former girlfriend. And my dog Vodka that I'd left behind. Vodka was a good-looking sturdy animal. A cross between an Ibicenco and a Zatopirsky. Thick short white hair with light brown spots. A personality. All the dogs lay down when he came by. He barked at the ones who didn't. Then they lay down too. He was king of the island. I'd always taken good care of Vodka, but when I took off for Holland, I left him with a sweet American girl, Peggy, who loved dogs and me very much. She was sorry she had to give Vodka back. Claudia liked having a dog around, as long as it wasn't too big.

Claudia and I spent our days shooting at home-made targets, reading a whole series of Saint detective stories sent to me gratis by the Dutch publisher himself, playing cards and riding our bikes to and from the city. We didn't have enough money to rent a motorcycle right away. (I'd left the Silver Monster—banged up, half dead, and falling apart—in Barcelona after getting back from North Africa.)

We ate in one of the cheap little restaurants. Sopa de Verduras, a deliciously greasy soup with beans, chick peas, and meat, the bouillon made from stewed pigs' feet. It tastes of pork and only costs three pesetas. Or else we'd have squid with onions—food for the balls.

Everybody on the island still knew me. Every bartender or paint salesman, restaurant owner or Mozo, hotel porter, and jack-of-all-trades. I'd spent more in one summer there than the average tourist does in a year (or the average Dutch tourist in five years). I had thousands of guilders that summer but, like my father always said, money's got to move, and I moved it around fast. Better to owe a month's earnings than spend

149

five minutes worrying. So Claudia and I had an easy time getting credit at the Music Bar.

208

The island of Ibiza is overrun with war criminals, swarming with ex-SS men. Half the island belongs to a Dutchman, Sprot. In 1945 Sprot sped down to the island and bought it up for what you'd give for two acres nowadays. He's a timid little guy who'll try almost anything to avoid speaking Dutch. He prefers to speak French, with a heavy Dutch accent. He rides around in an old gangster Buick driven by a private chauffeur. He has an exceptionally large nose, reddened by drinking Spanish wine.

He's wanted in a number of countries. In Holland he faces a life sentence for his activities during the war. In Germany, the bullet. In France, the guillotine. In Belgium, a portion of poisoned French-fried potatoes. In England, the noose. In Ibiza, however, he's perfectly safe. A few times a year he takes off on business trips to South America to see how his kinfolk are making out. He has a special plane with two specially trained (and unbribable) pilots.

Sprot is only one of the scores of war criminals on the island. There is also, for instance, the Man-Without-Friends. A guy with a wooden leg. You can hear him coming, his wooden leg bonking and squeaking, from a long way off. Apparently he'd been a notorious Jew baiter in Holland during the war—a genuine race-pure kraut with a bony, broad-cheekboned, bleached-out James Mason mug in blond. Every evening in his favorite café he challenged Negroes, Jews, Americans, and Germans who didn't agree with him to a fight. Nobody ever took him up on it because of his wooden leg and because all the Spaniards would stick up for him. He's the only human who ever really terrified me. I used to have nightmares about his face. Claudia couldn't stand him either. Sometimes I'd think maybe he's really a terribly nice guy, just got stuck with an unlucky face. The island's permanent nucleus was made up of war cripples, Korean war veterans, and war widows.

We heard about a little house that was vacant. Up back on the quay. A big room with a good-sized bed, a little living room, a kitchen, and a bathroom. Cheap. On top of a twenty-five-yard cliff with a view of the sea and the island of Formentera. It was smack in the middle of the city, which was good because we'd had more than enough of that peaceful little house stuck out in the middle of nowhere. Besides, Claudia's ankles were getting too thick from riding the bicycle, especially since she had to take me on back every night. I was always too drunk to ride my own bike home.

I rented a typewriter. I'd always wanted to write a book, ever since I was a kid. Besides, the easel and I had nothing to say to each other. I'd been sent copies of all the works of the Dutch literary colony, but I didn't find any of their stuff very exciting. Life on the island, including the local political structure, came out in a style you might call "Spanish bull." When the local Dutch colony learned I was a fellow countryman, brown-paper packages started coming in almost every day. They turned out to contain the literary efforts the local scribes had spent the best years of their lives on. Their books didn't seem to be breaking any sales records, so I was the sucker who'd somehow steer them ahead to fame and fortune. I glanced through their books and sent them back fast.

Claudia and I both enjoyed the dirty tales of Esteban Loops though. "My Mother Truus," "My Father Klaas," "My Sister Trien," "My Sister Trien and Me"—all out of the same pot. Literary smut masked a bit by his own long beard. Claudia liked him because she'd read his serialized account of "How I Spent My Summer Vacation" in the Dutch *Ladies' Home Journal*. Written under a pseudonym, but it was easy enough to recognize his style. Though I hadn't read this exciting series, I still found him pretty lousy in general.

André Kuitenkluiver lived on the island, too. A young Dutch man of letters. Very talented. Winner of stacks of literary prizes. The judges always consider him to be extremely promising. He started out writing radio plays and whole anthologies of short stories; now he can be regularly seen in walk-on parts on Dutch TV. A nice boy. A helpful boy. It wasn't his fault he'd wanted to be a writer. At least he saw the light in time.

And who should drop in at the island at his literary wit's end—following his leaders in this as in so many other things? Simon the Soggy Noodle, that great lover boy with so much love to spare. The island's literary output broke all records quantity-wise as soon as Simon started sticking his nose into things, writing down all the gossip about the island and its inhabitants. Considering how Simon stretched a one-night stay in jail out into a long chapter in one of his books, the reader can imagine all the mileage he got out of a four weeks' stay on the island.

Rumor had it that Remco Campert was also planning to settle a while on the island to write a few poems to stuff into his next Literary Pocketbook Giant. But on his way down he lost his glasses and consequently lost his way. He didn't let the missing glasses cut down on his literary productivity in Southern France, however.

One evening when we were talking about literature in general, Claudia said, "That guy with the big nose, the one who always hung around Leyden Square, that guy who writes too—Harry Muliz—what is he, Jewish or German?"

"Sweetheart," I said after careful consideration, "he's half and half, I believe."

"Oh," she said, bored. "Still, there were some nice parts in that book of his about the sugar factory."

It wasn't a book. It's a play.

209

After a big fight with Claudia I ran out of the house and came back hours later. It was dark inside. There was a letter lying on the typewriter—a messy letter, words crossed out here and there:

Declaration of Love for Jan

You know something I want to be with you
fight with you laugh with you
be jealous of you go to bed with you
in bed you're terribly soft and subtle
darling you're lovely darling you're fascinating
darling I love you

Signed with two overlapping hearts in the middle, on a messy scrap of paper.

210

Claudia, I love you. You're the only one in the world. I wish I could explain everything to you. I wish I could express all the things I feel.

I have never loved anybody as much as I love my lonely little Claudia. It was so hard to be happy for Claudia and me. We tried for months. We spent the most beautiful time of our lives together. She and me. A time that nothing and nobody can ever take away from us.

I'll always love you, Claudia. Never forget it. You once told me you were thankful for the chance to live with me. That I had a kind of diabolical influence on you. That no other man could ever take my place in your life. I knew what you meant. The same is true with you for me. Though women are always better at such things. I tried and you tried. We

152

were two children with shattered upside-down inside-out hearts. All mixed up. Still, we belong together, Claudia. Maybe not right now, but in a couple of years again, maybe. But if you want me I'll never leave you. Trust me. Trust nobody else, just me. I'll do anything for you.

On June 7, 1962, I wrote this for Claudia:

211

for me no problems or experiments
for me
purity & honesty
no ass licking please
nor untrue friend or enemy
no collaboration with phony brothers

even if it has to be
at the cost of
moving on
leaving sweet places behind
I'm not scared
What can I lose

for me no hearty brothers
for me
pure comradeship
no ass licking please
nor untrue friend or enemy
I don't mind
being betrayed or abandoned
as long as it's comrades
who do it
they can tie the noose
tighter & tighter
I'm not scared
what can I lose
wasn't I my mother's keeper
and didn't I come from a gigantic grave
wasn't I born with cannons roaring
amidst bleeding flesh
who is to say & who has the proof
& who will tell me
what to do in time of war

Jan Cremer *Claudia's Mother*

& disaster
me & myself & I
who will kick me & beat me
only he who's afraid of the crowd
only he who's afraid of me
I'm not scared
but then again
I've got nothing to lose

for me there exists
1 ruler, 1 god, 1 love
and that's me & myself & I
didn't I grow up admist smoking ruins
didn't I feed on garbage
when I was five years old
couldn't I turn on the stove & make a cup of tea
so who believes in me
me & myself & I
I shall love my true friends
even with a knife stuck in my back

& when
they pull the handle
& I try to dive in the noose
that's been knotted & waiting
for twenty years
I won't go under
just to show my dearest friends
that when I go there's 1 person who'll have made the decision
& that's me & myself & I

I love my life
because it's 1 big risk I'm consciously taking
& deliberately

when the earth splits in two
forming 1 roaring mass
1 person will look down from the edge of the abyss
& that's me & myself & I

212

Daan and Gerda, a Dutch couple, used to give us the Dutch papers and magazines when they were finished with them. In the middle of March, I

154

noticed an article in the lower lefthand corner, page 4, that initially seemed very innocent:

POPE SLIPS ON WAY TO THRONE

Pope John XXIII lost his footing today on the seventh step as he was approaching the dais of the pontifical throne in the Vatican Palace. He fell to his hands and knees and was helped to his feet by the major-domo, Monsignor Federico Callori di Vignali, and the chamberlain, Monsignor Mario Nasalli Rocca di Corneliano. The Pope had not suffered any serious injury and the day's schedule continued as planned. (From our Vatican correspondent.)

"Look!" I said to Claudia. "Look at this!"

When she'd finished reading the article, I asked, "Well, what do you make of it?"

"It looks pretty obvious to me," she said. "Somebody tripped him, the poor guy."

"Yeah, sure," I said. "But who? The major-domo or the chamberlain?"

"The chamberlain has a pretty suspicious sounding name," Claudia said. "No normal person would walk around with a name like that. Too fancy. His real name's probably Pietro Caneloni, or something like that."

"Exactly," I said. "Besides, there's something I don't trust about that seventh step. Why not the sixth or the eighth? You can smell something fishy a mile away."

"Yeah," Claudia concluded, "those guys are always up to something."

We decided not to think about it any more. It would have to remain a Mystery.

213

We lived in a little house on top of a sheer eighty-foot cliff. All day and all night we heard the murmur and slosh of the sea. The fishermen all knew us. With their anchors out, the fishing boats bobbed up and down out there for hours. The crews aimed their binoculars up at our house to try to get a glimpse of Claudia walking around naked. Peeping Toms spent hours glued to our keyhole. If we surprised them and opened the door, they scuttled off into the night.

Living there was a bit dangerous for Claudia because the Spaniards couldn't keep their hands off the girls. Some years back the bishop of the island had preached that they should keep away from the invading hordes of foreign degenerates, devils, and heretics—that big viperous brood come to drive the islanders off their native soil. However, when Ibiza started to be a popular tourist resort, the bishop impressed upon his flock that they shouldn't step aside, that they had just as much right to be wherever they wanted to be as those damned tourists who should have stayed home in the first place. Then the trouble really began. Girls were being constantly molested by Spaniards.

One foggy winter's eve Claudia and I were on our way to Es Vive (a villa neighborhood, populated mainly by Americans who "hibernated" in Nova Ibiza) when we heard somebody screaming. Ahead on the deserted, unlit road we saw a Spaniard pulling a girl down off her bike. I ran, but they were too far away and I knew I couldn't get there in time. I picked up a stone and threw it at the guy. It hit him smack in the back of the head (one of my talents, which has made me an unwelcome visitor in many circuses and amusement parks; when I want to hit the target, I hit it). He stumbled and fell, but by the time I got there he'd disappeared. The stone was still there though, sticky with blood. The upset girl thanked us.

214

At night we played cards. I'd taught Claudia every game in the book. It kept us in pocket money at least. Sometimes, though, we'd spend an evening writing serious letters of application in answer to ads in the Dutch papers:

> UTRECHT PHILHARMONIC ORCHESTRA
> seeks applicants for
> the position of
> subs. SOLO VIOLIST
> subs. SOLO CLARINETIST

In my clumsy handwriting, with lots of blotches and words crossed out, I wrote:

Dear Manager of the Utrecht Philharmonic Orchestra:

Having read your advertisement in the *Telegraaf,* in which you mention you are looking for a new solo clarinetist, I have the honor and pleasure of nominating myself as a candidate for this position and, may I add, I would be proud to accept the job. When I saw the *Telegraaf* hanging in the bathroom (my wife never reads it due to the political opinions expressed in it) and, consequently, your advertisement, it struck me that I was exactly the person you were looking for to fill your chair as solo clarinetist. Previous experience includes playing in the PMPBC (Practice Makes Perfect Boys Club), a ter-

156

rible club as I trust you know; a season with the Dutch National Patriotic Sons of Our Country Band, which, however, I left because (a) they found me intolerable and because (b) they never let me play solo. I have, furthermore, played the drums in the Amstel Drum Band and, while still in knee pants, sung on the radio. I was very good, if I do say so myself, so if you ever need anybody to liven things up with a bit of warbling, you won't need to worry because you can always count on me. Thus, the only conditions I lay down before joining your outfit are (c) that you promise me I can blow a good solo from time to time—a so-called solo solo, if you know what I mean—and (d) how about the dough? I trust, sir, you won't tell me to go blow, will you? Besides being a fine clarinetist and singer, I also happen to be what you might call a pretty good amateur M.C. (I've done my act at weddings and dinner parties, there isn't a boffo I don't know, and we've always had lots of laughs.) So if you need a master of ceremonies to keep things bouncing during the break, you know who to turn to. Me. It'll cost, of course, a little bit extra, but then, of course, it'll be worth it. I'm sure we can turn your outfit into a swinging band. I'll see to that. Rely, sir, on me, sir, for that, sir. You and me, sir, we understand each other. My repertoire: CLASSICAL (my favorites are Verdy, John Bach, and Chaucer). Also JAZZ (Dixieland and swing; Bill Haley). And let's not forget ROCK-AND-ROLL (the top ten; I was always good at *Chipmunks for Break-fast*—the solo in the chorus, know what I mean?). Now that I'm as good as hired, perhaps you would be so good as to send me a portion of my salary in advance so I can take the train to Utrecht for the first rehearsal of the season. Should I bring my own flute?

Sincerely
Your humble servant, truly,
Jan Cremer.

P.S. What???? Oh yeah. My wife says she wants to play the flute too! Either Suzie gets to play too or the flute stays at home. If Suzie can't come, I just don't know. (Idea: conference.) Well, that's all for now, sir. Bye.

We waited for months for a reply to our letter, laughing at the weird reception it must have got at the manager's office.

Naturally I didn't neglect our Royal Family either. After all, my heart and soul were, as always, with them every day. Like the hearts and souls of every self-respecting Dutchman. After all, Claudia and I *were* Dutch. Though the sight of the Dutch flag on the masts of the coasters coming into harbor may not have exactly brought tears to our eyes, still the smell of good Dutch bacon on a good Dutch frying pan did. I went on board and chatted with the boys (we always had some mutual friend or had worked on the same ship somewhere along the line), and I came away loaded down with slabs of bacon, giant bottles of Maggi sauce, *sambal oelek* (an Indonesian delicacy), "Jerry Cotton, G-man" and "Lord Lister" comics, bottles of black-currant gin, Very Old Dutch "jenever," and, naturally, packs of Van Nelle's Strong Shag. In exchange for all this I introduced the boys to all the girls I knew, or stood them a few drinks in the Music Bar where my credit was still good. In the spring whole fleets of Dutch freighters docked at Ibiza for the famous Malta potatoes. Sometimes we threw a big party at our house and the boys brought along food and liquor from on board. We always made sure there were plenty of chicks around. So I kept up my ties with the homeland pretty well.

When I read, then, that our Royal Family was about to celebrate their silver wedding anniversary and that back home Fantastic Festivities were being organized for the occasion, I realized that, as a true-blue Dutchman, I'd better get busy.

I promptly wrote a letter to Mrs. J. van Nassau, Queen of the Netherlands, Soestdijk Palace:

Your Majesty and Royal Highness:
On the occasion of your birthday and your silver wedding anniversary, I would like to proffer my sincerest congratulations.
As a Dutch subject, temporarily residing in Spain, and deeply devoted to both you and your husband, I consider it highly unfortunate that I will be unable to personally participate in the festivities of this national holiday.
Well aware of your deep interest in, and sympathy for, Modern Dutch Art, I would like to seize this opportunity to present you my famous million-guilder painting, *La Guerre Japonaise 1960*.
At the moment this painting is in storage in Holland but upon my return from Spain (late in 1962), where I am preparing for numerous exhibitions, I will have it delivered to your palace.
La Guerre Japonaise 1960 dates back to the beginning of 1960 and is 18′4″ long and 6′8″ wide. The canvas has been exhibited at a number of galleries, including The Hague Salon, 1960, and a wide range of art critics consider it a masterpiece—the crowning glory of my brief career.
I myself consider it to be one my finest works and, after having rejected various offers (generally of a crassly commercial nature), I sincerely desire that it may hang in a place befitting its quality. I am delighted, therefore, that your silver anniversary presents me with a perfect occasion to offer this painting to you.
Knowing that you will doubtless be pleased with it and that for a good painting no better place exists than a royal residence, I hope you will gladly accept my gift.

I, furthermore, hope you will fully appreciate it and that it may bring you lasting pleasure, happiness, and prosperity in the future.

I remain

Sincerely yours,

Jan Cremer

I thought it was a great idea. The same day I sent off a letter to the warehouse where it was stored, saying that if anybody from the Royal Family came to pick up my famous triptych it was okay, but that they'd have to pay the storage I owed on it. Only a Scrooge would refuse. Certainly our Sovereign Rulers would pick up the tab. I wrote to the Director of Transport and Storage telling him, "You can put the royal coat-of-arms over your door now."

I didn't get an answer, which is why, a year later when I was back in Holland, I sent off another letter:

Your Majesty,

Happy Birthday and many happy returns of the day!

However, I feel compelled to unburden my heart of a painful grievance.

To my astonishment, I once again discover that this year I have been omitted from the list of those invited to the festive Shower of Stars and Ribbons.

Since, in my own humble opinion, I have made a large contribution to Dutch culture, the least I expected (and have, in fact, been expecting for years) was the Order of Knighthood.

Alas, it is my sorrowful duty to inform Your Majesty—and please don't hold this against me, since I'm truly sorry and have arrived at my decision only after severe inner conflict—that I do not wish to be considered as a candidate for the next Shower of Stars and Ribbons. I repeat, I'm truly very sorry about this.

Sincerely yours,

Jan Cremer.

P.S. Likewise, I humbly request your Majesty to consider the offer I made when I was in Spain some time ago—to give you the painting *La Guerre Japonaise 1960* (18′5″ x 6′8″) on the occasion of your Silver Anniversary—as null and void, since I have never been honored by a reply or thanks of any kind.

I did, however, learn that my offer of this gift (price: one million Dutch guilders) led to an investigation by the National Security Men of all information relating to me in the files of the Kroller-Muller Museum at Otterloo.

I haven't yet received an answer regarding that, either. And they must have got the letters because I sent them registered mail. And rain, sleet, snow, or hail, our mailmen never fail—right?

159

I did everything I could think of to get my hands on some money. I heard the Dutch government gave out travel grants to talented artists, painters, and writers who lacked the means to set about broadening their minds abroad.

Naturally one big tight clique ran the whole operation, and if you weren't in, you didn't stand a chance. Past experience had made it pretty clear that only Talentless Painters, Pompous Penpushers and the most Flannel-Mouthed Film Directors ever got any of the goodies.

The person charged with advising the minister about who should get grants is a little old man called Jan van Kapot. He's on all the committees which award national or international prizes and no committee ever got around to crossing his name off the list. He should have been exed as well as axed ages ago. Kapot is also in charge of the (take a deep breath) National and Municipal Acquisition of Works of Art Commission, so he says who buys what. For years this prick has ruled the whole Dutch art world like a dictator. He's constantly surrounded by a crew of ass-lickers who hang on his every turd as they sit at his feet at De Posthoorn, a Dutch artists' hangout about a boulder's throw from the office where the Big Boss with the cigar waits for his baldheaded Art Dwarf to hand in his latest report. Almost all grants and fellowships are awarded either to Jan van Kapot himself or to close friends of his.

Among his other talents, Jan van Kapot is also a painter. Pale bitter-sweet still-lifes that give off a slight smell of vomit but never fail to win extravagant praise from the art critics and other artists. For years his name always popped up among the winners of art prizes awarded by paint factories, porcelain importers, and museum directors, as well as among the lists of judges or jury members.

The dimwitted paintings of our aged classical-Dutch artist were regularly exhibited at international art shows. And they always found a ready buyer in the Art Acquisition Committee. The chairman insisted on it—the chairman, of course, being Jan van Kapot.

It's a fact that the people at the Ministry didn't know the first thing about art. Their advisers knew even less about it, so everything fit. (Sorry, folks—I know you couldn't care less about all this but somebody has to say it sometime, and if I don't, who will?) So I wrote a polite letter describing my situation in Spain in detail and said I'd like some money. Even a loan would be okay, as long as I could go on painting. Besides, a travel grant would be a bargain for them because I was already there, so there wouldn't be any tickets to pay for. I sent the letter off to the Ministry.

Months later I got back a kindly, refined letter from the Secretary of the Ministry of Education, Art, and Science. In a friendly way he expressed his regret that, after consulting with a commission of experts (including Kapot, on whose dome I once squashed a raw egg for getting fresh with my fiancée, who also had a name in the art world), my application had been rejected this year. This year! Of course, I could go on applying year after year like so many artists did, and after you've applied for twenty-five years they can't turn you down. (One of the requirements before you can get an exhibition-with-catalogue at the Municipal Museum is that you've got to be collecting social security.)

I felt unscrupulous, sending that application in. Being a pickpocket is better than being dependent on the Dutch Art Establishment. But now that I'd been turned down anyway, I wrote them a note on the back of a picture postcard of a naked Spanish chick in full-blown technicolor. I sent it to the Director of the Art Department who'd signed the letter (no. 59106), since the Commissioner himself wouldn't dare. I wrote:

> Dear Sir,
>   In reply to your letter in which you refuse to accept my application for a travel grant, I would like to inform you that I do not take the above-mentioned refusal seriously. Having wiped my ass with your letter, I await the grant and remain,
>
> Yours,
Jan Cremer.

I hadn't, of course, because you can't wipe your ass with the kind of paper they use for official occasions. Too slick.

215

On the Queen's birthday, which was also the day of her Silver Wedding Anniversary, all the Dutch were invited by the Dutch consul at Ibiza—a Spanish freight-office owner—to drink a toast to the Royal Family that afternoon. A nice gesture. The cordial consul made a few remarks about the Queen in Spanish and after a Dutch Man of Letters (name withheld) had carefully enunciated "Long Live the Queen," and we'd all shouted "Hip Hip Hurrah," we got champagne and potato chips.

Of course glasses were emptied and the chips gone in no time. Dutchmen are easily identifiable abroad. At receptions they can always be found clustered in a semicircle around the table with liquor and eats. When the speech is over they clap with their mouths full. I had an appointment once with a delegate from the Dutch embassy and bought him a beer at a sidewalk café. The waiter brought two beers and I hadn't even seen mine was there yet while he'd already finished his off. Must be the effect of the war and the hunger-winter.

So Claudia and I didn't have much money. To get some, I sold the records she used to play day in, day out. Claudia was a sweet kid and soft. She could listen to Nina Simone and Billie Holiday for days on end. I loved her. She was a sensitive girl, very closed up and alone on the inside. Me too, but with me everything came out.

One day it looked as if we were really going to be wiped out. We didn't have a cent, not even enough to cover a pack of Spanish cigarettes. I'd sold all my records to the Music Bar for a good price. Good for them, anyway. Anybody hard up could sell records to the Music Bar for next to nothing, listen to them being played there, then buy them back later at a slightly higher price. Claudia's records had to go. It was all we had left that would bring in some bread. Though I dug Nina Simone as much as she did, one morning I said:

"I'm going to sell your records."

"Why?" she asked, shocked. "I want them!"

"Listen, honey," I said, "it's not that I don't like your records, but we're flat broke and we've got to raise some money somehow. Anyhow, I can't stand hearing that music any more. It makes me sad. It knocks me out. When I've got some money again I'll buy you all the records you want!"

So then for a while we could afford to sit down at an outdoor café and have a sandwich, *un bocadillo con queso,* plus a glass of beer.

We had a good time, the three of us—Claudia, me, and Vodka the dog. While I wrote or slept, Claudia went out for a walk with Vodka, and with that dog around you'd have to be nuts to try anything funny with Claudia. Vodka went straight for the jugular.

We didn't mix much with the Dutch. Most of the permanents were either fat slobs or just plain swine. Take Joseph van Polen, for instance. Joseph van Polen ran a combination art gallery-library-sewing-circle-informal-club-room-cum-knickknack-shop. He was known as The Stingiest Man in Town. In his prime, apparently, he'd lived in Indonesia where he managed his plantations in the way for which the Dutch were generally known and loved. And, of course, he'd put aside a pretty penny, which helped him set up shop in Ibiza. Until he married the daughter of a rich Dutch chocolate king who came to the island on a tour cooked up by a Dutch tour-manufacturing company and there bumped up against Joseph's large nose, which could smell money out in a field of skunks. This was the beginning of a truly meaningful relationship and the girl with the buck teeth and peeling nose married Joseph, who promptly expanded his business and bought up a farm. There he exploited the poor Spanish workers, setting their wives to work weaving straw baskets which he paid starving painters to decorate with all kinds of designs—abstract or classical, he couldn't care less. He sold them in his knickknack shop for astronomical prices.

Joseph was the official Dutch spokesman. He wasn't wild about me. He thought I shot my mouth off too much. Once an American chick was about to buy an expensive Inca statue in his store when I showed her it was plaster of Paris by scraping a layer of brown paint off with my thumb nail. Joseph watched one hundred good dollars vanish into thin air right in front of his eyes. Poof. Gone.

Though he and his wife were very fond of the cross, took a heaping spoonful of God in their coffee, and Joseph drank holy water on the rocks, he had the raunchiest collection of dirty books in his lending library I ever laid eyes on. Under the counter, only for special customers. Once Claudia took out a book, and when she brought it back it was two days overdue and she had to pay three pesetas. She'd taken the three pesetas along to buy a pack of Ideales (Spanish roll-your-own cigarettes) for me, who was waiting at home for her to bring them back. When she came back without them, I charged down to his shop. While he stood there with his holy face and his wife's mouth flopping open letting her teeth buck out like a beaver in a toothpaste ad, I let them have it.

"Who the hell you think you are, you sad-assed bastard? Giving my wife a hard time when I'm not around, huh, you shit-lip. Take all her money, huh? I'll give you something. Ever heard of the screaming crabs, hard-boiled hemorrhoids, prick-rot, face-flake, explosive sphincterosis? That's what I've got all wrapped up for you in your pimp suit and whore slippers trying to steal my wife blind for one of your lousy goddamn books, and you the tightest wad on the island, along with that herring-bone cunt-wife you've got, too! Yeah, you!" I yelled at the daughter of the chocolate king. "You, with that mouthful of tusks—that's right, you!" And I flashed out my own teeth and stuck a finger at them just in case she missed the point. "I'll fuck your business up so good you won't make another penny. I'll make you pack up and head for hell, you crotch-licking piss-ant. Any more trouble like this and I'll take care of you so fast you won't know whether you're coming or going. And don't think it won't be a pleasure. So, back on your knees now and confess all your sins, you dismal freaks!" And I swung back the beaded curtain and strode outside, feeling fresh as a daisy having said my say. Nobody was going to mess with Claudia.

216

I painted hard. Whenever money came in from Holland—somebody paying back a loan—I spent it on supplies. With my refined gift of gab I could always get paint and turpentine on credit. We ate at a restaurant next to the Music Bar, The Portico, owned by the guys from the Music Bar and

Canadian Al, a shrewd Canadian who started the Music Bar with the two others.

The Music Bar was a tiny cellar on the waterfront with a big bar, a few tables and chairs, and a loudly amplified record player. Artists, old-timers, hibernaters, tourists, and war widows all gathered there every night to hear jazz and drink cheap. The boys had played it right. An Englishman with a baby face had put up the money and ran the joint, together with Al and a six-foot-plus German. They advertised all over the globe: Come to Ibiza, free eats, free drinks on credit. Everybody's credit was good there. Which meant lots of customers and, since you couldn't just walk off the island, people generally paid. If you were short on cash, they'd take payment in records, jewelry, razors, clothes, suitcases, paintings, motorcycles—anything. And they were fair, too. Every once in a while some bearded beatnik cleared out without paying. No skin off the owner's ass. Free credit makes big spenders. It all went down on the list anyway. And when you finally had money, a few dollars more or less wouldn't make much difference.

Claudia and I lived a five-minute walk from the Music Bar. We got along fine with the Spanish waiters—even visited them in their homes. Nice men. Or we'd spend a pleasant evening with them, playing dominoes at their own favorite cafés. All over the world I've always gotten along well with the ordinary people. For the tourist, the waiter is a nice guy you don't get too close to. A man's job didn't make any difference to me. I often got buckets of fish, crabs, lobsters, and shrimp from the fishermen who sailed back into harbor in the blazing sun of early morning. I always stood them drinks at the Music Bar in exchange.

We always got up at the crack of dawn. Then we'd walk Vodka down to the post office where everybody had to pick up their mail in the morning. Then a cup of coffee at the outdoor café. In the afternoon we ate at The Portico, and either rode around the island or stayed home. I rented a small motorcycle, an Ossa 250—also on credit.

Claudia was great. We went swimming in the middle of December even though the water was freezing cold. The first night of the new year we plunged into the phosphorescent sea stark naked. We'd celebrated Christmas in the Music Bar. The restaurant served a special Christmas dinner for the regulars, with champagne and dancing afterward. Away from all the Dutch mistletoe and fir trees, we had a ball. Stuffed ourselves on turkey and put away a lot of champagne. Claudia got pleasantly plastered and we laughed like mad. Very nice. Though I'm against eating poultry, I munched away at our feathered friends and picked all the meat off the bones.

Until I suddenly recalled the time Barry and I stopped at a small

Spanish village near Valencia. And dropped the bone I'd been chewing on.

217

We'd stopped for the night and met a few half-stoned Americans in the local bar. The whole village worked at the American turkey and chicken plant—the village's sole source of income. The next day we had a look at it. The Americans had invited us to see their factory and have a drink. It was a gigantic plant that employed about a thousand people. A kind of low-slung airplane hangar. One big assembly line. A chicken never lived longer than three days there. Then they were packed up in plastic and shipped off by refrigerated truck all over Europe. American imports who'd never once seen the light of day.

A chicken lays an egg. The egg glides down the assembly line to a tester. If it's a good egg, it rolls on down to an incubator and twenty minutes later hatches. The chick is automatically dried and a kind of vacuum cleaner sucks all the egg shell and loose feathers out. A half hour after it's come out of its mother, it's a normal two-day-old chick.

A kind of cage comes down over the chick as it goes farther down the line. Pellets of chicken food are sprinkled in mechanically and at the end of the line suddenly two injection needles stick into the cage. The cage is automatically shaken. The chick loses balance and falls against one of the two needles. It can relax then. It is left alone for one day and one night. Meanwhile, all kinds of high-calorie food pellets pop out, which the little chick eagerly pecks up.

After that one day—and, of course, the injection—it's a healthy, good-sized chick about as far along in its development as an un-American chicken would be in two or three weeks without an incubator.

Twenty-four hours after the egg was laid, the chick continues its merry way along the assembly line. Gets an injection which makes it grow so fast you can actually *see* it grow. Then another twenty-four hours in an iron cage—this time with warm spotlights shining on it—and, again, all those nourishing pellets of food.

On the third day, the chick looks like a young chicken normally would, though the feathers aren't able to keep up with all the other fast developments. The chick is bald in some spots and fluffy in others, but essentially it looks like a two-month-old. One more injection and, in the afternoon, after the chicken has been on its feet for six hours, it moves on down the assembly line to the completely automatic slaughterhouse.

Here an iron spiral comes down out of the top of the cage and curls around the chicken's neck. The cage folds up and the chicken is left hanging from a little noose that, in turn, is connected to an assembly line. At the end of this line, razor-sharp knives flash back and forth slicing off the head. Blood gushes out of the chicken's throat.

Then the chicken is, for the first time, touched by a human hand. A guy wearing a blood-stained once-white coat and holding a razor-sharp knife waits for the chicken to come his way. Sticking one finger into the slit at the throat, with his other hand he slices the chicken from gullet to vent.

The chicken isn't given a minute's rest. Slowly it's nudged on to another guy who, with a practiced flick of the wrist, scoops its guts out with a kind of sharp little trowel. The chicken is then moved on to a roaring fire and boiling water, above which it dangles for a few minutes. Since the feathers never really had a chance to grow, it's not hard to pluck the chicken. Then off again to an inspector.

If the chicken's not clean enough, or if anything else is wrong with it, the inspector pulls the chicken on its hook off the rails and hangs it up on other rails headed the other way. Once it's passed inspection, the chicken moves on to a long wooden table where a line of men are waiting for it with short cleavers. The spiral around the chicken's neck lets go and the chicken falls onto a chopping block where, in three expert blows, its head and feet are chopped off. The men at the chopping block throw the chickens into big tubs of cold and hot water out of which the chickens are then lifted on big metal trays and dumped onto the packing tables. The men and women at the tables fold the chickens up at a fantastic speed— neck and legs tucked up just so; kidneys, heart, and liver in a separate plastic bag, a pat here and there to shape the product up, then the whole thing is packed into one big plastic bag. Packaged, the chickens are slung onto large square metal trays and carted off to deep freeze. The whole process takes just about one hour.

Three days after a chicken lays an egg, the hatch is already a piece of full grown, packed, and frozen poultry ready to be shipped to any of Europe's sizable supermarkets. America has thousands of these factories. Which is why Holland's flooded with chickens and turkeys. Dirt cheap at all self-service food stores. Chickens that make your mouth water, chickens that never saw daylight and are only three days old. They should have been sweet little chicks, fluffy as the ones in Easter ads. But these are all-American chickens, injected with all sorts of stuff to make them grow and grow and grow. Synthetic stuff that can give you cancer and poison you if you get enough of it long enough. No detailed research has ever appeared on the subject.

The deep-freeze chicken, the so-called ice-box chicken, was introduced to Holland after an American television company made a documentary on some of those assembly-line factories. Suddenly there was a sharp drop in sales. Since the assembly lines couldn't be slowed down there was a surplus of chickens, so the product was introduced to Europe at an incredibly cheap price.

The kind of chicken you buy at a poultry shop—a real big fat healthy farm chicken—costs ten times as much. Still, you can never be sure you're getting a genuine chicken, since poultry dealers may be tempted to make some easy money. After all, one pound of the deep-freeze export product costs only three American, or eleven Dutch, cents.

So Eat More Chicken! Special Chicken TV Dinner! Want More and Better Cancer? Eat More Chicken! When You're Having More Than One For Dinner, Make a Meal of Chicken! Be a Man—Eat Chicken!

Barry and I couldn't believe our eyes. The Americans proudly explained that this one factory alone produced thirty thousand chickens a day—roosters for slaughter, that is. If the candling showed the egg contained a female fetus, then an entirely different procedure was called for. These were the laying hens and they could live for one month. Minimum lay: two eggs a day. No egg? Off to the slaughterhouse.

Of course, our hosts explained with a laugh, little slip-ups will sometimes occur. Chickens are gripped wrong by the metal hooks and ripped apart; cages sometimes fall down on the chickens instead of over them. But they had solved this problem: whole cartons of drumsticks were sold off to restaurants and wholesale dealers; packages with thousands of drumsticks or breasts were stacked up in the freezers by little white-coated men.

Because of the super treatment they underwent, the laying hens weren't fit for consumption. When they reached the age of fourteen days their meat started to rot. Their innards weren't affected; they went on laying eggs. All that rotted was their skin and meat. Their liver, kidneys, and hearts were cut out and packed in little plastic bags or sold in bulk to some restaurant or other.

By the time those gutted laying hens were three or four weeks old their flesh had turned a sickly blue or copper-green. Even when they were still alive. Fed on synthetic foods, they never had a normal growth of feathers. They stared at us, pitiful and dumb—their flesh spotted with blue and moldy green patches.

"They're going to be thrown out, of course," we assumed. No, the cadavers were sold by truck- and shipload to Europe's big soup makers. They were boiled down to chicken soup. Synthetic coloring took care of the color problem.

Eat more chicken, we thought, and after reassuring our hosts that the notes I'd jotted down would never be used for publication, we headed for the exit.

"For publication?" I laughed. "No. No. Just a few technical notes. Planning to start a plant like this myself if I ever get enough money. There's a fortune to be made in this business!"

We didn't touch the whisky they'd offered us. It was hours before either of us could say a word. Every time I started a sentence, the whole assembly-line scene ran through my mind. I haven't touched a chicken in four years. (Turkeys got the same treatment, only the process takes a bit longer.) I still won't eat a chicken. Or only if there's no other choice.

If I were a chicken-eater, I'd make sure I was getting a real one. I'd point out the one I wanted to the poultry man. I would never eat an assembly-line chicken. When I told Claudia the story she got sick to her stomach and had to throw up. Just telling her about it made me vomit too.

Chicken Eaters of the World—Bon Appétit!

218

Far from the Fatherland we had a ball on New Year's Eve. Sooner or later everybody in the restaurant got pie-eyed. The whole colony was there. Fat Frank, who'd gotten his balls shot off in Korea, a fat slob but a nice guy who looked exactly like Henry VIII. In his hoarse boozer's voice, he was always telling grisly war stories or explaining his vision of the ideal sex life. And then there were the Well-Jumpers—aspiring suicides who jumped into the deep echoing wells from which the local townspeople pumped their water. Also elderly English or American ladies who resided on the island, hopefully waiting to get raped by Santa Claus or a wild young artist someday, who often saw ghosts rising out of the wells. They drove the ghosts off by throwing petroleum and burning cotton wads into the wells.

Daan and Gerda were there, too, a Dutch couple with children— little boys like young gods, blond hair, blue eyes. And a beauty of a daughter, Vera. A kind of Swedish wood nymph (the kind you always see in Swedish movies running naked through the forest chased by a couple of gullible yokels who think she must be an angel). A young May Britt, a younger version of Gerda, her beautiful mother. A German beauty with well-shaped hips and legs. A sweet, sensitive woman who made dreamlike paintings that sweetly expressed her sensitive nature. Daan, with a good head on his shoulders, was a good-natured guy always good for laughs.

He'd started out as a slum kid and built up an international business in intestinal canals, answering the needs of medical men and sausage manufacturers all over the world. Many an appendix has been sewn up with the help of Daan's guts. Good friendly honest people. I was glad I'd met them. A New Year's party back home came of our island friendship. Dreamy Gerda had a weakness for art, which lots of sweaty arty parasites took advantage of. They sponged off her, giving her a lot of bullshit about art in return for her charity and good will.

We took back some steaks for Vodka. We couldn't leave him out of the New Year's celebration. He was a good, playful dog with a personality all his own. Once he disappeared into thin air. Claudia and I looked everywhere for him. Nowhere to be found. Panic-stricken, we went down to the dog catcher every day to see if he'd caught Vodka. The dog pound, next to the arena, was run by the dog catcher, a slippery operator who wore a wide-brimmed official-looking hat and carried a big wire dog net. If you paid your fine, you got your dog back—if he hadn't been convicted, that is.

In Ibiza, the judge or the police chief could sentence a dog to jail. For instance, if a dog bit somebody, crossed the path of a bike, fought with the bishop's dog, swiped a sausage, barked too loud at night and woke up the neighbors, or committed an immoral act in full view of witnesses at an outdoor café, he could be arrested and sentenced to jail. Of course, you could always buy it out for a small fee to be paid to the chief of police and the dog catcher (who also netted dogs whose owners he knew and whom he knew were just napping or waiting for their boss who'd stopped off at a café somewhere).

I soon got in the habit of shadowing the dog catcher on his daily rounds. Every time I saw him tiptoeing up on a stray, just getting ready to clamp down his net, I clapped my hands or started singing at the top of my lungs, or accidentally bumped him or cracked Vodka's leash against the sidewalk. If he'd ever lifted a finger against Vodka, I would have sent his hat flying with his head still inside it.

Podencos, the indigenous dogs of Ibiza, had been left behind on the island by the Egyptians thousands of years ago. Now they were carefully bred and sold to tourists, who got a kick out of strolling around the island behind a native dog with its pointed nose and ears—a kind of slim greyhound. Lots of Podencos were shot or injected to death every year. Tourists heading for home, not wanting to go to all the trouble of getting the required papers and shots for their faithful companions, left the animals behind to look after themselves.

The *perro ibicenco,* the Podenco, is a rare breed. A breed found only in Ibiza (birthplace of Hannibal, who crossed the Pyrenees with a herd of

169

elephants back in the old days). They were originally smuggled out of Egypt by sailors who kept dozens of dogs on their galleons. When Empress Tamara promoted the cat to the status of holy animal and all dogs had to be exterminated so they couldn't chase holy cats, the Egyptian warriors were reluctant to give up their faithful Fidos. Especially since they didn't have any women on board. They decided to leave the dogs at Ibiza, as well as Moorish slaves captured on their expeditions.

Also, of course, Empress Tamara was famous for her eccentric whims. She was the first empress to introduce sex between her legs and flat on her back instead of the kneeling and in-from-behind position. This caused a veritable revolution in the Egyptian court. The method was gradually taken up by various other nations and meets with pretty widespread approval nowadays. The Egyptian galleon crews knew from bitter experience all about the Empress's whims. After all, she'd been the one who'd denounced hens' eggs as demons—proscribed items that had to be destroyed—so that soon there wasn't an egg left in Egypt. After a while, of course, there weren't any chickens left either.

The abandoned Podencos lit out for the forests and fields of Ibiza and at night wild dog packs plundered the cities and towns. This went on for years until finally the Bishop of Ibiza demanded the dogs be exterminated. Walking barefoot up the steps to the door of his cathedral, he'd stepped in a pile of dogshit a few times too often. In the fifties, a giant anticanine crusade was carried out by volunteers and lunatic bureaucrats who killed more than two thousand Podencos.

When the dogs later turned out to make nice souvenirs for tourists, they were quickly bred back again. By that time, though, the only dogs left were Podencos belonging to prominent citizens who pampered the hell out of their dogs. Used to a rugged existence in the wilderness, the dogs had grown weak from eating too well and being spoiled too much, so that the *perros ibicencos* you see nowadays are only the harmless and happy descendants of their strong and ferocious ancestors.

Three days later we saw Vodka out for a walk one evening with his fiancée. A big Podenco bitch. He was strutting along at her side, proud as a peacock, opening all the garbage pails for her. He hardly listened to our shouts—just nodded, a little annoyed, then walked off very dignified with his girlfriend. We were relieved. After all, a dog is a dog. And even a dog's only young once, so what the hell—more power to him!

Two days later Vodka came home. Fucked out and filthy, all dirt and fleas. But satisfied and swaggering, too. He'd had a four-day ball in the woods or a cave somewhere with his fiancée and now he was ready to return to his every-day life. We took him to the beach and I plunged into

170

the ice-cold water. When Vodka jumped in after me, I scrubbed him all over, my teeth chattering and my fingers numb, with a big bar of Maya soap. Vodka got out smelling of soap and I got out with a bad case of pneumonia. At any rate, he wouldn't need another bath for a while. And anyway, love is love.

Three times a week they showed a movie at the local movie house. Spanish or South American soap operas. Fortunately we couldn't understand Spanish, so we didn't have to cry. Every time they showed a sob story, the whole audience bawled and blew their noses into sheets brought along by each family or block.

The movie house was an old unpainted wooden one-room house with boxes along the sides and rows of straight-backed chairs. When I came in, alone or with Claudia, squeals, giggles, and laughs resounded from the balcony. As soon as the film began, the lights went out and the little Spanish señoritas started throwing me love letters. After the movies the girls paraded in chattering groups on the street, and the bravest one sometimes bumped into me or tapped my arm as she passed, which made all the rest of them laugh.

It was strictly forbidden to go around with the Spanish girls. You kept your hands off if you knew what was good for you. A couple of young foreigners had been found in wells or hanging from trees, castrated or mauled pretty badly when word got around that they'd been trying to mess with the virginity of local señoritas. The military commander of the island—an old war horse, a real hombre's hombre with a Stalinesque mustache and fierce but friendly eyes—was the father of the three most beautiful girls on the island. Very unwise to try anything with them.

The Spanish films were usually made in full-blown acnecolor and all the actors trapped in the serious dramas wept all the time. Every time a man and a woman were alone somewhere the camera looked away for a long shot of a raging waterfall. The comedies were simple slapstick—lots of banging on the wrong door and putting hats on backwards, which always brought the house down. Before the movie began, a portrait of Franco was projected on the screen for minutes on end. Anyone dumb enough to start talking if the national anthem recording didn't start up on time was in for trouble. Policemen with red hats and clubs were scattered throughout the room just waiting to bash your skull in for you. If you were a foreigner, that is. Otherwise you were under arrest. Thou shalt honor thy Fatherland and thy Motherland. Amen.

The sound track was off more often than on, and in dubbed foreign films the lips were always a full two minutes behind the words. Every film track broke at least three times and once a month the celluloid got over-

171

heated and caught fire, pulling the actors out of shape and then losing them completely in the dark as the audience booed again. At any rate it was an evening out.

219

Things were looking up. I was working on a book. *I Jan Cremer,* I thought I would call it. Or *The Beast, The Barbarian and I, Jan Cremer.* I'd taught Claudia how to make collages and while she bustled about with a brush, paint, colored paper, and paste, I typed up my adventures on an old typewriter I'd rented from the local book shop.

I got my hands on a radio and was paying for it in installments. A blue plastic Spanish-made radio. We hadn't had any music in the house for three months. We'd had to part with the record player and all the records one by one. At night we could get Holland on Hilversum 2. "Marimba" was the first program I heard in Spain, and late at night, jazz for the American soldiers stationed near Alicante: Gerry Mulligan and Zoot Sims.

It was starting to warm up in the daytime. At night it was nice and cool. We slept with the windows open and loved each other very much. Lots of German stations on our radio. Top hits from the time-honored German Reich. "Heimatlos" and "Kleine Rose auf die Borste."

Claudia was pregnant. We were happy. Every day her belly got a little heavier. A pointy belly. That meant a son. I asked everybody for names. Claudius Caesar or Cassidy Caleb, Clifford, or Clinton. Anyway it would have to start with a C like Cremer. Now that Claudia was pregnant she blossomed like a rose. She was lovely. More beautiful every day. She was so terribly beautiful I promised I'd always be true to her. No woman could even start to compete with her. Not a single one of all those fancy females that came to the island: American fashion models, English mannequins, German movie stars, Swedish millionairesses; famous women like Esther Williams and Romy Schneider had houses there. But nobody as beautiful as Claudia.

Living with Claudia was an adventure. Every time she undressed it was sensational. She looked like Ava Gardner, warm, sweet, sensitive, and moody. I designed a couple of thin dresses for her and had them made by a tailor, very cheap. Usually we'd go for a swim in the afternoon. Spring was coming. A warm spring. After we'd frisked around with Vodka in the waves, we walked back home over the hot yellow boulders, throwing stones for Vodka, who'd chase them, barking as he ran.

Claudia took off her bathing suit and when she put on her dress, since she wasn't wearing anything under it, the thin material stuck to her moist body and her big dark brown nipples jutted out like twin torpedoes. She had a great body, rounded and mature. Her calves were maybe a bit short but they had their own special charm. She was very slightly bow-legged in a very sexy way. Her skin was bronzed (her father was a South African of remote Vietnamese descent). She had fine broad hips and a sturdy protruding Mount Venus. On the skin just around her bra, a light brown line had formed over the years, like on the insides of her elbows and knees. It was always a great new adventure for me when she undressed at night. I felt the same way each time, like a little boy who peeks through the curtains when the lady next door starts undressing.

She was very relaxed, Claudia. She knew I loved her. Sometimes though, domestic life was too much for me and I had to break loose. Claudia didn't say anything, which is why I came back. Drunk or miserable. She consoled me. A lot of tension was caused by our being so dead broke so long. Fights. Swearing. Slamming doors. When I felt most helpless I hit her. Everything was against me. Everything went wrong. Who could I take it out on except her? There's a Javanese proverb that runs: "Beat your wife at least once a week; there shall be peace in your home. But don't beat her too hard or she will be angry and she will hit back and cause you much pain and sorrow."

There was peace in my home. Claudia and I had the worst fights in the world. She couldn't keep up with the pace I set and sometimes did things wrong; because I was so irritable about everything, about being broke, about not having enough money to go on working, about the future, I took it all out on her, which I shouldn't have done since she took things hard and sometimes couldn't understand my fits of rage.

She couldn't cook. Heaven in bed, hell in the kitchen. ("If you see a cloud of smoke, it's just my wife cooking.") I took over and made our meals. When she went out shopping she'd come back hours later and couldn't figure out what I was so worried about. Also, of course, she was pregnant. Felt sick every morning when she got up. The little money I could spare to give her to buy a few things for herself always got spent on the wrong things.

Once when we went swimming with some other people in Portinax, on the other side of the island, she forgot her bathing suit. She forgot it on purpose because she was ashamed to wear it in front of other people. She thought she looked ugly with her growing belly. Actually, she looked more and more beautiful.

She was a very impressionable girl. Jealous girlfriends tried to make trouble, telling her all kinds of nasty things about me. She didn't believe them; on the other hand, she couldn't be sure they weren't true. She was always in doubt. A very introverted girl. Sometimes all the misery came gushing out all at once—the miseries that thousands of war babies had had to live through but which had taken root in her and, instead of making her wiser and more independent, had weakened her. She was very awkward, slow and dawdling. She couldn't keep up with my insane tempo. She always went along with me, at least she tried, but sometimes she just gave up. She'd sit staring off into space for hours. Motionless and silent, staring at a far-off horizon.

She'd wake me up in the middle of the night, gaze at me with tear-filled eyes and ask, "Will you stay with me? You'll never leave me? I'm sorry I was like that to you this afternoon. I shouldn't have been like that. I didn't mean it that way. Please say you're not mad I said all those awful things to you."

"Sweet sweet Claudia," I said and took her tear-stained face in my hands and kissed her slowly. "I forgot you ever said it, okay? Of course I'll never leave you. You know that. Don't worry about what people say. They're jealous of you. Just stay yourself and everything'll be fine. You should never let them know you feel bad. Just tell me. Your so-called friends are just dying to hear all about your problems. They're so miserable themselves, it makes them feel better."

"Sweetheart," she said softly. "I'm so happy I can be with you. I hope it won't ever end."

She had problems and she was homesick. She was a bit strange.

220

Early one sunny morning we strolled along the wharf where the fishing boats sparkled in the sunlight. We were on our way to the post office. It was a warm summer day and Vodka was in a good mood; you could tell from the way he barked. We laughed and Claudia seemed very cheerful. We stood in line for Poste Restante and when it was finally our turn I got a letter from Holland. So did Claudia. A long letter from her mother.

We sat down at the sidewalk café to read our letters and enjoy a cup of coffee. I was finished with mine in no time. I saw Claudia getting whiter and whiter as she read through her letter. When she'd finished she folded it up and put it in her straw basket.

"Something wrong?"

"No, nothing at all," she said, trying to smile. "A letter from my mother."

"How can you get a letter from your mother if you don't want to have anything to do with her?" I said.

"Don't ask me," she answered.

I saw she was concealing something.

"Come on. Out with it," I said. "Yesterday we promised we wouldn't have any more secrets from each other. What's in the letter? Bad news?"

"None of your business!" she exploded.

Shocked at the sudden explosion, she smiled at me apologetically.

I diverted her attention from the letter by pointing out all kinds of weirdos.

"Hey," I said, "look at lover-boy—that guy over there."

A Spaniard came limping up on crutches, one foot in a cast, his neck and head wrapped in a turban of bandages. When he passed, I shouted, "What are you trying to do? Make us feel sorry for you? Get a move on!"

The man stared at us with hate in his eyes and we burst out laughing.

"You shouldn't make fun of people like that," Claudia said when she could talk again.

"Oh yes I can," I said. "He's an old friend of mine. He can take a joke."

"Who is he?"

"You see his turban?" I asked.

"Yes."

"Well, that's Lawrence of Arabia."

221

Late that night it all came out. After we'd made love. She had written her mother an emotional letter just after we'd had one of our worst fights. We'd made up a few hours later but by that time she'd already sent off the letter. Now she felt awful about it. But now it was too late.

"She wants me to come home," she said and suddenly burst into tears and grabbed me tight with both hands and pressed her tear-streaked face against my chest. "I want to stay with you. Please, don't let me go!" she begged me.

"I just wish you'd trust me for once," I said calmly. "Naturally I'm not going to let you go. But it can't go on like this. What made you want to drag your mother into this anyway? You know you didn't want to have anything to do with her."

"I didn't have anybody else," she said.

222

Claudia's mother was a bitch. A thoroughly evil person. A she-devil. To call her a "woman" would be a blasphemy to the "weaker sex." A person who the older she got the more she looked like a hippopotamus. A mother who prostituted her daughters in every possible sense of the word.

Claudia feared and disliked her intensely. Her mother's whole life was nothing but plots and intrigues. She'd had seven children from at least four fathers. She'd been divorced from Claudia's father for twenty years and Claudia and her younger sister had been brought up in children's homes. The mother had never shown any interest in them—until the girls started earning a weekly salary. She had a sharp appetite for money.

Sometimes Claudia would wake up in a cold sweat in the middle of the night screaming, "No, no, not the stick!" As a kid, when she had a nightmare and wet her bed, she used to get a merciless beating with a wooden stick. Her mother's current boyfriend did it. Her younger sister had stuttered ever since because of those beatings.

The girls led lonely lives in the various children's homes they were put in. No mother, no father. The brothers were sent off to children's homes, too. The oldest sister was the only one the mother kept with her.

When she was three years old, Claudia was raped by a senile old man—a shock she'd never got over. Her mother had never given a damn about her.

When Claudia first met me, her mother was overjoyed. She thought I could help out. She'd been trying to break up Claudia's marriage for some time. With no luck. She'd come up with a new plan.

Claudia's mother was interested in only one thing: money. Claudia worked at an office and went out on Saturday nights with her older sister, a half-breed flop who'd been happily married for years, then suddenly ran off with the circus, abandoning her husband and two kids. From half-assed housewife to circus performer. She worked as a lion tamer and rode elephants around the rings of various circuses and came back home after everybody had gotten fed up with her intriguing, backbiting, and general all-around bitchiness.

Mother and eldest daughter had one thing in common. They both hated all men and all happy women. Claudia's lion-tamer sister always dragged her along to jazz joints and night clubs. As usual: the beautiful woman had to provide the camouflage for the ugly one.

The sister, hooked on men with bulging wallets or big reputations, met an American impressario who took an immediate interest in Claudia. Claudia took none in the old fart, though. When the American told the sister he was wildly in love with Claudia, Sis quickly invited him to come meet Mama. Mama smelled a summer villa in Claudia's name on the Italian Riviera, an apartment in Claudia's name in Amsterdam, tons of money, a car for Claudia, clothes, and everything else her little heart desired—if, that is, Claudia would only accompany Old Fart on his business trips. He organized festivals and concerts all over the world. If she'd be his mistress in Europe, he'd give her everything in return.

Claudia wasn't interested. But Mama Dear and Big Sis didn't give up. Claudia flatly refused. She was married and expecting a baby. But Mother and Sister raved about the furnished flat, the villa on the Riviera, the trips she'd be making, the new world that would open up for her. And Claudia wouldn't ever have to worry about being lonely because Mom and Sis would come to live in her houses with her. Besides, she could always break with the old guy and still have the houses and the clothes and the presents.

Claudia, who'd never had so much attention from her mother in her whole life, told her husband all about it. He forbade her to ever go to her mother's house again. And, since the American impressario wasn't ready to make the same deal with the circus siren, the whole deal was off. Mother and sister set to work to convince Claudia what a fantastic life was awaiting her and how dumb she would be if she didn't take it. It was the chance of a lifetime.

Finally the poor impressionable girl gave in and one day, instead of coming home, got on a plane to Rome. Off to the Man of Her Dreams, leaving Mom and Sis already planning their own golden future in the Italian sun. A few days later Claudia came to her senses, told the American to drop dead, threw all his expensive presents at his feet, and flew back to Holland. Back to her husband.

Mother and sister didn't give up. They kept right on working away at her and nothing Claudia's weak and good-natured husband could do could stop them. They explained how stupid she was not to take what she could get while the getting was good. All those suede coats, those *haute couture* clothes, the Italian sportscar.

"Even if only for your mother's sake," they said. "All our lives we've worked our fingers to the bone for you."

Claudia lived on through one complex after the other. Aware of his mother- and sister-in-law's plans, her husband did his best to keep them out of the house. The two women kept right on scheming. Where there's a will there's a way. The American took the first Holland-bound plane he could get, but had to return to Italy—mission unaccomplished—to go on with his tour.

Then I came along. At first, the mother thought I was just what was needed. I would get Claudia away from her husband; then she'd leave me or I'd leave her and the coast would be clear. However, her plan backfired badly. Claudia really loved me and I wasn't going to let her go. In Amsterdam, before we took off for Spain, her mother used to come around sometimes when I wasn't home. She told Claudia the poverty we were living in was impossible.

"Here you go on living in poverty while that rich American is still crazy about you!"

Jan Cremer *Claudia's Mother*

She didn't make any headway with Claudia. We left for Ibiza and the mother saw her dream palace go up in smoke. The older sister, who was working with a circus in Germany, wrote me a few nasty letters when she got back to Holland. That I was no fucking good and that everybody knew it. She didn't even know me. Maybe from a distance. She joined forces with Claudia's husband and tried to talk her into coming back. Claudia didn't let them bug her.

She hated the mother. But her mother had a kind of satanic power over her and Claudia was too scared or too weak to break the spell. There was something weird about the whole thing. Claudia's greatest fear was that she'd become just like her mother. An embittered bitch interested only in money and in making other people miserable. The hate she felt for her mother always came out at the most unexpected moments. She'd see something or someone that reminded her of her mother, who'd never once had a nice word for her. Not when she was a kid. Not when she got married either. The mother had opposed the marriage. She used to come around every day to stir up trouble.

Her brothers were nice simple boys, with respectable jobs. One of her brothers she hadn't seen in years. The mother never visited him and never included him in the family get-togethers or at the big Christmas dinner. He was the son of an Indonesian and he looked too much like his father. If you lined the whole family up, it would be almost impossible to see the slightest resemblance between any two of them.

The older daughter was mother's pet. Both of them hated men, both of them as sly as they were dumb. The mother had a cunning bordering on perversity—a cunning born of paranoia, the cunning of a hyena. It often impressed people, until they got to know her better.

They tried repeatedly to get Claudia to leave me. Even when we were in Ibiza. Claudia had gotten jewelry from the American. Her mother kept it for her and pawned most of it—after taking the best things for herself. Later, when Claudia went back to Holland, her mother immediately got a hold on her again. Letters and postcards I sent her had to be sent in care of our friends. The mother censored Claudia's mail. All letters from me were destroyed.

"You see!" the mother kept trying to brainwash her. "I told you so Loves you so much, does he? Never going to leave you, is he? Well, one thing's for sure—he's fixed himself up with another woman by now. It's all over now with you. You'll be having the baby any day now and he won't show up, not him."

The stories Claudia told me later! About how her mother kept warning her to stay away from me. I was a "punk." "The worst sort of vermin. Just look at his friends! Like seeks like. And the only people he knows are pimps and gangsters. Nice man you picked out for yourself!"

178

Day in and day out she and Lena the lion tamer preyed on the poor trusting soul. When I finally came back to her, she couldn't believe her eyes.

Claudia was afraid. Afraid of everything. Afraid of her mother and afraid of the law. A girl like that—sensitive, a bit strange, bossed around too long by strict headmistresses or child guardianship boards, unable to absorb all the shocks, tortured by all kinds of traumas—is bound to develop a fear of the world. Sometimes she was so preoccupied with her own problems, she hardly knew what was going on around her. Her mother took advantage of this. Instead of helping her to accept the world—in all its beauty as well as its ugliness—her mother sabotaged every effort Claudia made to adjust and grow.

Her mother threatened and blackmailed Claudia constantly, told her what to do, how to laugh, how to think, how to feel. Claudia was battered inside. I found that out soon enough. I may not be a psychiatrist but I do have a certain amount of worldly wisdom and I use it. I keep my eyes open. I can sense good or evil intuitively.

I did everything I could to hold on to Claudia. I couldn't help it if I wasn't exactly a model husband. After all, I was also still studying at the School of Life too. Only nobody could get me down. If anybody ever wants to get me to knuckle under, he'll have to shoot me, then tromp me to death, then bury a dagger in my heart. Anything less than that and I'll be up and fighting again.

Claudia's mother had absolutely no respect for men. The only thing she respected was the sign of the holy guilder. Money. Her daughters and sons had to marry people loaded with it. Then she'd have it nice and easy in her old age. She'd played the divorce racket so well that her former husband, who'd thrown up his hands in despair and walked out on her twenty years before, was still paying alimony. If the poor devil was a week overdue paying up, off went the dynamic duo, Lena and Mama, to the city he lived in to make him regret it fast.

"The old man pays like clockwork now," she once told me grimly. And she told me in great detail about how she made her ex's life impossible. He worked at a simple but honest trade and for years she'd been making him switch from one job to another by hounding him down wherever he went and raising hell about him at each different place.

I'd already heard all these stories from Claudia. The woman made me sick to my stomach.

What she felt about Claudia was clear from the fact that she hadn't seen or written to her in eight years. When Claudia was about to marry a boy who looked as if he might make a wad later on, it took a lot of doing but she finally gave her approval. For me she had nothing but hate.

I met her once before Claudia and I left for Spain. She was very friendly to me. Too friendly. I was just as friendly back. Immediately a kind of armed truce was established.

"So you're Jan Cremer," she said politely as I entered the room. Her room. A little room with a lot of stuffed plush pillows, crocheted table mats, a bleak landscape on the wall. Delft-blue tiles, a plaster of Paris African head on the mantelpiece, and a parchment lampshade with little sailboats painted on it.

"What are you going to do with Claudia in Spain? Claudia isn't the traveling kind. You'll have to leave her here."

As friendly as possible I explained that Claudia and I had decided to go away to Spain together.

She ran an automobile appliance shop with her boyfriend who, surprisingly enough, was a simple, honest, good-natured man who didn't want to get involved in arguments and always sat in the corner reading the paper or a book. Her boyfriend, a broad-shouldered middle-aged man, lived with his mother and could only sleep with her on weekends. They spent their vacations together though.

That woman was so evil she never left off telling Claudia that an abortion was a serious crime. Just after Claudia had gotten married, she'd had an abortion. Her husband couldn't stand it and stormed out leaving her holding the battered fetus, already a few months old, in her arms. A pool of blood, an awful mess. That whole night she rocked the dead flesh like a baby. Until somebody found her the next morning staring off into space humming a lullaby.

For Claudia I was the only person in the world who could help. I really tried. If things went wrong it was because I was still growing up myself. I tried with all my might. It's like a ladder you have to climb together. All the way to the top. If one of you stops at one rung of the ladder, the gulf begins. He or she gets left behind and the gulf gets wider and wider. I tried to pull Claudia up with me. Rung by rung. Slowly and carefully. She had to get to the top. With me. I had patience. I hoped I'd be able to make it. The only person Claudia had in the whole wide world who knew who and what she was was me.

I've met a lot of people in my life. But none as evil as Claudia's mother. Too evil to live.

223

Circus Colombia came to Ibiza. Weeks in advance the brightly-colored circus posters with their stars, elephants, daring young men on flying trapezes, naked girls, and colorful letters were up on whitewashed walls all over the city. The renowned circus pitched its tent in the middle of the municipal arena. In the inside ring. It was a small yellowish tent.

Claudia and I went to the gala opening. The tent was packed with Ibizan farmers, yokels, and townspeople. Hard metal folding chairs were set up around a shaky stage. A real old-fashioned circus.

I'm crazy about circuses and so is Claudia. We finally elbowed our way to the front row—a few red-painted wicker lounging chairs right up by the round wooden stage. The posters had announced that Circus Co-lombia was touring the world. The tent was tiny; filled to capacity, it could hold maybe a hundred people. The circus started after half an hour of waiting. Somebody tripped over the wire so out went the lights. The tent was pitch black. Claudia screamed. In the dark somebody was feeling her breasts. People were making the most of the few minutes of darkness. Smooches and slaps all over the place.

The lights flashed on, off, and on again. The show could begin. We were right next to the band: two trumpets, drums, an accordion. When the trumpets started blasting out "Circus Renz," way off key, my left ear started buzzing like mad.

The opening act was a duo of midgets who came storming onto the stage on tiny bicycles. One was going so fast he stormed right off the stage—heading straight at us. Fortunately he landed in the band. The crowd roared with laughter. I wasn't sure whether it was an accident or just part of their routine. It looked like it had happened before though, because the drummer calmly put down his sticks, picked the midget up in one hand, the bike in the other, and tossed them back onto the stage.

A loud flourish of trumpets. A woman fat as a hippo clomped on stage wearing a glittering costume and high hat. She cracked her whip wildly a couple of times. On the other side of the stage, people clutched at their eyes and yelped with pain. The fat lady pretended not to notice and announced the program.

Loud applause. From the rear of the ramp leading off to the dressing rooms, two poodles were kicked on stage. Behind them came a sleazy-looking guy with a stick who made the dogs do all kinds of tricks. Loud flourish of trumpets. Suddenly one of the dogs jumped into a trumpet. The trumpet player huffed and puffed. The buttons popped off his jacket. Then out shot the dog back on stage and the player could play his trumpet again. Tremendous applause, once again.

The fat lady came on again looking very roguish. The ramp creaked and wobbled under her weight. This time she was wearing an old-fash-ioned bikini with sequins embroidered all over it. I didn't quite get the point of the act. She waddled back up the ramp, wagging her enormous ass. Claudia and I found it hilarious.

181

The magician was Mr. Magoo. He could make anything come out of a hat. An egg, a long string of handkerchiefs, flowers with pointed petals which he tossed onto the stage, except for one which he placed on the knee of the doctor who was sitting in a box seat with his wife. The doctor tried to throw it back but the paper flower unraveled, shot through the tent like a crippled dart, and landed somewhere in back.

Then Magoo tried the magic wand trick. But when he tried to break it in two, it suddenly became obvious he'd made a mistake. The one he was holding was solid wood. Everybody could see the paper imitation wand sticking out of his cape pocket. Laughter from the audience. Mr. Magoo hesitated. Take the wand out of the pocket? That would be a little too obvious. Finally, he just grabbed both ends of the wand in his hands and broke it over his knee. Feeble applause.

Suddenly a dove fluttered out from under the table where Mr. Magoo's magic hat sat. Everybody laughed and then tried to catch the dove which was circling around the tent just above head level.

"Silence!" Mr. Magoo screamed, so loud that he shattered two red lamp bulbs. The crowd quieted down. The dove perched on a curtain rod over the entrance. Cautiously Mr. Magoo came down the stage stairs, everybody watching him tensely now. Along the aisle people moved their chairs in to let him pass. In the breathless silence inside the tent, Magoo was inching up on the bird when, all at once, somebody pushed aside the curtain and came in, surprised to see the whole crowd staring at him. Scared, the dove took off again, sailed through the tent, turned, dove, and shot out through the entrance like an arrow. Enormous applause.

"Craziest circus I ever saw," Claudia mumbled.

"You can say that again," I said.

Mr. Magoo cursed the hell out of everybody—especially the guy who'd opened the curtain. He reluctantly went on with his act, but his heart wasn't in it any more. He did some card tricks—very confusing. He'd say "eight of spades" when the card he was showing was an ace of clubs and "king of hearts" when the card we saw was a deuce of diamonds. Applause. Getting feebler.

The two midgets zoomed on stage again on their bikes. This time they didn't fall off the stage, but when their act was over one of them did ride off the ramp. He crawled back up, his nose bleeding all over his shirt, and ran off backstage through the curtain.

The Bearded Lady came next. I recognized the Fat Lady but she'd pasted hair on her face and was strutting around now, pointing at her beard. She said somebody from the audience could give it a yank to prove her beard wasn't fake. The magician, in shirt sleeves and suspenders now, had quickly taken a front row seat. She came up to him and bent over, but a young Spaniard sitting just behind the magician beat him to the draw. A gentle tug and off came the beard from the lady's chin. Magoo swung around and—Blam!—thanked the Spaniard with a punch in the face.

Suddenly a whole pack of circus hands rushed in and dragged the dare-devil out of the tent. From the stage, a couple of muscle-bound types with cauliflower ears and bashed-in noses glared down at the audience menacingly. Anybody who laughed too hard got drilled by those eyes. They wore dirty blue overalls. One of them cradled a monkey wrench in his paws.

Intermission.

The whole scene reminded me of my own childhood Circus Matador. Except my shows were better than this one. A sucker born every minute. Barnum was right. I remember overhearing a conversation once between a Bearded Lady and her manager.

Bearded Lady to Boss: "If you don't give me a raise I'll show them my prick."

The intermission ended as the Fat Lady came barging out with her whip again and all the people in the front row seats shielded their eyes fast. Then on came Achilles, the Strong Man of South America. No doubt about it, he was a real mountain of flesh who padded out stripped down to his white undershirt and shorts. I recognized the guy who'd been fondly patting the monkey wrench a few minutes before. He flexed his biceps, ballooned a few other muscles, and straightened out a horsehoe—with a lot of sweating and straining. After he'd wrung some straight iron bars into U-shape, the backstage boys rolled a set of enormously heavy dumb-bells down the ramp. The audience was absolutely quiet now. Those things weighed at least a thousand pounds.

Working hard, he got the weights first up to his knees. Then, with another heft, up to chest level. Then, with the last of his energy, his huge muscles popping and quivering now, he suddenly hoisted the weights up past his face and over his head. Tremendous applause. A loud cracking sound. Achilles, a shocked look on his face, sank through the stage floor, dumbbells and all. All you could see of him now was just his head with its Erroll Flynn mustache. Soon everybody in the circus was busy getting the weights off Achilles, then pulling the giant himself up from under the floor. Another round of applause.

While the thug of a dog trainer whipped his dogs through their tricks —in their enthusiasm the dogs leaned so far backwards standing up on their hind legs they fell over backward and were thrown back on stage by the audience—other hands were putting up a metal cable between two tall poles.

Mr. Magoo the magician appeared again, this time wearing tights on his spindly legs. Longlegs tugged the wire a few times, twanged it for tension and strength, swung himself up, and took a few perky ballet steps in time to the music.

Dramatic drumroll. Mr. Magoo then asked if anyone in the audience had a handkerchief for him. A beautiful Spanish señora tossed hers up to him. He gallantly kissed it, though he wrinkled his nose at whatever he whiffed, and tossed the lady an elegant kiss. He put the lace hanky across the metal wire, then, after another roll of drums and a bit more high-wire ballet, he bent down and hung by the backs of his knees. Balancing himself with his outstretched arms, he then straightened his back and stared at the hanky lying on the wire between his kness.

Dramatic drumroll again. He leaned forward and tried to bite the hanky, tried to lip it off the wire into his mouth, but every time he got his big lips close to the hanky, he nearly lost his balance. Once he fell off. Onto the stage, fortunately for him.

The act dragged on and on. It was getting ridiculous. At first, everybody had laughed themselves silly, but after half an hour, with our jaws aching from laughing so much, the whole thing got sort of awkward. And Magoo still went on. Even when they were shouting from offstage that it was time to stop, he stayed right where he was, balanced on the wire. He was going to get that goddam hanky if it took him all night.

After about an hour of this the crowd started thinning out. Two hours later I looked around, no longer fascinated, and said to Claudia, "Come on, let's get out of here. The show's over."

As a matter of fact, the place was almost completely empty. The only people left were the señora who'd tossed up her hanky and the yawning man sitting next to her. The lady was still staring in fascination at the sopping wet, sweating Magoo. Every time his lips almost got the hanky, she hissed, "Sí, sí, sí."

Claudia and I walked out of the tent. The midgets were sitting outside on benches smoking their pipes. Before I let the curtain fall behind me I took one last pitying look at the empty tent with the acrobat still dangling on his wire. We had had a good laugh. What else is a circus for?

Outside on the cement patio a blind organ grinder wearing dark glasses was grinding away at a beautiful little hurdy-gurdy. Fantastic music came out of it. The music from *M* with Peter Lorre. A little monkey dressed in a suit was hopping up and down with a cup.

Claudia was delighted.

I gave her a few coins. She threw them in the cup. The monkey danced to the music.

184

224

Speaking of monkeys. One evening I was on my way back from Friesland. On the motorcycle. Fall weather. Cold, at the speed I was going. It was dark when I saw lights on in a small-town bar, and I thought I'd stop for a beer and warm up.

I parked the motorcycle and walked into the bar. One huge long room. A kind of tavern with wooden walls, wooden ceiling, plank floors, tables and chairs along the walls. A big heavy mahogany bar to the right as you came in. Not a soul in the place. Deserted. Except, at the far end, a tall sloppy-looking man with a mop of curly hair playing a piano. Fantastic music. All kinds of tunes. They went on and on.

Although it was still early in the evening, nobody else was there. I'd expected to find a nice cozy bar crowded with yokels. I slammed my hand down flat on the bar.

"Anybody here?" I yelled.

Again, louder this time, "Anybody here?"

No reply.

I banged the bar a few more times and then finally heard somebody shuffling around upstairs. A little later a sleepy-faced elderly man in a nightcap and nightshirt came in through a door behind the bar.

"Good evening," I said cheerfully. "A beer, please."

Mumbling, he poured me a glass, waited till the head settled down, then said, "Forty cents."

I gave him two quarters and said, "Keep the change."

He grumbled a thank you, threw the coins in a drawer and went out the door again. Soon I heard that same shuffling around upstairs again. Even with that guy hammering away at the piano I could still hear it. He was playing everything, kids' tunes, rock-and-roll, folk songs, everything.

It seemed pretty weird to me, that bar. But then what can you expect in Friesland? I stood next to the stove where it was nice and warm. When I walked back to the bar to pick up my beer, two hairy little hands suddenly popped up from behind the bar. A tiny monkey swung himself up onto the counter. Astonished, I looked at him and he looked at me. With his enormous eyes. He loped over to my glass of beer and sat down on top of it, straddling the glass, and while he kept his twinkling eyes trained straight at me, calmly proceeded to wash his balls. That was too much for me. I looked around. Still nobody there. What the hell was going on? The only human around was the piano player. I strode over to him, disgusted and mad, and tapped him on the shoulder.

He had unbelievably long hair, thick glasses, and wore a suit at least

185

three sizes too large for him. Fingers spread wide, he lustily clobbered the black and white keys. I tapped him on the shoulder once again, harder this time. With a start, he stopped playing, threw back his hair and glanced up at me with sparkling eyes.

"A monkey is washing his balls in my beer," I said indignantly.

He gazed at me thoughtfully, reflected a moment and said, "I don't know that one. Can you hum it for me?"

vodka & 1 gouged eyeball

225

I've had dreams about the Black Dog With the Pink Nose for years. A Canadian soldier gave him to me on Liberation Day. The dog's been following me ever since. I've petted or caught sight of him in Russia, Tunisia, Gibraltar, Spain, Sweden, and France.

In Sweden I had the Black Dog With the Pink Nose examined by a veterinarian. After conducting a thorough examination of the dog's paws, the vet said that since 1945 Blackie had walked more than five million miles. It was the Black Dog With the Pink Nose's assignment in life to follow and protect me. Wherever I go, he's always around somewhere.

226

It was Thursday morning. I crawled out of the warm bed bright and early. I had a date with an American chick who'd bought one of my paintings and was finally going to pay up. I put on a clean work shirt and strolled over to the sidewalk café. Claudia was still sound asleep. Vodka jumped up on me, wagging his tail, eager to go, but I pushed him down. I couldn't take him along; I had business to do. Go to the bank with the girl and get some money at last.

Spring was turning to summer. The mornings were scorching hot. By ten o'clock the sun had sucked every ounce of oxygen out of your chest. I kissed Claudia's warm face, then opened the window and the transom to get whatever breeze was going that day. The sun was shining full blast and the heat was lethal as I took off for Café Montesol.

Vodka looked at me expectantly. "Boss'll be right back," I assured him. Usually I take him along. This time I didn't. I don't know why.

We got our business over with fast and I had some cash now. Head straight back home, get Claudia up, then set off with her and Vodka on the motorcycle for Portinax. It's on the other side of the island, a little place where the water is emerald green from the salt and you can see a pebble sixty feet down. We could finally afford to buy gas for the motor-

Jan Cremer *Vodka & 1 Gouged Eyeball*

cycle and something to drink on our way. A glass of beer and a plateful of squid, I thought.

I put the key in the door and opened it. Claudia was up, walking around in her panties. I went over and put my arms around her.

"She finally came through!" I said, full of enthusiasm. "Get dressed. We're going for a swim."

But as soon as I turned and started walking away, I heard Claudia shriek with terror. In that split second, while I was turning back to see what had happened, I knew for sure it was something horrible. Visions of catastrophe flashed like a black lightning flash through my brain to my heart, through my stomach to the tips of my toes, and back to my brain again. For the first time in my life I was scared stiff.

I whirled around and looked into Claudia's shocked eyes, her hand to her mouth.

"What happened?" I screamed. "What's the matter?"

"My God," she moaned. "How awful!"

"What is it? Where's Vodka?"

Suddenly I knew it was Vodka.

When I came in I'd seen him stretched out on the window sill in the sun. When I'd gone over to Claudia, I'd heard his nails scratch the cement as he got up. While the shock of fear was still shooting through me, I heard a thud.

I raced to the window and looked down. A twenty-five-yard drop straight down. A sheer cliff. I scanned the pebbled beach, the white foam sweeping over it, hoping against hope that Vodka's fall had been broken, that he'd got caught in something on the way down. Then I saw him: brown, with white spots.

My first impulse was to dive right out the window to get down there and help him. Hysterical with fear, I turned and dashed out the door. Down the stairs, through the alley, to the twisting narrow steps carved out of rock. I flew down hundreds of steps. I've never run so fast in my life. Horror and shock gave me superhuman strength. I leaped the last four yards of steps and in those last few seconds thought of all kinds of miracles and flukes of luck that could save lives. I sank up to my ankles in the tiny pebbles. My legs could hardly move after all that running. After one last burst of energy, I collapsed at Vodka's side.

The whole way down, I'd been screaming, "God, please, God, don't let Vodka die, please, please." I'd prayed for a miracle.

I fell down crying next to my best friend. He wasn't dead. When he heard my voice, he tried to get up. I was his best friend, his master. He stared off into space, stunned. In desperation I screamed, "Vodka!

188

Vodka! Everything's going to be all right, old pal," and stroked him and petted him and held his head in my hands. He couldn't see me. He'd gone blind. His belly was completely smashed open. His hindquarters were smeared all over with blood, shit, and piss. Crying like a baby, I buried my face in his soft hair. He struggled to get up on his front legs.

I looked up. Nobody. Just Claudia looking out our window. What could she do? I patted Vodka's head and blew in his ears. When I'd jumped down onto the beach, I hadn't seen him right away. I was still hoping for a miracle, knowing it was impossible, thinking maybe there wouldn't be anything wrong with him at all, that he was just afraid I'd be mad at him for falling out the window and that he was just hiding somewhere. Till, a second later, I saw him. He was breathing. He was still alive. I racked my brains, trying to think what to do.

I'd sacrifice everything for Vodka, I thought. Everything—all my paintings, my house, clothes. I'd sell everything I owned if only I could save his life. He must have been suffering because he was having a hard time breathing. I was at my wits' end.

"Don't die, old boy," I begged him. He blinked his eyes, a sign that he'd heard me.

"Don't worry," I said. "I'll save you. I won't let you die, you crazy mutt."

Feverishly I wondered how in hell he could have fallen down from the window sill.

"Vodka," I whispered, "I'm taking you with me."

I lifted him up. Very carefully. His shit and guts ran down all over my clothes but I didn't give a damn. I walked up the steps as fast as I could, carrying Vodka around my neck, his front and back paws in my hands. I did my best to walk without jarring him. It was noon. I called to a few kids, "Quick! Get me a cab!"

I prayed, me who can't pray at all: Please keep this dog alive. Please. I'll do anything to make up for it. Anything. Just let him live!

That day was the first time I hadn't taken Vodka along with me. Every time I went out for a walk I automatically took him along. It was also the first time I hadn't greeted him and patted his head when I came in. Patting his head was an old tradition. I would say Hi to him even before I'd said anything to Claudia. The dog was my most precious possession. I could talk to him. Whenever I'd had a fight with Claudia, I'd take him to the beach at night and talk to him. He was my only friend. He just *couldn't* die. I could laugh, play, cry with Vodka. Coming home meant playing with Vodka for an hour. Romping, wrestling, throwing him onto the bed with Claudia, laughing. On the beach, after we'd gone for a swim, I always let him shake himself off right next to Claudia lying stretched out on a towel basking in the sun—a nice, quick shower. Vodka was my comrade, my everything.

The kids found a cab on the quay. Passing the outdoor café, El Barco Boracho, on my way to the cab, I heard people say "What a shame," and "Too bad," before hunching back over their expensive bouillabaisse and beefsteaks.

The cab driver, a dumb Spaniard, didn't want to take me. Either I had to wrap a newspaper around the dog or put him in the trunk.

"In the trunk," he said. "It's dead anyway."

"Like hell he is!" I screamed. "He's still breathing."

"Finished," he said. "Anybody can see that."

"Just get me over to the Abattoir," I shouted, "and fast."

"But . . ."

"But nothing," I snapped. "Get a move on or I'll drive your heap there myself. I'll pay anything you want, but, for Christ's sake, move."

He rammed his cab into gear and we started off. Vodka was lying on my lap. He was having a hard time breathing. I blew on his neck.

When we'd got to the slaughterhouse I put Vodka, still breathing, gently down on the floor of the car and ran to the office. The vet was just coming out the door. A well-dressed Spaniard, director of the slaughterhouse, also a vet. Stammering for words, I told him my dog was dying, that I urgently needed his help. He didn't have time. He'd just washed up and was going home for lunch.

"Please," I pleaded. "I'll pay anything!"

I took out the money I'd got just that morning—more than five thousand pesetas in one-hundred-peseta bills.

"Here," I said, handing him the money. "For you. Save my dog! Please."

He looked at me blankly and finally followed me over to the taxi. The driver opened the back door of his cab, grinning stupidly, and rolled his eyes at the vet as if to say, "Those crazy foreigners."

The doctor took one look at Vodka, who was still breathing heavily and said, "No use."

"What's no use?" I yelled. "Help that dog!"

"There's nothing I can do," he said, laughing. "It's a waste of money. I'd give him another five or ten minutes at the most."

"Save him," I said threateningly and never in my life have I been so determined.

He saw the threat in my eyes and apparently got the message that I meant what I said. At that moment I was the most dangerous human on earth. If he'd tried to walk off I'd have jumped him and beaten the shit out of him. I'd have flattened him and then stomped his head into applesauce. I'd have torn him apart until there weren't any pieces left.

"How?" he asked.

"How should I know?" I said. "But do *some*thing. Give him something. Drug him. Operate. Do *some*thing. I mean it."

"There's no point," he said. "There's nothing left of his insides. He's dying."

It was true. Vodka's breathing wasn't regular any more. I knelt down in the car and put my ear to his crushed chest.

"Vodka," I said, "I'll miss you like nothing else in the world."

A few minutes later he was dead.

I told the driver to take me out of the city, past the harbor, into the country. On the way I stopped at a store to borrow a shovel. I lifted Vodka out of the car and took him over to a green slope, then dug a deep hole. With tears in my eyes I laid him in his grave. His stiff legs pointed straight up, taking one last good stretch. I took the money out of my pocket and threw it in the hole.

"Here," I said. "This is what made me forget you for a second. I don't want it any more. It brings bad luck. Money stinks."

Feeling completely lost, I filled up the hole. The first few grains of sandy earth looked black against his white spots. Then I asked the driver to take me home.

I wanted to be alone. Alone, or with Claudia. To mourn the loss of a friend.

Claudia wasn't home and I didn't have the key so I had to go to the Music Bar. She was sitting out on the terrace and waved to me, smiling.

Suddenly I'd had enough of everybody and everything.

227

I wondered how Vodka could possibly have fallen out the window. An accident, of course. But he was accustomed to lying on the window sill. He lay there every day. Must have jumped up too fast when he heard me come in. Maybe he was in the middle of a dream, so drowsy he lost his balance.

Had he committed suicide? Because for once I hadn't paid any attention to him? Had he always wanted to commit suicide? Dogs do that sometimes. If they feel unwanted they commit suicide. Walk in front of a car or jump out a window.

Jan Cremer *Vodka & 1 Gouged Eyeball*

Claudia liked Vodka but was jealous because I paid too much attention to him. We'd had a fight about it once.

I've seen people die, people, young men with their guts hanging out. People who died right next to me, people I'd laughed with and talked with. Two minutes later, I'd forget all about them. The death of the dog made more of an impression on me than anything else in my life. Maybe I just haven't suffered enough. Maybe there's plenty of suffering ahead.

I hate people that don't love dogs. People who don't like animals aren't really people. Something's wrong with them. They're incomplete. Something's lacking. I'm no fanatical animal lover myself, but I do respect everything that lives and grows. That's why I don't like the Spaniards. Stupid, primitive people. I would have had a ball beating hell out of that bastard of a vet. Bullfights are equally vicious and lousy, and the people who flock to them are dumb, low, yellow, and mean. Bullfighters are maniacs. All those glorious stories about bullfights and fighters are so much bullshit. Let a sober healthy bull into the ring and fight him with your bare hands. With a bayonet if necessary. But not with fourteen men. As it is, the bulls are dopey with sedatives and the picadors gleefully stick long lances into their spines. Nothing could give me more satisfaction than to see a toreador get his balls horned out or to watch him go hurtling ass-over-end through the air.

I spent the rest of the day alone, in the dark, in bed. Feeling miserable. Nothing could cheer me up. Late that night Claudia and I went to the Portico to have something to eat.

"We'll get another nice dog," Claudia consoled me.

The restaurant was packed. The Bad Boy of Ibiza was sitting with a friend at the table next to ours. They were both friends of mine, but on this particular evening I didn't feel like talking to anybody, no matter who.

Alexis was a pretty wild character. Nightclub owner. Noble family. Franco's nephew. The island's man-sized problem child. A totally paranoid playboy generally good for a few laughs. He tried a few jokes on me. Didn't know what had happened to Vodka.

After a while I told him to screw off. Unexpectedly, while I was hunched over my bowl of soup, he slashed me in the right eye with a dog leash studded with metal disks. Dazed and stupefied for a couple of seconds, all I could see was stars. It was all I could do to keep from passing out flat on my back. The second I came to I jumped up. Howls from the neighboring tables. Children quickly being led out the door. I couldn't see anything with my right eye. I tried to feel it with my hand and got the shock of my life. My whole right eyeball was hanging by a couple of tendons, dangling down on my cheek. My eyelid was torn off and, still attached at one corner, hung over the socket. My other eye saw red.

Jumping up from the table, I grabbed Alexis, shoved him down across a table, and started socking his head. Suddenly his whole face was red from my blood. I was so mad I tried to murder him. Nothing mattered any more. I was blind in one eye anyway and, besides, killing him would be a kind of revenge for Vodka's death. I kept pounding away at his head.

He was an ox of a man. A head taller than me. Much better built and stronger. I needed both hands just to keep him down on the table. People tried to break it up. I shoved them back. I saw a knife lying on a table. When I had a free hand I grabbed it. If fourteen hands hadn't lunged for it fast, I would have stabbed him.

Alexis was scared shitless. He knew I wanted to kill him and started screaming for help. A friend of his, a lawyer, managed to calm me down. Alexis shot out the door. I was led to the bathroom. What I saw in the mirror knocked the breath out of me. My whole eye was dangling down on my cheek, the eyelid flapping over the empty socket, my eye all the colors of the rainbow—green, blue, orange, red. I'd lost a lot of blood.

Douglas, an Australian, took me to the hospital in his Triumph. I hated Alexis and decided to get even with him no matter what. I had downed too much alcohol to make it safe for them to give me anesthetics at the hospital. A lady doctor, a sweet woman with gentle hands, put everything that was hanging out back in and sewed up the eyelid. A thick needle and thread worming their way through your eyelid hurts like hell. Douglas had to promise not to leave without me. The doctor asked lot of questions. How it had happened. I said I'd bumped into a door.

"It must have been a very special kind of door," the doctor said sarcastically. "A tenth of an inch more of that door and you would have been blind in one eye. As it is, we'll still have to wait to see whether it heals properly. I'll have to call the police about this. It's a nasty wound inflicted by some sort of instrument. You try your door story out on the police."

A few minutes later a detective from the precinct station entered the room, sat down at the foot of the surgery table.

"Now just tell me what happened, please," he said.

I told him about the door.

"We know as well as you that Alexis did it. He did, didn't he?"

"Alexis? No," I said. "I just bumped into a door, that's all."

I thought, I'll get even with him myself. Anyhow, I didn't have much choice. Being the Big Boss's nephew, in the eyes of the law Alexis could do no wrong.

After three hours on the surgery table I was allowed to leave the hospital. Claudia was waiting for me in the waiting room.

"Okay, Douglas," I said nonchalantly, "thanks a lot. I'm going for a walk. Got to get the ether stink out of my system."

Claudia and I walked. I was still dizzy. I could hardly see with my left eye. The right one was all bandaged up. Two blocks from the hospital I got into a fight with three French sailors who tried fooling around with Claudia. I was raging mad, furious. All that in one day.

A French flagship and some submarines had called in at the harbor. The boys were out for a night on the town. We couldn't shake them. We happened to be passing an outdoor café where people were sitting around having coffee when they started in on Claudia. I grabbed a bottle of brandy from under the noses of the surprised coffee drinkers and smashed it with a dull thud right in the face of one of the sailors. The bottle broke in his face in a shower of blood and brandy. While he staggered back against the wall of the café, I rammed the jagged top of the bottle in his mate's face, who let out a scream, covered his face with both hands, and planted his ass in a potted palm.

The third one was getting off a kick straight for my crotch and would have won the ball game if three Spanish fishermen who recognized me hadn't happened to pass by just then. They jumped him and then started booting him and his pals down the quay toward the harbor.

Suddenly whistles were blowing and a horde of white-clubbed and white-hatted militia came charging down the street. Claudia and I were quickly escorted inside. Hidden away in a back room.

The bandage on my eye was one big red blotch. I was writhing with pain and had to go back to the hospital. The detective came back, too, with his little black notebook. He looked like Victor Mature, wore two-tone shoes. He took us home. Dazed and dizzy from sedatives, I fell asleep.

228

Two days later Alexis hesitantly came up to me in the Music Bar. He offered his apologies. I accepted them. He promised he'd take care of the doctor's bill and I kept him to his word, in fact made him pay me four times the bill. Small compensation for damages incurred. He was a good guy. We often made the same chicks. He still couldn't get over the fact that I'd once gone off with the only chick he'd ever loved. A Brazilian countess, Flaminia.

The next day I saw him on the street. On crutches, one of his legs in a cast, one of his eyes all bandaged up and Band-Aids all over his face. I honestly didn't know how it had happened, though I had my suspicions. The fishermen weren't too fond of him. As a matter of fact none of the Spaniards were. The night of the fight the fishermen whispered in my ear that they'd get him some day. That "some day" had obviously already come and gone. For months Alexis walked around with a sore eye.

We bought a slender young Ibicenco puppy from the dog catcher. Named her Zuef after the Egyptian goddess. As soon as Claudia and I had finally gotten used to the slim and delicate creature, she had to be put out of her misery. She coughed all day and all night and her nose was too wet. Distemper. I asked a guy from the Portico to finish her off.

Claudia went along on the back of the motorcycle to the open field where the Spaniard killed Zuef with a well-aimed shot between the eyes. Claudia met me at the bar of the Portico.

"How did it go with Zuef?" I asked.

"What a sight!" she said. "PAANG! and she was dead. Nothing left of her head but one big hole."

229

Once when I was thirteen I bashed the hell out of a ragman who man-handled his old gray mare every day. Everybody was afraid of him. Not me. One day when he was whipping his skin-and-bones horse and happened to hit me instead, I dragged him down off his cart, yanked a piece of iron out of his wagon, and let him have it right on his head. A nice sound, that dull thud. Like hitting a pumpkin with a poker.

230

We were stone broke. Claudia had to eat because she was pregnant. Her beautiful belly grew bigger every day. We left the house in the morning to avoid running into the landlord—a cranky old man with dark glasses who rented us the house. The town was so tiny we ran into him every day anyway in one of the many narrow streets. Or he'd come to the Portico at mealtime and find us there. I knew how to handle him.

"Mañana," I said. "Eleven o'clock on the dot. I'll have the money ready."

We made damn sure we weren't home the next morning at eleven o'clock on the dot. We worked this racket for weeks. I simply didn't have the money. At the restaurant we ate on credit. We were the best

195

customers, made the most racket. We got everything we wanted on credit. Even cigarettes. All the liquor we wanted at the Music Bar, all we wanted to eat at the restaurant.

I even bought my new dog Provo on credit. The German co-owner of the bar had a big black German shepherd who'd just had puppies fathered by a blue-snouted Moroccan shepherd. A so-called blue-nose. He let me pick out the one I wanted. I picked the cutest—also it turned out, the dumbest. At first I called him God Damn It. After a while I changed his name to Provo. When I shouted his name on the street, loud, because he hadn't learned to obey yet, all sorts of characters in short pants, knee socks, flowery sportshirts, and peeling noses looked up at me, bewildered and surprised. In their buttonholes they proudly wore our national flower, the carnation, or little red-white-and-blue Dutch flags.

We fed our little blue-nose the best steaks we could lay hands on, much to the displeasure of the restaurant owners and the other customers. Spaniards aren't particularly fond of animals.

I once threw a bone at a big fat greasy Spaniard who was enjoying an elaborate outdoor feast with his overstuffed, tight-assed family. He was teasing a cat with a chunk of meat—a little alley cat, one of the many strays that rummage around behind cafés and restaurants and are habitually harassed and tormented by the natives. When the cat had finally inched up closer and, hesitant and scared, tried to take a bite, the fat Spaniard stabbed it in the head with a fork he'd kept concealed in his other hand. Joyous roars of laughter from Fatso, from his whole damn family. Two young girls—one a real looker, the other not bad, probably his daughters— were practically popping their bras with laughter. Impulsively, I grabbed the big T-bone steak lying on my dish and hit the bull's-eye—the thick back of Fatso's neck. The whole family swiveled around and glared at me. With a withering look the two girls stuck up their noses at me as if I didn't exist. How could I possibly spoil their fun? Peculiar people, the Spaniards. Peeping Toms too.

Every time we spent an evening at home we heard soft footsteps out in front of the door, could hear somebody trying to open the transom far enough to look in. Peeping Toms were peering through the narrow crack, hoping to see Claudia walking around without any clothes on. Finally I couldn't take it any more. I shut the transom and locked all the windows. It got broiling hot in our place. And still the fumbling went on out in front of our door.

Sometimes I went out at night. Took a walk with Provo. Every time I opened the door one of the peekaboos darted like lightning down the stairs. Head over heels. They'd discovered a new peephole. The keyhole. The big old-fashioned kind!

Things had gone far enough. I took my loaded rifle—the one Claudia and I used in rifle tournaments (Claudia often won, she was damn good) —and when I heard shuffling in front of the door and was sure somebody was on the other side of the wood (I could hear heavy breathing and, above the murmuring sound of the sea, somebody's fingernails scratching against wood), I poked the barrel into the keyhole and pulled the trigger. I heard a terrible scream. Howls and yowls of pain. I gave the Peeping Tom, the Keyhole Voyeur, a few seconds getaway time, then opened the door. Not a soul in sight. I decided to let it go at that. But I would keep a sharp look-out for somebody with a bandaged eye. There was only the playboy, Alexis.

231

Of course my creditors and I hoped the paintings I was working on would make a big hit like my other exhibit. I hoped to sell a lot and make a lot. There was one hitch. A lot of Dutch artists, smelling cash in the air, flocked down to the island like vultures in the wake of all the publicity I got when I'd gone back to Holland. All eager for a piece of the easy life. Aside from the fact that these brown-nosers went in droves to the gullible gallery owner and told him I was their best friend and that I'd sent them over to see him, they also imitated my style. I made "action" paintings. Suddenly they were all making "action" paintings. Et cetera.

Two weeks before my exhibition was scheduled to open, another Dutch painter was giving private showings prior to the opening of *his* exhibition. A small-town boy from Twente with a full-time witch for a wife. An ex-nurse who'd worked for the Salvation Army. Vacationers who brought their Dutch-licensed cars over on the boat to Ibiza soon wished they hadn't. Seeing those tell-tale plates from Holland, Nursey accosted them in the middle of the street. She'd practically drag them out of their cars and over to the studio. They rarely escaped without first having bought at least one "work of art."

Nursey and Hubby weren't exactly wild about us. But they invited us over. I promptly ate up all their cheese (Edam, brought all the way from Holland to impress prospective buyers), stuffed myself on their little canned sausages, and drank up their entire supply of beer.

"Good food makes safe drivers," I explained between belches.

It was a broiling hot summer day and, after all, we were broke. Claudia's popularity dipped fast when she enthusiastically exclaimed, "Why, these look just like Jan's paintings. Are they yours, Jan?"

To top things off, Provo strolled across some still-wet water colors, much to the distress of both painter and wife, then scratched around, unexpectedly lifted one leg and peed smack on a canvas. The couple concluded we must be anti-Art and we were politely but urgently asked to leave.

"You know," I said to Claudia when we were out on the street, "yellow was just what that picture needed."

232

After dodging our cross-eyed landlord, I started up the Silver Monster. I'd picked up the Monster in Barcelona after prying some money loose from Holland (not from the Welfare Department). Crossed over on the night boat, came back in the morning. Some of the island's Korean war vets knew a thing or two about Harleys. Used to ride them straight through huts, in one wall and out the other. With their help, Silver Monster was soon as good as new. It was easily the biggest motorcycle ever to land on the island since Hannibal threw one together in his spare time for rounding up elephants.

In the meantime Claudia's belly grew and grew. The baby was starting to live. Sometimes she'd wake me up in the middle of the night.

"Listen," she whispered, "he's kicking."

I wanted to say, "Well then, kick it back," because I don't like to be waked up at night. But I listened with one ear pressed to her warm belly that hopped up and down. Until one time the little dear gave me a good hard kick in the ear. My bad ear too. It had gotten an inflammation when I was a Navy frogman and stayed under too long. That was the last time I'd ever listen to that brat. With my ears tingling and my head bursting, I settled down to sleep again next to Claudia. I couldn't. It took a whole tube of aspirin to calm my ear down so I could sleep again.

We went to a quiet peaceful beach where nobody ever came.

Ibiza was big. Before I stepped off the boat, I'd always thought it was a tiny island, that I could trot from one end to the other every night before turning in. Great sport. I know a nut who jogs through the woods at six every morning.

Claudia's bikinis were too small for her now. They hardly covered her bush. So we swam in the nude. Delicious feeling. Claudia had a beautiful mature body. Now that her belly had swelled up she looked very grown up. Plump and filled out.

We dried out on the hot rocks. And when we were dry, made love. Her enormous buttocks rolled back and forth on the hot stone. Basking in the sun we dozed off. Until we suddenly felt something slithering across our bodies. Lizards who climbed you like a mountain. If you caught them, they shed their tails and scurried away. They reminded me of the monsters in *King Kong*.

At sunset we headed back to the city. I parked Silver Monster on the pier under our house and we strolled hand in hand down the Paseo. At the stand we stopped to buy some pinchitas—a kind of *sateh* minus the peanut sauce—sharp peppery chunks of meat on a skewer, then had a glass of Montepetillo, the famous Montepetillo wine from Montepetillo.

Life certainly was a ball. The only things we missed in Spain were croquettes, fresh herring, and real Gelderland salami. I mean the real stuff from Gelderland. They had salami in Spain. But not Gelderland salami. More like Nomansland salami. Gooey orange salami made out in the street in front of the butcher's store in a sort of cannon. Grimy orange flour with chunks of blubber tied up in a pig's gut. The butcher's specialty. People came from all over the place to buy his orange salami.

I remember one afternoon when I went to the butcher I saw this gray-haired old guy stumbling along followed by a gang of curious island-ers. He'd come all the way from Canada in a boat that sank on the way. Took him three years to get to Ibiza. Just for that orange salami. Wife dead, kids dead, everything kaput, and he'd even lost his passport. The butcher hadn't had a tribute like this since he'd emigrated from Israel. Neither had his orange salami.

When he first opened up his salami stand he'd found some sacks of orange powder in the basement of a former paint factory. He tasted it as soon as he saw it. It was tasteless, so he used it to brighten up his ground slabs of fat and dead cats. It was this that had made him famous.

"Sammy," he'd say to himself, rubbing his hands with glee, "you did all right by yourself."

He graciously took a piece of salami out from under the counter, a piece that had been returned by various customers four times that month. The salami had gone bad, they said. It stank. Fooey, he thought, those nudniks, those goyim. What do they know about salami?

The old gray-haired Canadian crawled up on his knees, hoisted his body from the sawdust-covered floor, grabbed the piece of salami from the tip of the butchers' knife, gobbled it up, and dropped dead.

"Oi," said the butcher. "The Lord of Hosts has wrought a miracle!"

He pointed his knife to the ceiling. The pious on-lookers nodded meekly. Clearly, the Lord had taken the wretched gray-haired Canadian back into his Arms. The Lord had been kind. He had granted the old man his last wish, had let him taste a fine piece of salami. The real orange salami of Popperto.

I was one of the butcher's best customers. The store didn't have any doors. You just walked right in. Every evening I walked in with my dog and ordered five pesetas worth of "carne por el perro." I knew he'd have to go way to the back of his shop because he put away all his bones and scraps in the ice box at around six. It took him a long time to find a few bones for five pesetas. Which gave me plenty of time to select a nice steak from the meat on the counter or the chopping block and slip it in between my shirt and bare belly. At night Claudia and I would have a steak and Provo could gnaw on the bones. Usually he got the steak also because it was tough—like it was so tough nothing is tough compared to how tough that steak was. Meat on the island was so bad the good restaurants used to have KLM bring in meat from Holland.

I couldn't put really big steaks in my shirt. Too conspicuous. So I trained Vodka to steal—may he rest in peace. When I went to the butcher, Vodka hung around outside. Outside the place where the door would have been if there had been one. When the butcher went to the bone department I whistled, in came Vodka, and I slipped him the meat I'd picked for that evening's meal. He disappeared immediately. With the meat in his jaws he went straight home. Up two flights of steps, through an alley and there Vodka stood, proud as a peacock in front of the house, the meat on the stairs. Had to be washed off but it made a fine meal.

No sense trying to teach Provo the trick. He was too stupid. I once tried it with a piece of salami. He just gobbled it up. A day later I tried it with a big steak. Gobbled that up too. The next day I decided to try it for the last time. The butcher disappeared into the back of his shop grumbling about meshuga customers bothering him for five pesetas worth of bones. I took a complete leg of lamb off the chopping block. Too big to gobble. Provo eagerly sunk his wolf's teeth into it.

"Ssst! Scram!" I said. "Go home!" and gave him a kick in the ass to help him on his way. He promptly vanished and the butcher came back with a few dry bones in his hands. When he saw the chopping block he started screaming bloody murder. The meat was gone. His leg of lamb. The right buttock of Rosabella, his favorite lamb. Who could have done a thing like that?

"Not me," I said.

"Then who? Who?" he screamed.

"I don't know from nothing," I said in simple Spanish. "But a creep in a black suit and mustache came in just a second ago. Not that I'm trying to say he did it. Far be it from me. God will punish the guilty. Still, as soon as I laid eyes on him I knew he wasn't the kind of guy you can trust."

Just then Provo shot past the store, skidded, turned back, peered inside playfully and in a flash was gone again. The butcher thought he'd seen a mirage.

Suddenly Provo appeared again in the doorway, proudly wagging his tail, his floppy ears standing straight up. Once more the butcher screamed bloody murder.

"Whose dog is that?" he screamed. "Yours?"

"What dog?" I said.

"*That* dog" he screamed, pointing at Provo who dropped the leg of lamb down in front of him and wagged his tail cheerfully across the dusty ground. He was waiting for me to grab for the bone and then race him home.

The butcher bounded over the counter aiming a cleaver at Provo, who immediately tried to pick up the leg. But it was too heavy. He dropped it, then circled around at a safe distance, carefully following the whole scene with his big mischievous eyes. What kind of game was Big Jan playing with the butcher now?

The butcher pointed the cleaver at my belly and said, "That's your dog. You pay for that meat or I'll call the Guardía Civil."

I knew from Federico García Lorca what those guys with the green uniforms and the squashed-in caps could do. So I changed my tune fast.

"Provo, get over here," I said. "You naughty dog!"

I barked commands and pointed to the ground in front of me while the butcher eyed me suspiciously. Provo had the good sense to stay away. So there was nothing else to do except eat that leg of lamb, including Rosabella's right buttock, all by myself since, after all, I'd had to pay four hundred pesetas for it. Claudia had to sell her suede jacket to a girlfriend to raise the money. The beautiful light brown suede jacket I'd bought for next to nothing in Barcelona when I'd gone over to pick up the Monster. Now it was gone for even closer to nothing.

Rosabella's buttock was as tough as they come. After I'd hammered at it for hours with a rolling pin, I put the meat on a chair, sat on it, then bounced on it for another quarter of an hour. The Huns used to tenderize their meat by putting it under their saddles when they went out for a ride. They could have crossed all of Asia without putting a dent in Rosabella.

After an hour of slaving away over a primitive charcoal fire, I tossed the stuff to Provo. He gnawed at it for two weeks. Then I had to sell my motorcycle because he attacked three sheep and finished them off down to the last bite. Once he'd got a taste of mutton, he couldn't get enough.

233

We were invited over to a big party at Formentera. Four pigs were slaughtered for the occasion—Americans celebrating Thanksgiving and not enough turkeys to go around. The pigs were roasted on spits and eaten steaming hot. Early the next morning we took the first boat back to Ibiza, everybody chucking up pigs and wine, including Provo. Some Thanksgiving.

234

After first giving me a lot of bullshit, the gallery owner finally decided to help me out. Put me in charge of publicity for the gallery. Gave me money for supplies and a small salary to live on. The gallery's artistic director was a cute Spanish piece. She painted, too. Ever since I'd given her a lesson with the Special Brush the year before, when I was with Barry, she was after me for a refresher course. She didn't like the fact that I'd brought Claudia along this time. "Still," she said to the gallery owner, "maybe we ought to give Cremer one more chance."

As publicity director I got a slave's wages, had to put up posters announcing exhibitions all over the island, had to hang them up in hotels, nail them up on trees. All over the island. The gallery paid for the Monster's gas, plus not very much. Just enough to allow me to buy art supplies every once in a while.

Naturally I took Claudia and Provo along. The first month we took our work pretty seriously. I slapped the badly printed posters up on windows, trees, and bulletin boards in various big tourist hotels in all the nearby resorts. But our enthusiasm soon wore off. We hung the posters upside down, slapped paste on the walls of first-class hotels, and got chased off. I knew the owners of most cafés on our route so we'd stop in for a little drink and by the end of the day be lushed out of our nuts.

We had to get rid of the posters. Then our work for the day was done. So I nailed forty posters onto one tree, pasted two to a passing donkey and then made off for a shady spot on the patio in Santa Eulalia under the trees. There a delicious bottle of wine helped us slowly doze off. Montepetillo wine, the real Montepetillo wine from Montepetillo.

235

There was only one whore on the island. A colossally fat madam with one tit. She'd lost the other one in a trench somewhere during the Civil War while doing her thing with a general or some other big shot. She spent her evenings behind the bar in the only cathouse in Ibiza. Since she was the only hooker with both licenses A + B + the Yellow Stamp, her place did a landoffice business. Hordes of horny Spaniards stared glassy eyed at that one tit of hers. But though she only had one, it was big enough for five, a tit to remember, a tit to write home about! She kept this enormous boob slung up at an angle under her low-cut dress so the nipple came up for air right under her armpit. A fascinating sight. Still, all things considered, I was well off with Claudia. No monkey business on the side. Not even out of curiosity. I hope the fact that I resisted the one-titted madam didn't do me any serious psychic damage. If she'd had two twats it might have been a different story.

236

Things soon went sour between me and the Spanish painter-cum-artistic director of the gallery. She had a boyfriend, a dried-up fig from Switzerland, a fairy I figured. At least judging by the way he painted. All very abstract. She was having her troubles because he wanted a new exhibition of his own paintings about every two months. It was high time he was discovered, he thought. This led to sparks and whenever they really blew up at each other, she'd start hunting around for me. I was never hard to find. Where the beer keg was, there was Jan. I didn't feel like consoling her though, I'm hip to the kind of mess consoling arty girls like that can get you into. Also I had something better already in Claudia. Besides which, Little Miss Arty had a clitoris the size of a football.

So then she blew up at me. Slowly and very politely I told her exactly what I thought of her painter friend. Insinuated that he'd been trying like mad to lay the two French chicks from Biarritz. Two fabulously wealthy chicks, millionairesses, young, pretty, and sweet. What I didn't mention was that he never got to first base with either of them. I myself had affairs with both of them—at the same time. Out of one, into the other. Very exciting and complicated. Only a genius like me could have got into something like that.

They were close friends. Both of them wanted me and were jealous of each other. They slept together in a room the size of a dance hall. When I slipped out the door after a session with one of them, I had to sneak in through a window to start in on the other one. A feat demanding vast organizational skill and enormous concentration. It worked out fine. The Swiss often helped me without ever knowing it, just by sitting outside in the moonlight chatting romantically with one of them about the stars. He could go on for hours. In French. He came from the French-speaking part of Switzerland. In the meantime I had the other one all to myself.

The girlfriends never told each other about their affair with me.

However, on the pier, shortly before their boat was to leave—it had already sounded its big horn for the second time—it all came out. A hysterical exchange of words in French. One of them sat down on her suitcases and started sobbing her heart out. The other slapped me as hard as she could and then she, too, started bawling. She'd just found an orange crate to sit down on when up stood the other and—whammo!—another slap right in the face.

I'd tried to spare them. I'd spent a lot of time coaching them: "Don't tell your friend about us because I think she's sort of fond of me. Whatever you do, don't tell her we're in love. She might feel left out, the poor kid."

What really pissed me off was that they'd both invited me to go skiing in Biarritz that winter. Two slaps ended all that.

237

I spent my afternoons with the gallery owner. We chatted. About anything and everything. Art, etcetera. Claudia and I enjoyed the delicious sangría. We drank out in the back yard between the tall cacti under big green fig trees. I told him about the coup d'état I was going to carry out to revolutionize the art world. About my "New Directions for the Art World."* He took it all very seriously, compared my plans with Hitler's *Mein Kampf*—also a kind of New Direction. The more sangría I drank the bloodthirstier I got. Before long, I'd developed a whole new manifesto. "Hitler wanted the very same things and he failed," he said indignantly.

Well, he should know.

238

The boat pulled in. I looked up and saw a friend of mine, Pretty Willie, standing at the rail. We sat down at the sidewalk café to have a cup of coffee and Jopie started telling me all kinds of crazy stories about what he'd been up to lately. Suddenly he stopped and waved. I looked around to see who he was waving at. Whatever Pretty Willie laid eyes on was generally worth looking at. My mother always said you have to look for the beautiful things in life. What I saw almost made my heart stand still, from sheer shock. Pretty Willie was waving at a broad, motioning her to come over and join us at our table.

I couldn't believe my eyes.

She was a horrible freak with a big bulge of a head. An American

* *The New Style,* volume 3.

who came up to my armpits. I didn't get it. The notorious cocksman Pretty Willie with a Gnurp? I didn't expect this kind of thing from him. Beautiful women, young or old, they were all the same to Willie. As long as they were loaded.

Besides the fact that the Gnurp had this crazy head, her face was covered with a rash of tiny pimples. Her teeth looked as if they hadn't grown since she was five years old. Just got yellower. Dressed like an over-grown schoolgirl—not even a well-dressed schoolgirl—she had greasy straight hair, a stumpy pair of piano legs, and her nails were bitten down ragged right to the quick. In short, she wasn't beautiful. Not Willie's type at all. He only liked beautiful girls. Or old ones. Or ugly ones.

"What the hell's got into you? I said. "Are you *that* hard up?"

"No," Willie replied, earnestly. "It's a very sad story. I'll tell you about it later."

"Yeah," I said, "I'll bet you will. Those sad stories of yours. God help you. How can you even walk down the street with a thing like that? So Snow White gave one of her Seven Dwarfs the day off—does that mean *you*'ve got to look after it? A real Gnorf, a Gnurp, a Troll. What a spook! I never thought I'd see the day you'd come up with anything like this. God knows, I've seen a lot of freaks in my life, but anything this bad? Never. Why, man, she's an insult to the human race!"

"I'll explain it all later," Willie mumbled. "You just don't under-stand."

When he actually patted the girl . . . excuse me, the Gnurp's chubby knee, I practically vomited.

"Hey," I warned him, "You don't still believe in fairy tales, do you, Willie? I mean, you don't think this toad is going to turn into a Beautiful Princess any minute now and make you her one and only heir, do you? The odd thing is," I went right on, "that I don't smell anything. And she must be stinking rich. Otherwise you wouldn't be sitting next to her."

Pretty Willie was obviously embarrassed. He was deep in conversa-tion with the troll and I heard him say he'd walk her back to her hotel. I knew the theory: If the cunt's good, the rest must be good too. But I couldn't believe Pretty Willie believed in that line of crap. With him, I figured, the theory probably was: If the money's good, the cunt must be good too. And I burst out laughing.

> Cunt is cunt.
> Come again?
> Cunt is cunt said the farmer
> as the farmer fucked his pig.
> Cunt is cunt said the farmer
> as he sank into his wife.

Pretty Willie and his dwarf took off soon after. He chivalrously carried her suitcases, and was back about fifteen minutes later.

Before he could even sit down, I said, "Come off it, man. I don't want any more of your bullshit. What are you doing with that miscarriage?"

He told me a moving story. Genuinely moving. I had to swallow all my sarcastic cracks. The American girl had come over to him on the boat, they started talking. She had a fatal disease. Diabetes or something like that. Anyway, they gave her only two more months to live. The doctors had lost all hope. So she'd sold everything she ever had and come to Europe to get the most out of these last few precious days of life.

It was really awful, I thought, to be just in your twenties and off you go. Still, for a girl like that, maybe it was the best thing that could happen to her.

"Willie," I said, "you've just risen in my esteem. At least you've got a heart. You're a good boy. Still," I advised him, "if I were you I'd take along a nice thick newspaper. At least you can cover up that head."

I was glad I hadn't been on that boat. What if I had been the chosen one to screw that monster? The thought alone turned my stomach.

Pretty Willie did his duty. Went above and beyond the call of duty. He screwed her twice. Then he fled the island. At any rate, he'd done a good deed.

The troll, however, stayed alive. She haunted the island for months. Always coming on with the same damn story. Two years later I ran into her in Paris. With a good-looking guy walking at her side bashfully, looking everywhere else except at that pumpkin head and pimply face. Maybe medical science had worked wonders after all and had postponed her date of departure.

Six years later I saw her in New York. One afternoon on Madison Avenue. Arm in arm with a good-looking blond Romeo. He looked as if he was on his way to the electric chair. Puffing along beside him on her two-ton piano legs, she looked pleased as punch.

239

One afternoon Claudia came home and said, "An American artist wants to paint my portrait. I told him I'd have to ask you first. A nice guy, with a beard and sandals. He draws very well." I was stunned.

"WHAT? Have you gone stark mad? I wouldn't dream of it. I don't want you running around with—with a horrible, dirty, filthy, contemptible, untrustworthy, seedy—with an artist! The scum of the earth. Naturally he wants to paint your portrait up in his room, doesn't he?"

"Yes," she said. "He has a room at a boarding house."

"Sure he does," I said. "Look, honey, for the time being you stay right where you are. Don't you dare leave this house," I commanded. "I don't want you fooling around with any hippies."

Claudia started whimpering.

"Well, how can *I* help it if the guy comes over and asks me. Is that *my* fault? I was just sitting there eating. And Provo was there, too."

"Yeah, sure he was," I said. "I bet you sat there staring at the bastard. You think a beard's the greatest, don't you, huh? Well, you're not going to leave this house. And if you do leave, you can leave forever. I don't want any playing around. Get me?"

It turned out later he wasn't even a painter. Just sketched and drew in his spare time. He was a good-natured broad-shouldered American who'd worked on the highway patrol in Grand Canyon for nearly a year, saved up some money and lit out for Paris where he'd studied at the Académie la Grande Chaumière where Zatopek was teaching, then set out to take a look around Europe.

240

Living without money was getting pretty rough. There wasn't much we could do about it. Still, something had to happen soon. Our credit was still good at the Portico. Since we'd run up a big bill there anyway, we stuffed when we went there and always walked out with a basketful or more. We took everything. Sausages, cheese, meat, bottles of wine. Everything. Every day. The owner watched us with diminishing joy. We owed the biggest debt and made the most racket.

I ordered pancakes.

"Sorry," the waiter said. "All out of pancakes."

"What? Well then, make some, dammit! I want pancakes every day, understand?"

I brought friends along who ordered tremendous meals. I'd sign for the bill, they'd pay me back once we got outside, and I was back in business. That way, anyway, I always had some loose change. Meanwhile I worked my ass off on the pictures I had to have ready for the exhibition. It was coming up in a few weeks. I hoped to make a fortune off my pictures. Then be out of debt. For a while, at least. The older I get, the more debts I run up. "A man is worth double his debts," as an old saw made famous by Bobby Baker goes.

The studio in the peña, the casbah of Ibiza, was about thirty yards from the public shithole where the whole neighborhood came to squat. Near the well where we had to draw up our water in earthenware jugs.

A very Moorish scene. The people didn't even look like Spaniards. Years ago Moorish pirates had hung out in our neighborhood and it was their offspring that lived in those little clay huts. I always felt like I was in North Africa when I went to the well. If the wind blew our way, all the houses along our street stank of shit for days. Even the smell of charcoal burning out in front of the house couldn't drive that stink away.

In spite of being broke we lived the good life. The only trouble was, there's not a hell of a lot you can do without money. I had my hopes set on the exhibition. I'd painted some good pictures. I'd also made some sculptures in iron. At the blacksmith shop near the bull ring I welded, hammered, and worked like a madman. I made my "La Hora del Morir" there. Now a national monument in Ibiza. A big round globe, like a half moon. More than a yard in diameter with a convex rusty surface. I welded a huge knife onto it plus hundreds of bolts, nuts, clasps, nails, screws, and rusty sheet metal. With the oxyacetylene torch, I improvised on the forms and gave the whole thing a nice golden brown color. A handsome piece of sculpture. Whatever Cremer does, Cremer does well. It made a big hit. I gave it to the Portico as collateral.

Every Sunday we begged, borrowed, or stole tickets for the corrida. Claudia only went once. After that she stayed at home. I loved her like never before that first time she saw a bull get killed. The specialty in those particular restaurants right after a bullfight was bull kidneys and bull balls with mushrooms.

Somebody told me about a *finca* I could rent for practically nothing. A huge, rambling farmhouse about three miles outside the city of Ibiza. Two enormous rooms with thick walls, at least two feet thick. Upstairs, three rooms with connecting doors and a covered balcony. A gigantic kitchen with open fires to cook on. A hacienda around the *finca* where you could put out tables and chairs. I rented the place as soon as I saw it.

Nearby there was another big farm. We got all our food there—mainly eggs. No meat. There was also a well nearby with a blindfolded horse trudging around in circles pulling the lever that watered the fields. Around the house an immense plain, acres of almond trees and fig trees in full bloom, lemon trees and orange trees, pine trees and ordinary trees, cactus and shoulder-high plants. A true paradise—for people who want to live in peace.

There wasn't any electricity. We used candles and gas lamps to light our rooms. The place only cost about nine dollars a month, a ridiculous price, even if we didn't have any money to pay it with. The farmer offered us eggs and slabs of bacon if we'd look after the horse. Let it loose every once in a while, feed it twice a day. We immediately agreed. The first time I unstrapped her, I got up on her, bony as she was. The horse trotted happily to the pasture, but still going in circles. Dizzy as a wall-eyed lizard, I jumped off into the sweet smelling grass. Neighboring farmers often came over to visit our farmer neighbor. They all watched us like hawks, sometimes for hours on end. Friends of ours from Ibiza came and stayed for supper. All we had to do was go out to the garden to find everything we needed. Artichokes, grapes, mushrooms, *scorzonera,* cabbages, enormous melons, potatoes, green peppers, celery, tomatoes, garlic, et cetera. So we could cook up a terrific stew.

I brought out all our junk from the city. We wanted to stay there for good. Claudia and I had each other to ourselves. We were happy. I worked all day in the big room which I turned into a studio, while Claudia sun-bathed naked up on the roof, concealed from view by four low walls built to catch rain—when and if it ever did rain. At night we cooked our supper, or at least I did, and ate in the dim light of a gas lamp outside among the chirping crickets and the sounds of the countryside. It took a while to get used to the quiet out there. I didn't really trust those Spanish farmers. For three nights I didn't sleep at all. Although we were only about three miles from downtown Ibiza, I felt we were stranded way out in the wilderness. If I stood on top of the chimney—a funny chimney capped with two tiles leaning against each other like a tent—I could see Ibiza in the distance. I was homesick. All day long I stood there on top of that chimney. I'd had to leave the motorcycle behind because the battery was shot again. The evening of the third day I couldn't stand it any more. The silence, the darkness, the sounds.

Provo was a good watchdog. When we went outside for supper in the evenings we had to keep fishing beetles out of our food. Claudia kept stepping on toads and yelping with terror. At any strange rustling in the bushes, Provo would jump up furious, perk his ears in the direction of the sound (brave dog, I thought), bark once, then shoot like an arrow through the beaded curtain into the house, his tail between his legs, and up the stairs. You could always find him under the bed in the very last room in the house. No amount of persuasion and no juicy bone could get him out of there. You had to drag him.

After walking for hours (there weren't any busses), we finally made it into the city, staggered into the Music Bar and tanked up like crazy.

Claudia adjusted to country life easily. I, a city boy, couldn't. Downtown Ibiza was the most peaceful outdoor life I ever wanted to know. I rented a motorcycle again. If I wanted to get into town, it was no sweat at all. We invited everybody we met to come out and see us so we had plenty of visitors. The farmers found this very intriguing. Dozens of them hung around our *finca* day and night. Peering through the bushes. I borrowed a rifle from an American friend of mine and at night I lay in bed with Claudia on one side, the rifle on the other. Staring at the ceiling. I didn't shut my eyes once. When it started getting light I finally fell asleep. There was a surplus of food. As far as you could see, there was this dim blue glow of ripening grapes.

One day a friend and I went out hunting. The hills were swarming with rabbits and other small game. I tucked my pants into my boots like a real hunter, slung the rifle over my shoulder, and started wading off into the scrub. My American friend was the beater, whacking the bushes and trees with a stick. Provo followed us eagerly, completely devoid of every hunting instinct even though his father had served in the Foreign Legion. We didn't see or find anything. Once a fat hare popped out from the bushes, sat up and looked us over from head to foot, but by the time I'd swung my rifle around and aimed—slowly, to give it a chance to clear the hell out—it was gone. We started back home. At any rate we'd enjoyed the scenery. I had visions of Indians and Eskimos who, whenever their wives yell, "We're fresh out of meat, honey," slip off to the woods to pick up their supper. The Spaniards ate little birds. They shot whole flocks of them down out of the trees. We were cutting across our neighbor's yard where he and his cronies were enjoying their afternoon pipe, when suddenly I saw a big plump bird on a branch of the tree, aimed, squeezed the trigger, and—BLAAM!—down it came. Then everybody started howling and bawling. I'd shot a dove. La Paloma! The symbol of peace. The holy bird. I felt sorry about it, too. Claudia could hardly believe we'd really brought something back. But she refused to clean the dove. We opened a can of corned beef instead. We conducted services for the dove after supper. Dug a grave, laid it in, covered it up, planted a cross, sent up a prayer. After all, it hadn't asked to be born any more than we had.

241

The roar of an airplane above the island made me glance up at the metallic blue sky and follow the silver specter. I wondered where it was going, who was on board. In those days the airport at Ibiza was just one big sandy plain. The runway had been stamped flat by human feet. When it rained it turned to mud and no planes could take off or land.

I once flew from the island to Barcelona. On the way to the flying coffin—a single-motored old wreck—we passed the remains of two airplane crashes that had never been cleaned up, just shoved over to the side of the runway. We took off, just missing a couple of looming boulders, leaving behind an enormous cloud of brown dust. The plane was a pretty ramshackle affair. Halfway to Barcelona a door suddenly flew open so everybody had to hang onto his seat for dear life. The trip took an hour.

The whole crew was drunk. They were the relief crew, standing by for the regular crew. I sat next to their table at the airport canteen. There was a two-hour delay so they had plenty of time to booze it up. The biggest lush, a heavy-set guy with a pencil-thin mustache, had to be carried out and slapped awake when it was time to leave. He was the pilot.

242

Claudia's mother tried twice to get her to come back to Holland. The American impressario had written Mama that he was going to be in Europe for a while and would like to see Claudia again. Claudia and I had a furious fight about it which, of course, was just what the old bitch wanted.

Claudia was pregnant and I said. "Look, I've had enough of this shit. You keep sending that woman postcards and letters and every time things get a little rough you send off a ten-page, full-scale, tear-jerking report. If you want to go back to Holland so bad, go ahead and do it. If you don't know how to deal with a little problem now and then, clear out. Living with a genius just isn't the easiest thing in the world and that's all there is to it."

Claudia didn't want to leave. She loved me. She was crazy about me, but I was worn out, competely bushed. Like a watchdog I had to keep my eyes on her every minute of the day and night. I had to take her with me wherever I went. I had to stand up for her. I lived, thought, and worked for two people. Former girlfriends of hers, who spent their summer vacation on the island catching up on their love life—in a different bed every night, growing older every day—tried to turn her against me. The situation got out of hand. I couldn't handle it any more. I knew she didn't want to have anything to do with her mother any more, but her mother seemed to have a satanic hold on her. She was still scared of that woman, scared silly.

After one fight, when we still lived in the house on the cliff, I walked out and slammed the door. I came back hours later and Claudia proudly showed me a doll she'd made. I'd told her to do something, anything she wanted. She could use all my paints and brushes, which she did. She used to make fantastic collages and drawings. She had talent. Anyway, this doll was made out of all kinds of pieces of material, colored and checked, the face made out of orange wool. My heart skipped a beat. She had sewn a

211

tiny crown onto the doll's head. A crown of gold. Cut out of the Badge of Courage I'd got in the Navy. To wear with full dress. It was the only souvenir I had of those days. I used to show it to everybody with a kind of cynical pride. Claudia had fished it out from the bottom of a trunk, taken it out of its leather case. She couldn't understand why I was so angry. It was things like that that led to misunderstandings.

Claudia was an introvert. She was afraid to show her emotions. She'd been beaten up too often. Just after Vodka died and I was looking for her to get the key to the house so I could lie down—I was feeling wiped out—she smiled when she saw me, a very cheerful smile. I didn't get it. Hadn't it made any impression on her at all that he'd plunged to his death? When I told an old friend of mine about Vodka falling out the window, hadn't he immediately asked, "Where was Claudia? What was she doing? You don't think maybe she pushed him?" But that was impossible. If she'd done that I would have pushed her out too. It was because I found her behavior so strange that the big misunderstanding arose.

Once I asked Claudia, "Why were you smiling like that when I got back from burying Vodka? Had you just forgotten all about it or didn't you give a damn?"

"I smiled because I knew how miserable you felt and wanted to cheer you up. I thought, if I start crying now, he'll feel even worse."

I was mad about Claudia, even after all our rough times together. One day though she was gone. After one of our blow-ups a friend of hers named Marie Antoinette (a tall pale freckled girl, ex-housewhore for a culturally oriented brewery) told her she shouldn't put up with the way I treated her any more. That I was always scolding her but never said a nice word. She helped Claudia pack her bags after Mama-bitch had sent money for the fare back—Claudia's own money since her mother had pawned all of Claudia's jewelry and possessions. Although she was a prosperous business woman, Mama wouldn't spend a penny on Claudia. Never had and never would. So I came back to an empty house. I felt awfully lonely. Abandoned and deserted. I knew she couldn't have left the island. The boat didn't leave till the next day.

She'd left a note: "Dear Jan, I love you like nobody else in the world. I don't want to leave you. But I've got to. I'm just keeping you from your work. I'll always be yours. It'll be better this way. I love you. Please come and see me when I have your baby."

I cried a bit but stayed put inside the house. If I went out I'd either run into her or start looking for her. I jumped up when somebody knocked on the door. My heart pounded with joy. Looking as nonchalant as I could, I slowly opened the door. It was Marie Antoinette. She'd come to pick up a few things.

212

"Where's Claudia?"

She wouldn't tell me. Thought it would be better for both of us if Claudia went back to Holland. We were too much in love to get along with each other. In the meantime she, Marie Antoinette, would move in to console me. I managed to squeeze out of her that Claudia was staying at the hotel near the Air Terminal, waiting for the bus to the airport which would come in a few hours.

I ran to the hotel and found out at the desk which room she was in. I knocked on the door and she opened it, happy and grateful. First I cussed her out, told her maybe it wouldn't be a bad idea if she finally did get the hell out. Her sad eyes looked at me inquiringly. I was only playing a game. I was wildly in love with this girl. She sat on the bed, trying to hold back the welled-up tears of joy. We made up. I promised her I would stop tearing up her clothes.

"But don't you understand," I said, "that everything you wear, everything you have, belongs to your past? All I want you to wear is things that come from now and me. As soon as I get some money I'll buy you anything you want and we'll throw the other junk away. Why don't you ever wear those dresses I designed for you?"

I also promised I wouldn't hit her any more. Sometimes I felt so completely helpless I had to hit out. It was when I was feeling most vulnerable that I started slapping her, punching her, kicking her suitcases to pieces, tearing her clothes up. Just because I felt so powerless. I knew Fate had brought us together, that neither of us would ever know a love like this again. I felt like a tiger cub chained and caged before he's had a chance to prowl the jungle. They used to call me "Jan with the itchy hands." I couldn't help it if I hit her. As soon as I'd done it I knew it was wrong. That I would only hurt Claudia. Hurt myself even more. I did it anyway.

Sometimes she was unbelievably stubborn. Not on purpose. She just wasn't interested in what anybody else wanted. I didn't have the patience to deal with this. She was also terribly jealous—even of my dogs. Which often led to violent arguments. It wasn't that she didn't like animals. She protected Zuef, the sweet little bitch I gave her, like a mother protects her weakest child. It only led to sorrow. The dog had an incurable disease.

Claudia's one of those people who've been knocked around by society so long they don't know which end is up any more. By a society that always knows better and is supposed to watch over little lost children. Her whole life, anything she ever wanted she couldn't have. Either somebody grabbed it away or it went smash all by itself. Inside of her was a big chaos of pent-up sadness, anxiety, and insecurity. I knew all about

213

it. I could feel it. I suffered from the same thing myself. But I didn't let it get me down. She did. At any rate she was resigned to it. She was too sensitive to rise up and rebel. Day in and day out I tried to talk sense into her. She knew I was right. She agreed. She kept trying to break away from her fears yet kept crawling back into her shell. I was too young to play the analyst bit. The best I could do was control my temper. Sometimes I couldn't even do this and then all hell broke loose once again. Both of us were searching for "happiness" and "love"—two words that I begin to think only belong in a lexicon of archaic expressions.

Her girlfriend Marie Antoinette intimidated her, brainwashed her, and convinced her that she was only getting in my way, that the only reason I didn't kick her out was that I pitied her, that it was obvious I was only waiting for her to pack up and go, that I didn't want her, didn't even like her. Couldn't she see that? Was she blind?

"Dear sweet Claudia," I said, "do you really think I don't want you? Do you think I'd sleep with you one night if I didn't want to? Don't you think I'd have kicked you out long ago if I'd wanted to? Baby or no baby? Ibiza or Vladivostok, if I didn't want you, you wouldn't be here."

"But," she said softly, "Marie Antoinette said. . . ."

"Claudia," I said "it's always the other people who know what's best for you, who know what you want, who are so fucking eager to tell you what to do. But you are you. You have to live your life. I want to help you but I can't do it alone. You have to learn to help yourself. Now come on," I said, "put on your coat. We're going home."

I picked up her bags and she followed me, smiling happily. When I was just about to open the door she suddenly hugged me and whispered in my ear, "I was so scared you didn't want to see me any more. I was so glad when you came to get me. I don't ever want to live without you."

We got the money back for the ticket—enough to cover a few nights out on the town and a bottle of cognac. The rest I used to calm down some creditors, and for a beautiful present for Claudia.

243

Everybody was convinced I was expecting money from America. That kept a lot of people from showing their fangs too openly. The magic words were "check from America." Every morning I went down to the post office to ask if the check from America had arrived yet. This went on for months. Or I would go to the bank and ask the same thing. Ibiza is a small island. Word got around fast. I never missed a day.

Sometimes I walked into the post office and shouted to the guy at the window where a long line of people was waiting, "Alfredo, my check from America come in yet?" Of course not, because what fool in America would ever send me a check? Still, I don't know how I would have survived without that check that never came.

My check from America was something people believed in like they believe two and two is four. Gossip and exaggeration helped the legend grow. Somebody once complained about how much money I owed him. One of the bystanders happened to have been in the post office that morning when I came in to ask about the check. A bartender once said something to a customer about that Cremer who was months behind with his bills and didn't have a cent to his name. And one of the customers, who happened to be a bank clerk, said, "Oh, but he's expecting money from America. Comes in to ask about it every day." In this way I could get as much credit as I wanted. If anybody objected, all I had to do was utter the magic words.

244

Late at night Claudia and I would go by the bakery near the fortress wall. We'd buy a bagful of cookies—crisp and fresh, delicious—or a warm loaf of bread and eat it at home with fried eggs or a tortilla.

One night we were roaring down the path back to the farmhouse. A winding path about a foot wide that twisted between boulders and rocky ledges for hundreds of yards, a real country path I could take fast with my eyes closed. Since Claudia was pregnant I was taking it easy that night. Suddenly something glittered in front of me. I tromped on the brakes and stood there pressed up against a wire stretched across the road between two trees. Right at my throat. If I'd been going any faster or hadn't seen the wire, we both would have been headless. I broke off the wire on one side and we rode home on the lookout for any other surprises.

We often heard strange noises at night. One evening I went into town alone. To do some shopping. Claudia wanted to stay home. When I came in Claudia almost bashed my brains in with a hammer. She'd heard somebody fumbling at the door and had almost unbolted the door thinking maybe I'd forgotten something. She'd asked who was there. No answer. It gave her the creeps and Claudia can be very emotional. She'd put the hammer within easy reach and gone back to reading *Elle* and *Marie Claire*.

After the wire incident I decided not to take any chances and never to leave Claudia alone at home again. Very early the next morning I stole back to where the wire had been stretched across the road. The wire was gone. All that was left was the little piece on one of the trees, up to where I had broken it. I took it to the police station that afternoon. They couldn't do anything about it. Somebody had to be wounded or killed before they could step in. They weren't surprised though.

"You've got to look at it this way," the police chief said. "The country folks around here are very primitive. Where you're living, three miles from here, the farmers don't come to the city more than maybe once a year. There are people here, old people, who've never been off the island in their lives. People like that—why do you have anything to do with them anyway?"

As a matter of fact, why did I? A bunch of ignorant old hicks who thought I must be the devil or something, who'd never seen their own wives naked, and then suddenly all those cute chicks start running around in bikinis on my rooftop. The farmer sometimes came over to bring eggs and complain about Provo eating another of his chickens. He brought his son along, a shrimp of a kid. When I turned on my transistor and Franco's voice boomed out at us, the farmer took off his straw hat and stood at attention. The eggs smashed to the floor. After the speech there was music. The shrimp started howling hysterically and the farmer had to take him home. The kid had never heard any music before except for bird twitters and cricket chirps.

I borrowed a Luger from Korean Paul (an American making his way around the world in a sturdy old yacht). I wore it under my belt, hidden by my shirt, loaded. I didn't use the safety catch at night. The gun slept with me. I thought, if those yokels try any more funny business at least I'll help a few of them on their way to heaven.

245

As a simple city boy I didn't find getting used to life among the birds and the bees and bushes and trees any snap. I came down with a bad case of paranoia. Behind every bush I saw the enemy, behind every tree a division of hicks lying in wait for me. More than once I emptied my Luger into the shrubbery.

We decided to go back to the city. We moved into the biggest and most expensive hotel, the Montesol. No point in doing things half way. Naturally we took the most expensive room. If you took a cheaper room or haggled over the price, people would start to wonder. We had delicious sandwiches sent upstairs. Ate in the dining room. Mealy soup with lumps, waxy potatoes, sick peas, and cardboard meat. To pick up some quick cash, I periodically ordered a few bottles of whisky, slipped them in my pockets, and sold them out on the street. I also ordered cigarettes by the carton. There was a flourishing black market for tobacco and cigarettes. Anything from Chesterfields to Mary Janes.

246

The big day finally came. My fantastic paintings looked even more fantastic up on the gallery walls. The tremendous success of my last exhibition was still fresh in the memory of the island regulars. My new stunt had been the talk of the town for weeks before the opening.

The gallery was packed. Among the gay art lovers I noticed swarms of creditors drinking to my success with hope in their eyes. And I drank to them.

To make a long story short, the exhibition was a great commercial success. Not for Jan though. The gallery owner screwed me so cleverly that all I wound up with was two packs of Ideales, a bottle of Spanish cognac, and a hangover.

junkies' paradise

247

Friends—close friends—came to the island that summer. Dutch intellectuals: Brains, a guy who'd built up a fantastic reputation as a Man of
Letters without having written a single poem; Conrad Bamzaai, who'd
pasted on a false mustache to match his goatee. Just temporarily. He'd
burned off his own mustache while lighting a cigarette on his mother's gas
stove. ("Otherwise my Ibizan fans wouldn't recognize me," Conrad explained.) They were accompanied by Norman, the poet-journalist from
Zeeland who'd written some nice articles about me in the paper he worked
for, and who, in turn, was accompanied by his wife Gonnie, a robust
blonde nymph. A girl who'd met Norman who at that time was just starting out on one of the local papers. They fell in love. Et cetera.

I was delighted to see them at the pier. They'd written they'd be
coming. I'd made up my mind to be their guide, maybe pick up some cash.
Claudia and I had spent hours studying possible solutions to the financial
fix we were in. After my exhibition turned out to be a financial flop (for
me, anyway) my creditors began leaning on me. Hard. Even threatened
to take me to court and God knows what else.

In the meantime I decided to send Claudia back   Holland. She
could live there for at least a month on the money I'd ␣nt to all sorts
of shady characters before we left—that is, if they would only pay up. I'd
give her a few paintings to take along to sell to art collectors. Besides
which, since we'd decided to spend the rest of our lives together, she had
to get officially divorced. Before I could marry her we had to have the
divorce papers. And of course the baby had to be called Cremer. Another
thing that complicated matters was the fact that if my creditors wanted to
get really tough they could keep me from leaving the island, until I paid
up. Keep Claudia from leaving, too.

First we needed money for Claudia's fare. We fixed up a place in
Holland where she could stay for a while anyway. At Anton Kotshut's, an
energetic freeloader and con-man from Zwolle, a so-called actor who'd
slept on our floor for months and eaten us out of house and home. Until

218

he met up with a rich American Gnurp whom he wanted to take off to Mexico and marry.

"You can live in my house in Holland," he offered in a fit of generosity. "This broad is made out of money. We're getting married. I'll show her what freeloading's really like. It'll be years before I get back to Holland."

"But your contract with the Ring?" I asked astonished.

He was the leading man of a theatrical company, and for children of all ages he starred as the Boogie Man, the Old Witch, and Farmer Beet. (The critics considered the latter to have been his most important role. His impersonation of an old fart of a Dutch farmer was hailed as genius. It was. He was made for the part, didn't even need any make-up.)

"Stuff the contract," he said. "That bitch will take care of me."

Claudia and I were going to stay in his house for a couple of months, until we could find something better. We wanted to stay in Amsterdam until the baby was a little older.

My friends came through like champs. When we were all toasting our reunion with coffee and cognac I took Brains aside.

"Listen," I said, "I need some money because Claudia has to go to Holland. Due to circumstances—incredible developments known only to a few top men in the banking world—vast sums of money owing to me in Holland can't be forwarded. If you'd advance me the money, Claudia could be back here in two weeks. There's also a small sum I owe the hotel, but we can fix that up later. Besides, just think how happy you'll be to come into a wad when you're starting to run out at the end of your vacation. Think of lending me money as an investment in your future."

Brains, a loyal pal, lent me some and the next day I saw Claudia off on the boat to Barcelona. From there she had a couchette to Paris. Change for Amsterdam. I gave her a pile of drawings to take along.

When she said goodbye the tears were streaming down her face. I said, "I'll be with you again in less than a month. You can count on that. Have the coffee ready."

Wistfully I watched her leave. It gave me a hollow feeling in the pit of my stomach. I'd have to finish up my business on the island fast. Then I could follow her. I was determined to make one more stab at becoming a Respectable Member of Society in Holland.

Brains also paid the "small sum" I owed the hotel. A big dent in any wad, but we'd square that later. "If you've got money spend it; if you don't, don't" was the rule he lived by. He was a true friend, much to the consternation of the poet Conrad Bamzaai, the pack's self-appointed Treasurer.

By pulling a few strings, I got them a huge beautiful apartment for next to nothing. View of the beach. Brand new. In an apartment building the local doctor had just put up. There was one hitch in this business of moving into a new apartment. Overnight Ibiza had turned into a tourist resort. The airport was being modernized and enlarged. Old Spanish houses were being torn down to make way for gigantic apartment buildings or skyscrapers. Since everything had to be finished fast, there were a few little flaws in the construction. Underpaid masons stuck the bricks together with spit. Thus it happened that on the fifth floor of a brand new building (christened the previous day with a bottle of champagne), when the American poet Philip Fink hammered a nail in the wall with the sole of his shoe to hang up a portrait of Allen Ginsberg, the whole front wall of the building collapsed. Like in a war movie. On the third floor a few naked broads hid in the bathroom. On the ground floor, surprised people looked up from their plates and out to a gloriously unobstructed view.

There were two apartments empty in the luxurious building. I still owed some money to the doctor, but since I brought him four new customers he was willing to let bygones be bygones. The idea was that Brains, Conrad, Norman, and Gonnie would all move in together and split the rent. Gonnie would do the cooking.

I took Brains aside. After all, he was my best friend. He also had the most money because he'd worked for a year at a chewing gum factory. He was smart enough to sell the formula for invisible chewing gum to a rival chewing gum factory, whose name will remain undisclosed and which made a fortune out of it. So did Brains. Ibiza was full of freak fortunes like that.

Canadian Cooper, a former bank clerk, stole a million Canadian dollars from his bank, hopped a plane to Ibiza and invested it there. He stashed it away in various banks, a bit here, a bit there, and had a ball. Soon he had his own lavish villa built with a big swimming pool in the shape of a dollar sign. Stretched out on a rubber raft puffing away on Havana cigars, he cruised around his pool all day reading detective stories. The Spanish government refused to extradite him. Two years later Cooper's money was gone. Squandered. The next day the police handed him over to the Canadian authorities. Canadian Cooper's property was confiscated. The government took the place over.

I took Brains aside and said, "Listen, Brains, I like you. You know that. Well, take it from a friend that you shouldn't move into an apartment with them. The four of you? It'll be a disaster. Especially with a broad there. Okay, they're good guys, nice guys, always good for a laugh. But you don't want to sit around laughing all day, do you? You want to get some work done, don't you? And with Gonnie there, there's bound

220

to be trouble. She's a nice girl, sure, but what's going to happen? You'll be sitting around at night, having a drink, getting harder and hornier the longer you look at her—you know what I mean. In short, trouble with Norman. Okay, she can cook like an angel. Granted. But you know as well as I do that angels can't cook, and even if they could, what's that got to do with Gonnie? No," I said, "if you don't want to break up a lifetime friendship with the boys, you better move into a separate pad. Know something, Brains? It just so happens there's a beautiful empty apartment on the top floor. Better move fast. Otherwise it'll be too late. I'll take care of it. Then I can come and keep you company, because what's the fun of living in an apartment all alone? We can work all day. I've got a book I've got to finish too. We'll work all day and at night we'll drop down to see Gonnie and the boys. Son," I said, "we'll have a ball together! A bit of swimming, a bit of writing, and at night out we go. No women though," I said. "They only get you into trouble. Besides, I'm sort of married to Claudia. Don't even look twice at anybody else. Well, naturally if you happen to bring up an extra broad I'll do what I can for her. Not that I wouldn't enjoy it. But that's different from going out and finding them myself."

Brains moved into the apartment on the top floor and the others took the one two floors down. I brought my suitcases over from the hotel and brought Provo along too. A few good weeks followed, weeks of hard work, but plenty of kicks, too. Brains had a car which we used every morning. We'd have a hot cup of coffee at the sidewalk café, I'd read the letters from Claudia, who loved me more and more as time went on. Wasn't love beautiful! I worked hard while the others took it easy. Just work, work, work for me. Provo spent his days with Gonnie, a sweet girl with beautiful blue eyes and blonde hair. A knockout. But I had my Claudia. Besides Gonnie was married. Nothing in it for me. So I plunged ahead with my writing. Didn't even think about the ladies any more. Literature was much more important.

I wrote good stories and long love letters to Claudia. The future looked brighter. I hoped she'd be able to sell some of my pictures and that I'd be able to see her soon. How big would her belly be now? I loved her. No getting around it. Whenever I felt sunk or low I took out her picture and kissed it. I hoped she'd feel it.

248

In the evening after work we all got together. "Listen," I said to the boys, "you know what? I'm going to cook tonight. I'll cook up something special for you. And when Cremer says he's going to cook up something special, you can bet your ass it will be. You weren't planning to eat at one of those Spanish restaurants were you, or at the Chink place run by a Dutchman? If what he serves is Chinese, then sauerkraut is Egyptian. Besides, you can't even sit comfortably. That's typically Spanish—those awful chairs that crack your back. Shaky little tables slopping soup all over Gonnie's new dress. People all around jabbering German or Dutch. And on top of everything, the food's bad. Bad and expensive. You order a big paella, the Spanish national dish, lumpy rice with a few shrimp and fish thrown in, a few beers, a bowl of soup as an appetizer, soup that the chicken waded through in the kitchen, you have some salad on the side, dry lettuce with sand sauce or maybe it's dripping with olive oil, tomorrow you all pop out in pimples from the oil, to say nothing of the nausea, then pudding straight out of the package for dessert, coffee, ice cream, a few shots of cognac and then comes the bill, and what a bill! And what do you get for it? Nothing. No," I laughed scornfully, "if I cook, then you'll see what real cooking is. Good food, solid stuff with an exotic tang. And plenty of beer afterward, plus pudding or ice cream, whatever you want. At any rate, plenty of everything and cooked by a master. Don't forget, the cooks they put on in winter are just dressed-up garage mechanics or fishermen. They're moonlighters, that's all they are. But if you leave the cooking to me, you'll get everything and no closing time, no rush, no waiter trying to get you the hell out. You can slurp your soup and," I said to Brains, "belch as loud as you want. We won't mind. We're used to it. If Gonnie finds it too hot and wants to take anything off, fine with me. Play a game of cards, have a good chat. And if anybody wants more later, he can just get up and help himself. That is, if there's anything left. And the whole thing, except for the beer and other drinks, will cost you no more than one hundred pesetas. A hundred pesetas for heavenly food, especially prepared by Yours Truly. Look," I said, "I'm only doing this because I like you so much. Besides, I don't want to take advantage of your generosity. I want to offer you something in return for all you've done for me in the past."

I took the money, Provo, and a big straw basket and went out to shop. First stop was the butcher for a good piece of meat and some soup bones for Provo.

(Claudia and I kept alive for weeks by asking everyone we met on the street, "Can you spare five pesetas for some bones for the dog?" I pointed to Provo. "The poor thing hasn't eaten all day. Neither have we but that doesn't matter. We'll manage." In this way we picked up some money and Provo always got his bones.)

Then I stepped into a Spanish restaurant. I sat down and ordered myself a real feast. I had a delicious paella with all different sorts of fish, crabs, and lobsters. First a delicious bowl of chicken soup, afterward a nice salad with olives on the side and some ice cream with whipped cream. After a coffee and cognac I went shopping with the leftover money. Well, I thought, that meal's tucked away and it'll take some fast thinking to make me give it up again. After I'd bought everything I needed for the meal, I picked up a few packs of Ideales with the few pesetas I had left.

I rolled up my sleeves and started to work. While Gonnie peeled the onions, cut up the green peppers, shelled the beans, peeled the carrots, washed the lettuce, and seasoned the meat, I sat back, drank my beer, and pondered. Now that I had all this stuff, what should I do with it? It had to be something Romanian. I thought of the famous "Plagiata Romania," the Romanian meat dish known and loved all the way from the Black Sea north to the Kremlin. I concocted a fantastic pot of "Plagiata Romania." After a few hours of expert cookery I brought the steaming pot to the table. It was incredible, out of this world. We finished it up with wine and cognac, ice cream and coffee. We all felt heavy and drowsy.

I had a deck of cards and we played deep into the night. Black Jack. I couldn't lose. Kept on drawing the good cards. In three hours I'd won three hundred pesetas. Luck, that's all. Luckily I'd recalled a little trick I learned once from Jesserun Doremus when we spent a summer together at Scheveningen. The boys paid up reluctantly.

Conrad was mumbling in his goatee.

"I could win, too, if I played that way. You were cheating, Cremer," he said.

"Cheating?" I retorted. "That's what a poor loser always calls another man's good luck. Anyway, if I was a poet with a paper mustache, I wouldn't talk about cheating."

249

They liked the meal. They damn well better. It wouldn't have been the first time I'd punched somebody who dared to complain. Any insult to my cooking is an insult to me. In fact, they even asked me to cook more often. A few days later I surprised them with the Ibiza premiere of "Mongolian Monk's Tail," a very spicy dish which Mongolians frequently eat just before setting out to do some serious monk-tailing or Flipping. I got the recipe from a Russian grenadier wandering around the whore's quarter in Amsterdam. He charged me two quarters which he promptly fed into a food automat and yanked out two egg rolls. It was a great recipe and after keeping it secret all these years I think the time has come to reveal it to my readers. So here it is, the secret recipe:

Mongolian Monk's Tail

3 big ox tails and 3 teaspoons of salt

Slice the ox tails into small pieces. Simmer for four hours in enough water to leave ten cups of bouillon for the sauce. Just before the ox tails are done, add salt. Remove the meat. Let it cool and freeze it in ice. (Easy enough in Russia, but in Europe a refrigerator may be used.) Cool the bouillon also and keep it under the ice (in the refrigerator) to use for the sauce.

Ingredients for the sauce:
10 cups of ox-tail bouillon
1 tablespoon of suet
5 chopped red onions
6 cloves
16 grated peppercorns
2 sliced green peppers
3 bay leaves
3 sprigs of parsley
3 stalks of celery

Cayenne pepper
salt
black pepper
paprika
nutmeg and garlic
3 tablespoons of flour
1 tablespoon of Maggi or Marmite
1 pint of sherry
½ pint of cognac

Melt the suet in a frying pan. Add onions, cloves, peppercorns, green peppers, bay leaves, parsley and celery. Let simmer for ten minutes. Add salt, black pepper, paprika, Cayenne pepper, garlic, and nutmeg. Add a few spoonfuls of bouillon. Mix the flour in one cup of water. Add the Maggi or Marmite. Let simmer for twenty minutes. Cool. Remove meat from the bones. Warm up in the sauce. Pour on sherry and cognac just before serving.

It's a delicious dish. As an added attraction you can make it a "Special Mongolian Monk's Tail" with potatoes or corn on the cob. Everybody sits at the table naked by candle light (or an ordinary lamp as long as it's dim enough) and the dish is served by a Mongolian eunuch.

250

I made good progress on my book, and Brains, who was both editor-in-chief and managing director of an avant-garde magazine, wanted a couple chapters for advance publication. He thought highly of my work and said so.

"Well," I said, embarrassed, "I'm just a beginner. Just trying to keep myself alive, that's all. I just write what I feel. I don't even care if it gets published or not. Maybe I'm too young. Real writers are always pompous old perverts with beards and thick glasses, aren't they?"

Often while I was slaving away and Norman and Gonnie were fooling around and Conrad crocheting himself a new purse (at first I thought it was a pretty weird hobby, but I've since got used to writers' eccentricities much weirder than Conrad's), Brains would say to me, "Jan, you're working too hard. You never stop. It's not normal. You better watch out. It's not good for your health."

I just shrugged.

"Brains," I replied, "haven't you ever heard of work horses? Well, I'm one of them. I love work. I'm crazy about work. Vacation? Basking in the hot sun, burning yourself to a crisp? Not for this cat. You can vacation as long as you want when you're dead. No end of vacation then."

And I went back to work.

Trientje Spits, a talented young Dutch poetess, came to visit us on the island. Brains offered her a place to sleep. I slept out on the balcony and woke up early in the morning to the smell of my own body, broiling in the red hot rising sun. Trientje wrote out on the balcony. I often listened to her read her poems. It must be great to have been born a poetess. And a good one, too. Nice and experimental. My melancholy thoughts frequently slipped off to my father, the old troubadour, may he rest in peace, whose motto was: "Work is for idiots." The poor guy didn't know what he was missing.

251

It was high time to start thinking about going back to Holland, because every time I wrote I promised Claudia I'd be there as soon as possible. She missed me. I decided to earn some quick cash to help me on my way.

The Soggy Noodle had appointed himself Cub Scout leader of a pack of pimple-faced punks who met secretly at night to smoke pot. They thought they were the cat's ass—the real elite. I smoked with them once in a while, just to show I was a good guy or if there wasn't any shag around. I didn't make a big deal out of it. Then somehow Simon heard I knew where to get the forbidden grass. I was glad to be of service. Provided he could pay, of course. Doesn't a poor artist have a right to earn an honest living?

"What exactly do you want, Simon?"

"Well," Simon said bashfully, "marijuana. You know—weed."

"You mean *cannabis sativa*," I said. "For one hundred pesetas I'll see what I can do."

I had a friend, a Russian, who lived down by the caves, hibernated there all winter and cultivated his own weed garden. He gave me some and I rolled a few sticks. When I made my delivery, Simon asked nervously, "I . . . I . . . I . . . I'm not going to get hooked, am I?"

I laughed.

"No, Simon. Just smoke that joint and tell Uncle Jan how you're feeling. Better sit down first. Don't worry, I'll catch you if you faint."

He lit the cigarette with trembling fingers.

"I . . . I can't go through with it," he whined.

"Oh, come on, Simon," I said. "I'm with you. Be a real beatnik. Think of Allen. Nothing's going to happen to you, believe me. You've just got to stop being afraid, that's all. It's kicks. There's always a first time. You're not supposed to blow it all out, Simon. Just inhale. Suck in the smoke. Let it go down. Keep it down and in as long as you can."

He did. First he turned bright red, then green, then he started coughing up the fragrant smoke in a fit.

"How do you feel now, buddy?" I asked.

He looked seasick.

"I'm high! I'm high!" he squeaked. "Quick, give me another drag!"

He lunged clumsily for the butt between my fingers.

"I told you I'd get hooked," he reproached me indignantly but triumphantly. And he slapped my wrist as punishment.

"I can't live without it. I'm hooked! Hopelessly hooked," he shouted gleefully.

"Listen," I said, "there're a couple things you ought to know. *A:*—Marijuana is forbidden by law. So what do you do? You smoke illegally. *B:*—Illegal means punishable. So you smoke anyway but you've got to know how."

I showed him how. I lit up his joint and took a deep drag. Then I turned around, hid the butt in the palm of my hand, and glanced around nervously to see if any pigs were around.

"Now take it and be cool about it," I told Simon.

He did it. All wrong.

"No," I said, "first you have to glance around suspiciously a few times. After all, man, you're doing something illegal, illicit, forbidden. So you take your drag without letting anyone see, except for all the other people around who are all wondering: What is Simon doing now? Simon is doing something very naughty. Simon is smoking a Forbidden Cigarette."

After an hour he got the point.

"First smoke these sticks here," I said. "Always be sure there're lots of people around. Shut your eyes tight, squeeze hard, that makes them red. That's part of the whole scene. And there are a couple of things you might try saying to the people, like 'love love love love.' That way they'll know you're turned on."

That night Simon and his wife walked into the Music Bar. I was sitting in one of the booths talking to Brains about literature. We weren't paying any attention to all the chicks staring at us seductively and accidentally brushing their butts against us as they passed. Simon came up to us.

"Can you still see that I smoked that joint?" he asked eagerly.

"No," I said. "Go to the john and have a joint and squeeze your eyes real tight, or rub some soap into them."

"I'm scared," he stuttered.

"Come on, Simon. Don't be silly," his darling little wife chimed in. "You always said you wanted to be a junkie. You can't back out now. Don't you boys agree?" she asked us. "The thing is," she went on, as if talking about a defective sewing machine, while Simon slipped off to the can, "Simon's heard so much about marijuana and now he wants to see some of those visions himself. So I said to him, 'Well if that's what you really want, sweetheart, you just go ahead and do it.' And," she confided, with a malicious little chuckle, "he can't even smoke an ordinary cigarette. It upsets his tummy. Why, when he got home this afternoon after smoking with you, Jan, he had a dreadful case of diarrhea. But he's stubborn. He'll never give up. He's so set on being famous somehow or other."

Simon came back with bloodshot eyes and a pea-green face.

"I took an overdose," he mumbled. "Gotta go home now. I'm not feeling very. . . . Bye."

And he shot out the door clutching his stomach.

252

Simon was a good customer. And steady. Since he'd told everybody he was addicted to the dangerous narcotic marijuana, he was more or less obliged to buy large quantities of what I had in stock. I needed money for the trip back. I had a whole bale of the stuff up in my room. I smoked a bit of it every now and then, but what I wanted to do was to sell it fast and get some money. Simon was my big customer. And by far the richest. Brains and the boys had spent all their money. After a few games of cards Conrad had lost his whole vacation allowance to me. He was now living on money I lent him.

I had to think up some kind of story to make Simon take that marijuana off my hands. He already had half a pound of it at home but I had more. One night I took him aside, glancing around suspiciously since that's part of the game. "I've got something for you. Something absolutely out of this world," I said rolling my eyes to heaven as if that's where I'd got it.

"What is it? What *is* it?" he asked eagerly.

"A shipment of kief. There's no words to describe the stuff. And the ef*fects*. Something for the true connoisseur. You're my best customer, Simon, and besides you're a good friend, so naturally you're the first person I thought of."

I thought, I've got to cinch this deal now or never because he's got plenty of exactly the same stuff tucked under his mattress. A couple more twists and I thought I'd have him.

"Let me warn you though, Simon. Don't mention you've got hold of kief. Not to anybody. Not to a soul. Because if you do, they'll all want some. Here."

I gave him a stick.

He inhaled, reddened, coughed and said "Fan*tastic!* Must be Moroccan!"

I raised my eyebrows in surprise. "You know what you are, Simon? You're an expert. If you can tell that after just one drag, you're one in a million. Here," I said, "take it. For only three hundred pesetas you get two match boxes. The Boss would kill me if he found out. But then you're a friend."

He grabbed for the boxes and I grabbed for his money.

253

Ibiza, island of grapes. Ibiza, island of the clap. Ibiza, Junkies' Paradise. The torrent of tourists sweeps all kinds of oddballs ashore. It's a haven for beatniks, junkies, punks, poets, spinsters, men of letters, clerks and tellers, snobs, lunatics, gigolos, playgirls, playboys, underdogs, and loners.

Strait jackets are put into use at least six times every summer. Victims of delirium tremens break into the church and stone the statue of Jesus Christ. Four successful suicides every summer, twelve attempted suicides. Countless marriages, relationships, and friendships are shattered. Hate contracts are drawn up and signed.

Many thrill seekers come to the island drawn by articles and rumors. One of them was Bart. A clean-cut boy with big brown inquisitive eyes, accompanied by his wife Barbara. Bart was studying medicine, Barbara

I knew from Paris. When I last saw her she was a pimply kid working at Duncan's Art Gallery (Duncan, an eccentric old man who walked around in home-made sandals and home-woven Greek togas) and terribly eager to meet some real artists.

When Bart and Barbara stepped on shore they were both as naïve as they come. They soon bumped into Simon (of course) who made a big show of being hooked on marijuana. Bart wanted to try it too. When he smoked his first stick his face flushed through the rainbow and then he threw up right there in the café. He was hip. The next day he'd already discarded his jacket, taken off his tie, and with his sleeves rolled up and his shirt open at the collar he was already one of the boys. He was studying at the university and therefore could throw around lots of Latin words and expressions, which greatly impressed the whole gang of masochists, beach bums, and pseudo-intellectuals.

One day after being introduced to him, I took him aside and said sympathetically, "You're an addict, aren't you, Bart?"

"How could you tell?" he asked, overjoyed.

"Aw, it's easy," I said. "I can spot a real junkie a mile away. I can see it in your eyes!"

"Really?" he asked coyly, and rushed to the bathroom to look in the mirror.

There was absolutely nothing out of the ordinary about his clear brown eyes but he was delighted with the idea. So I continued, "I have something special for you. Horse," I whispered. "Heroin. For two hundred pesetas. Here!"

I passed him the goods, very secretively. I'd filled little twists of wax paper up with flour. I wasn't worried about his finding out because the guys who were always bullshitting about how addicted they were had never seen a needle in their lives. Except maybe when Mama was patching a hole in their shorts.

A few days later Bart was wandering around the island wide-eyed and bewildered. Barbara had gone out sailing for the afternoon with Korean Paul. On the way back the mast broke and they had to row back, which took three days. Meanwhile Bart stumbled around barefoot, his gray linen pants rolled up to his knees, shouting at everyone within range; "I have seen The Truth. I'm not at all jealous. I'm not at all jealous. I haven't slept for three nights. I haven't eaten for three days. But I don't care. I don't feel a thing. Because I have seen The Truth."

Poor Bart. He was worshiped and admired by a bunch of mixed-up Negroes and some spoiled rich men's sons. He, the lad who'd gone three days without either eating or sleeping, took nothing but pills. Centramine and pervertine. Poor Bart.

229

Encouraged by his Ibizan success, he later drilled a third eye in his forehead. How was I to know what Spaniards put in their flour?

254

I taught Simon how to swim. Though he was close to forty, he'd never gone in deeper than his waist. Except under the shower. It was pathetic to see him hanging back, playing quietly on the rocks with his son, a sensitive kid who could already see through his papa.

I had my own method of teaching him to swim. He was floundering around in the water holding onto a blown-up inner tube. After peering underwater through his goggles, he shook the hair out of his eyes and shouted enthusiastically, "Beautiful!" In fact, it was beautiful under there I thought, as I dove off a thirty-foot cliff aiming straight for the tube so he'd suddenly be on his own. Sink or swim. That was the way I planned to teach him. If he sank I'd be able to save him easily. But my aim was a bit off target. I landed half on the inner tube and half on Simon. Down went the Noodle like a brick and came up panting and coughing. It wasn't easy to save him, either. He thought I was trying to drown him.

In the evenings there were pot parties all over the island. To take the edge off my boredom I often put the pot heads on. Though Brains appreciated my sense of humor, the others didn't. Conrad Bamzaai discovered a kind of cabbage used by the locals in a special kind of soup which was supposed to cure asthma. *Datura stramonium* was the name of the stuff. One evening Provo and I came home after our daily raid on the town. I knew Conrad Bamzaai was there. Out in the hall, in front of the door, there was a panting and yapping pack of dogs. Conrad was an animal lover, and ever since he'd once jerked off a stray puppy the news had spread like wildfire through the underdog world of Ibiza. Every day he was trailed by dozens of dogs all yearning for his magic touch. The animal lover didn't have any time left to crochet his new purse. His old one, actually an old leather wallet given to him by his grandmother, was all worn out.

Conrad mixed the *datura stramonium*, which you could buy quite openly and legally at the grocery store near Hotel Noray, with the potatoes, and Simon, Elise, Conrad himself, Norman, Gonnie, and Bart all sat around the table and enjoyed the meal. Brains and Trientje Spits were off somewhere wisely listening to poetry.

"Anything left for an old bum and his dog?" I asked. Provo and I both had the cabbage. It tasted a bit odd. But not bad. I even had seconds.

After the meal the others sprawled out on couches and chairs. Conrad had said the cabbage could give you an enormous kick. You could even go blind or crazy. Gradually the guests started acting funny. Simon was the first, of course. After all, he was later to dub himself the High Priest of Marijuana.

In the days when Simon was still a normal citizen holding down a respectable job at an unbiased weekly newspaper I often used to write him letters. Finger exercises. After all, I thought, he was a writer who some day might write a good article about me. Which he did. He even opened some exhibitions of my work with his squeaky little voice.

"I'm high!" Simon screamed. "I feel it coming. Oh, oh, oh, I feel awful. I'm going to be sick. I know I am. Elise," he cried. "My pill. Quick!" (Miracle of providence, Simon had remembered to bring along an antidote.)

That started the rest of them off. Soon they were all talking strangely, roaming around, their brains blown, tapping against the wall. I saw him but since the others hadn't he did it a couple of more times. He wanted to jump off the balcony and started crying. Conrad picked up his wallet, dug a few coins out of it, and actually threw them over the balcony wall. That *was* strange. Norman stared blankly into space and Gonnie chatted away at somebody who wasn't there.

Provo and I exchanged knowing glances. We looked around as if nothing had happened. What a crowd of phonies. All because of some simple cabbage. Obviously the boys hadn't built up much resistance.

I went out on the balcony. A beautiful evening. Twilight moved in from the island of Formentera, bright red against the dark blue sky and the glistening sea. A sultry breeze blew from Rat Island into the apartment through the open doors. From below, hushed voices of people going by, out for a walk, and close by from the pool of the Hotel Ebeso loud German voices shouting jokes across the water.

I stuck a big fat cigar in my mouth, a present from Antonio Malo. I licked my brown arm and tasted the salt, the sea, the sun. I peered out over the sea. In the room behind me the noise and jabber rose and fell in waves, half drowned out by the blare of Radio Tangier.

A hundred yards out on the mirror-smooth water, a motionless swelling: Rat Island. A big round bare boulder. Fifty yards in diameter. Brown, ochre, and yellow stone, covered with light gray guano, here and there a yellowish stretch of dried grass. Rat Island, *Las Ratas,* the former torture island from the days when ships flying the skull and crossbones deposited their prisoners there.

Many years ago before Figueretas Hill was built, and before anybody lived by the bay, Rat Island was used by the police and the Falangists as an execution ground. The island was overrun with rats. Big broad-shouldered guards wearing hip boots and dressed in leather suits brought crates of rats over to the island, staked iron chains onto the bare yellow rocks on which rusty handcuffs from pirate days still dangled. The rats spread out and multiplied. Soon the island was swarming with them. In the beginning, the guards dumped garbage there for them to feed on. Later the ravenous rats started in on each other. No one dared come to the island. Only suicides who came to be eaten alive.

Once a month heavily armed guards came out with a shipment of prisoners. Before they came ashore they threw grenades to drive the rodents into their holes—for a short time anyway. Then they chained the exhausted prisoners, men and women, political prisoners, to the rocks. And left fast.

Dizzy from the hot sun, chained, powerless, weak (having been long underfed in jail), the prisoners soon gave up fighting off the approaching hordes of squeaking rats. They were eaten alive, their bones picked clean of every scrap of flesh. All the way to the *finca* of Don Villangomes you could hear the bloodcurdling shrieks of the dying prisoners.

Years later skippers used the island to store contraband. Still later, I opened up the narrow twat of a lovely German virgin on that island. Wistfully I recalled all these things as I stood on the balcony, while, inside, they were still off on their long trip. Provo and I walked back into the room. They were all sprawled out on the floor gazing off into space. I made myself a cup of tea.

While the water was heating up on the gas stove, I suddenly heard something scratching and sucking by the bottom of the door. The dust near the door mat was being sucked out of the room. I couldn't figure out what was going on. It couldn't be the dogs out there still waiting for Conrad. I opened the door. There, standing in the twilight, right in front of me, was an elephant. A little mousy gray elephant, the last descendant of Hannibal's famous elephant herd. Trumpeting loudly through his trunk, he tottered inside. He had a hard time squeezing through the door, but he finally made it. He stared at me with his large mischievous eyes. Provo started barking. The elephant, after clearing his trunk like a good after-dinner speaker, then proceeded to tell the following story.

255

New Year's Day, 1962. I knew Holland was (still) in urgent need of good playwrights, which is why I decided to take some time out from writing my book and other miscellaneous daily chores to jot down a fast-paced, action-packed, little drama. A one-acter which I was later to publish in my *Collected Plays*.

It would be easy enough to cast. The role of the Young Man fits Lucia's husband like a glove (Lucia, the Dutch-provincial version of Florence Nightingale). If only he weren't still playing the part of a ballerina in the Dutch Royal Ballet Company. So instead of him I'll take the resistance hero Robert de Bries for that role. The Lady must be played by the eternal bachelor Hans Culeman, and the Dog by Joop Admiraal. All three well known (in Holland, at least) as bright stars of stage and screen. A sure-fire guarantee for success. My one-acter would be the pride and joy of the Dutch theatre world—a pearl of a piece.

Sold Out
One Act

Scene: Modern grocery store. Behind the counter a clean-cut Young Man in a clean-cut white coat with clean-cut neatly combed hair neatly parted. Enter a sultry Lady leading a sexily-trimmed poodle on a leash.

YOUNG MAN: Well well well well. Good morning, Mrs. Fuckman.

LADY: Well, good morning to you, Mr. Pickapecker.

YOUNG MAN: May I be of any service, Mrs. F.?

LADY: Yeah, hotshot. A pound of Dog Balls, see-vous-plate.

YOUNG MAN: Oh Lordie, Mrs. F'man, I'm awfully sorry but Dog Balls are the one thing we're fresh out of today. The cupboard, Mrs. F., is bare. Bare is our cupboard when it comes to that delicacy. Sold out! Awfully sorry, Mrs. Manfucker.

(YOUNG MAN *stares off toward distant horizon, wringing his hands. As the* LADY *turns to go, the* YOUNG MAN'S *hand dives into his pocket, dives deeper, ostensibly scratching.*)

YOUNG MAN: We do, however, have something else in that line that might interest you. For instance, Moth Balls, Cloth Balls, Blue Balls, Screw Balls, Ferret Balls, Parrot Balls, and, of course (YOUNG MAN *laughs subtly*), the famous Ding-Dong Balls!

LADY: But no vacuum-packed, skin-sacked Dog Balls?

YOUNG MAN: Madam, I'm terribly sorry to let you down like this but I sold our last vacuum-packed, skin-sacked, cracker-jacked Dee-Bees to Mrs. Feelmeup. You know how it is, her old mister still keeps trying. You can't keep a good man down, as they say. (*He winks to* LADY).

LADY: You'd be surprised, Charlie. Well, I'm clearing out of this

233

joint. I can get better service elsewhere. Just one word of advice, Scrotum.

YOUNG MAN: Of course, Mrs. . . .

LADY: Mister, if I was you, I'd take better care of my balls.

(LADY *exits, slamming the door behind her, leaving the* YOUNG MAN *bewildered.*)

CURTAIN

256

I went out a lot with Dianna, the widow of an American pilot shot down over Korea. Dianna would be collecting her pension every month for the rest of her life and, like so many others who shared her fate, she could live on it luxuriously in Ibiza. She was a good kid. Had a good sense of humor. She lived right next door.

She had a finely carved face and a degree in psychology. Two reasons why we got along so well. She was the daughter of White Russians who immigrated to the States early in the 1900s. She was very superstitious. We would talk about the weirdest things for hours. I had dreams about being chased by snakes and I'd wake up in a cold sweat, or I'd dream about women's breasts blowing in the wind. I was fascinated by her explanations.

One evening the Music Bar was packed with American sailors. The fleet was in. Two big destroyers on their way to join up with the Mediterranean fleet.

We ordered absinthe.

"I'm damn glad I don't live in the States any more," Dianna said. "Those poor kids. They must be horny as hell after being at sea for so long."

"Why don't you help them out?" I said.

"You wouldn't mind?" she asked, probing my ego like the psychologist she was.

"Of course not," I said. "As long as you bring me back an American sailor's shirt with an eagle on it. I've been a fanatic Americanophile ever since I was a kid.

She turned to talk to some of the sailors. Soon after, they all went out together. I stayed behind, my heart pounding. Dianna was a cute piece of ass but a little too independent for me.

Hours later she came back tired, her face lined with what must have been an extraordinary experience. Exhausted, she plopped down on the bench beside me.

"Did you help them out?" I asked.

She took out two white cotton shirts and laid them down on the table. Good sturdy cotton with big Blue Eagles stitched on.

257

You come alone
You live alone
You die alone

258

My Spanish period was coming to an end. I wanted to go back to Claudia. There was a hole in my heart. I missed her more and more every day. I had so many debts on the island I'd never get away except by pulling a fast one.

Brains, Norman and Gonnie, and Conrad were planning to leave on the Monday night boat. They'd already packed. That Sunday afternoon Brains and I went out for a farewell drink—much to the displeasure of Exchequer Conrad, who was scared we'd drink up the money for the fare back. It wasn't easy to shake him.

"Go to the bullfight. We'll see you later."

I maneuvered Brains to a big deserted café which I'd described to him as "a very notorious hang-out, home turf for pirates and the Spanish mafia, but don't worry, you'll be safe if you're with me."

I had to make sure Brains and I weren't being followed. If Conrad found us he'd tug his sleeve every time he ordered a drink. He was a real poet, that Conrad Bamzaai—always looking at the dark side of life and skip the fun if it's going to cost money. He'd even brought a piggy bank along in his suitcase.

The only café on the island I'd never been in was right behind the post office. It looked pretty grubby from the outside. It was completely empty. A scrawny girl with a patch over one eye and a thick German accent asked what we wanted.

I said to Brains who, from his saxophone-playing past, still dug Thelonius Monk, "You know what, why don't we try a Monk cocktail!"

"What's that?"

I pointed to the bottle-lined shelves. "You drink your way from one side of the shelf clear across to the other."

We had a Monk cocktail: First a big glass of cognac, then whisky, then liqueur, then gin, absinthe, and pernod. We gulped them down one after the other. The idea was to forget the problems of the day and get stoned as fast as possible. Then came glasses of plum liqueur, cognac, screwdrivers, bloody marys, crème de cacao, whisky—it all went down the bottomless pit. We were completely blind.

It was time to go to the bullfight. I could have gone on a while longer but Brains wanted to leave. A strangely-shaped brown bottle caught my eye. The label said Calisay. I decided to take a chance.

"Did you know they sold a famous aphrodisiac here?" I asked.

"They do?" Brains' curiosity was immediately aroused.

"Yeah," I said. "Over there." I pointed to the Calisay bottle.

"What is it?"

" 'What is it,' he asks," I laughed scornfully. "Man, don't you know how Napoleon managed to make all those broads? He drank Calisay."

"What does it taste like?"

"Well," I said, "like pine trees, like grass with dew on it, like a sun-baked pair of bare buttocks. Give some to a chick," I went on, letting my imagination run wild, "and she'll lie down and spread as fast as she can."

"Really?" Brains asked.

"Really."

I told him how I'd seduced the wife of an American millionaire after just two shot glasses of Calisay.

"I couldn't keep her off," I explained apologetically. "Not that she wasn't fantastic to look at. Unusually well-developed muscles, too. It all started with Calisay. By the way, it's forbidden to sell the stuff. Prohibited by the church because of overpopulation."

I dangled visions of erotic grandeur before his eyes. Any broad at all, if he wanted her all he had to do was give her a glass or two of Calisay and she'd melt like butter. "And," I said, "you can try any position you want. Nothing's dirty when you're in love."

My own stories made me wonder what it tasted like after all. We tried a glass. It was liqueur—nice, sweet, ordinary liqueur.

"Fantastic! Man, I can feel the difference already," Brains shouted.

He bought three bottles to take back to Holland.

259

We drove over to the arena feeling no pain but almost clipping a couple of Spaniards. Laughing at everything, high as a kite, Brains paid for our tickets. We sat down on the cement steps of the newly-built arena.

The huge throngs of tourists at the weekly corrida had called for a bigger arena. It had gone up in no time. So there were a few little cracks here and there, and the bulls climbed up in the stands more than they were supposed to, and too many spectators climbed down into the ring. One after the other the badgered mountains of flesh pawed their way up the barrera.

The bullfight came through a little blurred, through a mist of drinks. Conrad came over and sat down beside us. We'd brought along a few beers from the pirates' den and quickly finished them off.

"Why don't you get some more beer?" Brains said to Conrad.

Conrad pretended he hadn't heard, looking off engrossed in the bullfight. I started in on him.

"Yeah. A good idea, Conrad," I said. "A couple of beers. Or have you got the current on in your wallet again? Wouldn't want you to get electrocuted."

Swearing at me softly through his mangy goatee, he went over to the beer vendor and came back with three tiny bottles of beer.

"Almighty God," I said, "could you afford it? You're beginning to look more and more like Shylock every day, with your scrubby goatee and hunched shoulders. You know who I mean—the miser in that play by. . . ." I hesitated.

"Molière," he supplied hatefully.

"Shakespeare, cretin," I corrected him. "Don't try to teach the classics to me. By the way," I continued, "did you get sunstroke or something? I mean, how come you're sitting here in the shade seats. They cost a lot more, you know. I thought you always sat in the sun with the poor people."

"That's right," he laughed triumphantly. "I just walked over here and sat down, even though I bought the cheapest ticket in the whole damn place."

"Let's see it," I said.

When he took out his ticket I called the ticket checker.

"This guy's sitting in the wrong section," I said.

"Go back where you belong," the man said to Conrad. "If you want to stay here you'll have to pay the difference."

Conrad paid the difference, swearing a blue streak, taking the coins out of his worn-out wallet one by one, sniffing and blinking. His nervous tic.

"I've had it with you, Cremer. Up to here," he snapped viciously.

"Oh come off it, man," I said. "Can't you take a joke?"

We watched the bullfight. The matador had to drive in his sword time after time before the beast finally lurched and toppled over. I wasn't too wild about the Spanish national pastime. But what else could you do on Sunday afternoon?

When the second bull crumpled up after the matador had stuck him only three times, the fans let out a deafening "Olé" and the bull buckled, shuddered, and died. The audience went wild. The applause and cheers went on and on until suddenly a voice came over the loudspeakers calling for attention. This was the first time that season that a bull had been killed in only three *estocadas*—a memorable event.

"What are they saying?" Conrad asked curiously.

"That matador just set a record," I said. "Killed the bull with only three *estocadas*. Now everybody has to pay the price of their seats all over again. Otherwise they'll stop."

"But that was only the second fight," Conrad whined.

"Yeah," I said. "They're a bunch of con-men. Well, should we pay up or take off?"

"I want to see the whole thing," Conrad said. "This is the last chance I'll have."

"Then you'll have to pay up," I said, very businesslike. "Just give me the money. I'll go get the tickets. It's one hundred fifty pesetas for the three of us."

With trembling hands Conrad counted out the money. I went down to get a beer, then looked around for some official-looking stubs in the sand by the entrance.

Conrad, his pale face staring out at the bullfight from behind dark glasses, was in bad shape.

"I'm getting sick and tired of Ibiza," he mumbled. "What kind of bullshit is this anyway? If they think I'm going to stand for it, they're crazy."

By the time the last bullfight began, Brains and I were so completely bombed that suddenly Brains stood up and sailed a bottle straight down at the strutting matador. Bong. A perfect hit. The matador stopped strutting, clutched his head, and sat down in the sand for a couple of minutes to chart the stars going off in his skull.

We were arrested by a fierce gang of Guardia Civils who came storming up to take us off to headquarters, clubbing us down the aisles and out into the street. Boos and curses from the fans. We could make a deal with these bulls but it would cost money.

"My friend over here," I said pointing to Brains, "is crazy about the corrida. He was only trying to wave at the matador. He just forgot he was holding a beer bottle."

Conrad had to cough up another three hundred pesetas, which wiped out what was left in the treasury. Conrad went right to bed complaining of a terrible stomach ache. The experience had been a blow he would never get over. He'd never spent so much money in one day in his life.

260

With a lump in my throat I waved goodbye to my friends as they steamed out to sea in the big white boat. I was all alone now with Provo. Brains had taken as much of my luggage as his car could hold. I'd get off the island as soon as I could. Somehow.

I holed up for a few days, then got a nice letter from Claudia. She'd sold some of my drawings and scrounged up some money. I deposited it in the bank, got a checkbook and managed to cash the same check twice. So now I had enough ready cash to convince my most panic-stricken creditors that deep down I was their best friend after all.

Although boat captains, shipping companies, and the flight-booking office had all been forbidden to sell me a ticket before checking me out at a certain address, I still managed to get hold of a first-class ticket for the boat leaving that evening. Just one hitch. Provo suddenly disappeared into thin air. I searched the whole island. Nowhere to be found. Dianna promised to send him on later. I couldn't let him hold me up now. This was my only chance to escape.

Somehow word leaked out to a few people that I was leaving. They hunted all over for me and when they finally caught up with me, I said, "Hey, I've been looking all over the island for you. I'm taking off for Madrid for a couple of days. Just to make some money, then I'll be back. Let's see now—how much do I owe you again?"

"Five hundred pesetas," they spit the words out viciously. "You weren't trying to sneak out on us by any chance, were you?"

"Who me?" I asked, surprised, laughing that innocent open-hearted laugh of mine, a kindly twinkle in my honest blue eyes. "Am I the kind of guy to double-cross his friends? Would I cheat a poor Spaniard out of his hard-earned money? Not me. Here," I said and I handed them a check for one thousand pesetas.

"That's much too much," they said.

I smilingly brushed aside their protests.

"You helped me out. Now it's my turn to help you."

I walked away, leaving the Spaniards in a cloud of brotherly love. They were crazy about me. They wouldn't be able to cash the check until nine o'clock the next morning anyway, by which time Uncle Jan would be well on his way through France. If he played his cards right.

I pretended I'd be coming back the following day. I sauntered along the quay in dungarees and a shirt. I had some friends bring my bags on board. At the very moment I said goodbye to my dearest friends Daan and Gerda and kissed Dianna goodbye in the shadows of the Music Bar. Just as the gangplank was being hauled up, I jumped for it and sprinted aboard. I ducked into the crowd of waving tourists and waited until the boat was a safe distance from the pier.

I waved. I blew kisses to Dianna who ran alongside the boat until it passed the tip of the pier. I waved until she was only a dot.

Fantastic girl. Big and beautiful. Gorgeous body. I'd had some wonderful nights with her. Though I was madly in love with Claudia, the flesh is weak. And what the hell, can't a lonely lad lay a gorgeous girl once in a while?

We got to Barcelona the next morning. At first, though, nobody was allowed off the boat. I'd met a group of Dutch tourists on board, seamstresses from Tilburg, and then a squad of police came on board with a plainclothes detective, obviously looking for somebody. I decided not to take any chances. Surrounded by chattering girls, I made my way through the exit. The detective shouted "Completo" to the policemen, and if it was me he was looking for, tough luck, buster.

A schoolboy who'd been on vacation with his mother agreed to carry my suitcase if I'd give him a bottle of Centramine. I had one hundred bottles of Centramine in that suitcase—pep pills (Spain being the only country in the world where you can buy them at any druggist; they're very expensive on the black market)—plus ten cartons of American cigarettes. I'd invested everything I had in what I thought would keep me going for at least the first few weeks back in Holland. When we came to customs the boy stood in one line, me in another. I got the shock of my life. The customs inspector asked him to open the bag and suddenly I saw the kid pointing wildly over to me. I walked over to the counter. The customs inspector asked me what I was doing with all those cigarettes. He hadn't even seen the Centramine. I smiled at him, and handed him one of the cartons.

"For you and the ladies," I said. Always good for a try. He smiled back and marked my suitcase. I didn't even have to open the other one. I broke out in a cold sweat. Any delay could be fatal. By nine, when the banks opened, I had to be safely across the border. I jumped into a cab and made it to the station on the French side in record time.

The train was leaving in half an hour. I'd bought my ticket and was strolling around when suddenly I saw Nollie, an Amsterdam chick who used to live on Ibiza and was working as a waitress now at the Jamboree Jazz Club on the Plaza Real. We had a coffee together before my train pulled out. Homeward bound. Back to Claudia.

deutschland uber alles

261

I rang the bell. Nobody at home. Maybe Claudia hadn't got my card. It was cold. Gloomy weather. It would take time to get used to Amsterdam again. Everything was so tiny. My train had just pulled in and I'd grabbed a cab. It was worth the money. I wanted to be with Claudia. Fast.

Not sure what to do next, I stood there on the stoop of Kotshut's house in the center of town until suddenly, at the other end of the street, I saw Claudia's familiar walk. She'd gotten a lot bigger.

"Christ, how I missed you!" she said. "Are we going to stay together now? Always?"

"Always," I said as I lugged my suitcases up the narrow stairs.

It was a narrow two-story house. There were rats downstairs so Claudia had fixed up a nice room for herself upstairs. My picture on the wall and a little transistor radio. I felt like I was finally home. A great feeling to have a home, I thought. And a beautiful woman waiting for you. I loved Claudia. I unpacked the big suitcase and gave her her present. A pink baby-doll nightgown edged with purple lace.

"Try it on," I said. And when she stood there in that nightgown I knew I'd got her just the right thing. Her big pointy belly bulged out voluptuously and her big brown nipples jutted out against the material. Her breasts had grown enormous.

I'd also brought her a pair of Turkish slippers, a box of hankies, Maya soap, eau de cologne, and a scarf with a bullfight hand-painted on it. While Claudia was hanging up my clothes I lit the oil stove. The room was damp and chilly. I washed up in the sink down in the basement and, feeling fresh again, went back up to smoke a good cigar and enjoy a glass of the absinthe I'd brought back. For Claudia I'd brought a bottle of Frigola, a liqueur made from herbs and a specialty of Ibiza.

It was only seven o'clock when we rolled into bed and the feel of Claudia's soft warm body—the body I had missed so badly—made me feel life was all right after all.

262

Provo was found. I got a letter from Dianna. She'd heard that a German girl had taken Provo to another village on the island where she'd later sold him to some tourists from Paris. They'd taken him back with them. Dianna was a born sleuth.

I borrowed some money and a car. There was this girl who had a crush on me. Her father worked at an office and had a Ford Consul which he parked in front of the house every evening, and at eight-thirty every morning got in and drove off to work. I got the girl to get the keys from her father one evening when she was sure he wouldn't be going out. Told her I had to take a few paintings someplace, that I'd only need it for a couple of hours. Norman, who had a driver's license, drove down to Paris with me where we found the address without too much trouble. It was pitch dark on the stairs. The whole house sacked out. I rang the bell a few times and then heard a dog growling and sniffing on the other side of the door. My heart skipped a beat.

"Provo?" I said.

The dog started barking like crazy, jumping up and clawing the door. Dazed and still half asleep, the people opened the door. Provo had awakened the whole house.

They turned out to be very nice people who'd more or less adopted Provo when the German girl's vacation was over. They'd had to buy him from a Spanish bum who claimed he was Provo's real owner. They stared at me through half-shut eyes. All the kids had crawled out of bed to see what was going on.

"Bon sure, joy voo mon shyen," I said patting Provo, who was climbing all over me and licking my face. We had to get back to Amsterdam fast so I just said "Bon sure, oh refwar," and off we went. With Provo. Taking turns at the wheel, we made Amsterdam just as the sun was coming up. It was a race against time. At exactly eight-thirty we turned into the street and quickly parked the car. Norman and I were walking Provo along on a rope leash when the girl's father came out the door. He looked surprised when he saw his car. He'd parked it on one side of the street at night and now there it was on the opposite side. He nodded to me and said, "Good morning. Nice weather, isn't it? I didn't know you had a dog."

So the family was reunited again. We had Provo. Another mouth to feed.

263

It was ice cold. Fall. We were as broke as ever. We stopped up the cracks under the windows and doors with old newspapers. Our only heat came from an old oil stove that started smoking every ten minutes. Everything stank of grease and soot. One afternoon I swiped a few empty bottles from the crates stacked up in front of the dairy. I took them in and with the deposit money bought a bottle of milk. Now that the baby was due, Claudia needed lots of milk.

It was one hell of a mess. Even our transistor was dying out on us, the music growing fainter and fainter. We stared blankly at each other slurping tea (with no sugar) and smoking cheap cigarettes the guy in the store let me have on credit. I was seriously thinking of becoming a Respectable Member of Society when the doorbell rang.

It was Norman. He asked if we'd like to have a beer with him at the Square. Claudia and I sailed down the rickety stairs and off we went, down the dark silent street to the lights of Leyden Square.

It was Friday night. Payday for state-subsidized Artists, the unemployment-insurance set, and for bearded and unbearded young men in general. The arty café was packed. We pulled up some chairs and started filling up on beer, cognac, cheese and sausages, with side orders of beer, cognac, etc. Above the deafening roar of voices in the smoke- and artist-filled room, the waiters were bellowing out their orders.

One of the waiters tapped me on the shoulder and said, "There're two Krauts here. Theater people. They're looking for somebody to do stage sets for them. Might be something in it for you. Never can tell." And he pointed out two shady-looking runts standing off in a corner by themselves.

I invited them over. They stood us all drinks which seemed like a promising start to me. They said they were from a big theater in Kwammerschlagen, a town in the Ruhr, and that they'd come to Holland for a few days to see some exhibitions and plays. At the same time they were looking around for a scenery designer, somebody who could go back to Germany with them to design sets for experimental plays.

"Ach soo," I said, "das ist interessant." Come off it, I thought. They're only out scouting for cunt, so where do they go? To the big artist hangout where the line to work is to say you're a painter or connected with the theater. Not that I gave a damn. As long as they kept on buying us drinks anything was okay with me. Still, I was surprised that these two sex fiends knew all the names of the museum directors, theater groups, top actors, etc. They could have dug that out of a tourist guide, of course.

They sure didn't look like theater people. But then again, you never know with the Wirtschaftswunderkinder.

One of them, the one who claimed he selected the plays for the theater and who looked as honest as a three-dollar bill, went under the name of Karlheinz Beinkrampf. The other one, a dumpy little bubble of a guy, was Gunther Krappsalaten. He was the director. I quickly made Norman my manager and he played along nicely even though I spoke better German than he did. He told them what a gifted painter I was and how many stage sets I'd already designed. Didn't even have to lie. The Germans said that they'd heard about me, of course, and I thought, where's the end of this line of bullshit?

I said I'd go to Germany with them (they were leaving early the next morning) and design some sets. "And congratulations on finding me," I added. "It's not everybody who can go into a country and pick the best artist the way you've just done." I still thought it was all a joke. After a few more beers though, Beinkrampf and Krappsalaten asked whether they could see some of my work. Norman explained that at this time of night museums were closed in Holland but that I probably had a few things at home. The best ones had already been sold, of course, but if they really wanted to see something, why not?

I only lived a block away. Who knows, I thought, maybe they're in a buying mood, so off we went—Claudia, Norman, the two Krauts, and me—to my temporary studio and residence which was ice cold as usual. Without taking their coats off they looked at my pictures, mumbling appreciatively. I gave Claudia a pinch in the ass and said, "Before you know it, we'll be rich!"

The fattest one said, "Maybe we can have a little something to eat and talk things over. Okay?"

"Sure thing," I said. "There's always room for a little something, I always say."

We rushed back to the Square and I steered us all into the Café Modern. I thought, a little something? We'll see about that. I was getting pretty tired of their arty act and anyway we were starving. I ordered an appetizer (big enough for five people), a king-sized steak, and pudding for dessert. Claudia had a steak, too, and after weighing his conscience against his hunger so did Norman. The Germans each modestly ordered a grilled cheese sandwich. But what the fuck? Who'd brought up the subject of eating in the first place anyway?

They were real beauties. Beinkrampf looked incredibly weird at first sight. A ragged beard, straight lank hair combed straight back, his bright blue eyes squinting away, his suit too big for him, big rings on his fingers. He chain-smoked delicate little ladies' cigars. He looked like the kind of guy who hustles dirty pictures and "gold" watches in night clubs. Bein-krampf didn't talk much but when he did his German came out sounding raw and hard. His sidekick, Herr Krappsalaten, was a nonstop blabber-mouth. As wide as he was tall, he wore glasses that looked like aquariums. He didn't just read the menu, he sniffed it, holding it about an inch away from his eyes in his chubby little hands. His suit was too tight, the cuffs of his pants up above his ankles, the sleeves of his jacket not quite making it down to his wrists, a watch chain stretched tight across his big belly. He wore soft black suede shoes and light blue socks. He never stopped smil-ing. The other one was a Dostoevski type. They would have made a great stand-up comic team.

I savored every bite of my meal while the Germans nibbled their sandwiches. Tubgut kept staring hungrily at my plate and at the big meals people at other tables were putting away. He asked me about eighteen times if my steak was good and I said, "Ja, oh ja ja ja!" between mouthfuls.

While we were all puffing away on dainty cigarillos it was settled that I'd go to Kwammerschlagen with them the next morning. I'd take my scrapbooks, meet the director and the producer, and if all went well start work on Monday. Why not? At any rate there'd be at least one more meal in it for me. And a nice train ride can sometimes be very inspiring, even if it is to Germany. I decided I'd keep my date with them—ten the next morning at Hotel Mongolia—though I still thought the whole thing was some kind of joke. We said goodbye to Beinkrampf and Krappsalaten. Norman took off and Claudia and I went to bed full for a change.

264

I got to the Hotel Mongolia half an hour late, only half shaved (people on the street nearly fainted as I shot by still stinking of cheap aftershave lotion), with a bag stuffed with scrapbooks, photographs, slides of my pictures, newspaper clippings, my toothbrush, plus some paintings I'd removed from their frames and rolled up. To show the director. In my worn-out, one-and-only (cobalt blue) shiny suit and cheap blue sneak-ers, since I didn't have any other shoes.

They were waiting for me at the sidewalk café in front of the hotel, glad I'd showed up after all. We only had half an hour to catch the express train to Kwammerschlagen. If we missed that, the trip would take two hours longer. We hopped into a cab and took off for the Central Sta-tion. All three of us were very quiet. Not yet noon. Too early to talk. Krappsalaten glumly stared out the window. Beinkrampf's eyes were red, swollen, and not quite open yet. As for me, I was ready to get back under the blankets again, too. But work is work and Arbeit is Arbeit and I needed money.

After they'd bought our tickets (they bought a round-trip ticket for me; a good thing—I didn't have a cent), we still had ten minutes before the train left. Plenty of time if only Krappsalaten hadn't stopped to buy some postcards to send off to Mutti at the last minute. His passport disappeared along with the postcards into the mailbox. Panic!

We had to wait for the mailman to come to empty the box. He came up just as the clock struck twelve. A tall guy with an aristocratic nose dressed in plain clothes but wearing the regulation post office hat. We all three rushed him. He studied the Germans as if maybe they weren't for real, said something like, "Keep your shirt on, Mac," then opened the mailbox and caught the mail in a big sack. Krappsalaten was so impatient he started rummaging around through the letters. This was too much. The mailman barked out some German and finally found the little green book himself. "Just a minute, gentlemen," he said in a solemn tone and began leafing through the passport, studying each page like a scholar. This was too much for the Germans. They tried to tear the passport out of his hands. "Don't you know," said the mailman, "it's strictly forbidden to deposit official documents in a mailbox?" After I'd convinced him we really hadn't done it on purpose he said, "Okay. Just make sure it doesn't happen again!"

The next express train was due to leave at three. We decided to go for a walk. We checked our suitcases and strolled down a wide store-lined street. All three of us feeling pretty cranky. Me because I'd gotten up too early. We looked in the windows. I tried to start up a conversation with my future employers. No luck. Until I happened to say to Krappsalaten, "You know what I like most about Germany?"

"No," he said politely but without the least curiosity.

"Cheesecake," I said. It was, in fact, the only good thing I could think of about Germany.

"What?" he asked.

"Cheesecake," I answered.

"No!" he screamed, surprised and delighted and clapping his fat little hands.

"Yes," I said. "Cheesecake and apple strudel."

I'd turned him on.

He rattled on and on and on about his Mutti. About how she could make such great cheesecake and that her apple strudel outstrudeled all other strudels. About how cheesecake had to be made with skimmed milk and how the cows in southern Germany had the best milk in the world for cheesecake. He whispered that he had noticed the night before that I was a true gourmet and that eating happened to be his favorite hobby too. We would have a good time together in Kwammerschlagen. He promised to take me to a few restaurants where I could enjoy the cream of German cooking.

"You're not hungry now, by any chance?"

"Sure," I said. I figured it was about time the lean life came to an end. An hour later I could have eaten my words. Gunther Krappsalaten's favorite pastime really was eating. By the time we were through, pea soup was coming out of my ears.

265

The train for Kwammerschlagen pulled out of the station at three on the dot. Packed. We sat across from each other jammed into a compartment full of bulging bags and baggy women sitting or standing. The aisles were packed too. With luggage and standees. Mostly women. Probably on vacation. Or going off to visit their boyfriends. They gave me some very nasty looks as they clung to the luggage racks. I think they wanted my seat. Nothing doing, baby. A bulletproof row of corsetted buttocks walled me off from the Germans sitting across from me. I looked out the window. Little Holland looked beautiful. Flat countryside. Endless horizon.

266

The doors to the compartment were shoved open at the border. Passport inspection. I felt really proud of our Royal Military Police. Just the way they stood, the way they carried themselves. Big tall healthy broad-shouldered boys in their beautifully fitted fancy uniforms. Handsome caps shining with a fortune in silver. Neat braiding, whistles dangling. I was feeling patriotic until one of the boys snapped at me to step outside. Immediately the solid block of fat asses started buzzing. "You see?" "I told you so." "Hippy!" "Provo!" I was panic stricken. What had I done? Me, the nicest guy in the world. Had the Spaniards finally tracked me down? Had the milkman minded when I balled his wife in the butter freezer? I couldn't figure out what I'd done.

"You're in the Black Book," said the Royal M.P. "Did you know that?"

"No, Your Honor," I said. "What did I do?"

It turned out to be a minor offense from way back. (At a circus once I'd dropped cotton candy in a lady's hair from the top of the ferris wheel and was sentenced to either six years at hard labor or a fifty-guilder fine. Which I'd never gotten around to paying. Still, publicity is publicity. Not everybody gets into the Black Book.)

I said I didn't have enough on me to pay the fine just then. Tough luck. They'd have to lock me up until I could. I told them I'd come back that same night to pay off the fine since I was going to make a lot of money in Germany. Even offered to let them keep my passport until I'd paid. No luck.

Everybody, including the two Germans, was following the whole scene through the glass doors of the compartment. I stepped back in to ask Krappsalaten if he could lend me some money—"just an overdue parking ticket, nothing much"—otherwise I couldn't cross the border. At first they flipped and flatly refused to help me out, but finally Beinkrampf said all right, but just this once. Just in time. Because three colleagues had joined the Royal M.P.'s and now there was a whole squadron of uniforms lined up out there in the aisle.

"Okay, buddy," they yelled, "either you pay up now or off you go." Beinkrampf only had German marks so we had to go change them into guilders in the M.P.'s special compartment at the other end of the train. We had to squeeze through crowds of people and past stacks of suitcases while everybody watched the parade of first one uniform, then me, then Beinkrampf, then two more uniforms. All we needed was a marching band.

I could hear people saying things like, "It's written all over their faces," and "That runt with the beard, isn't he the creep we read about in the paper?" which didn't cheer Beinkrampf up any. After he'd paid and I'd been given an official-looking receipt—proof of my innocence (it would come in very handy later)—we had to file back past all those people all over again. They seemed disappointed we hadn't been shot or at least kicked off the train.

We spent the rest of our trip in silence—me, glad not to be in jail; Beinkrampf and Krappsalaten glaring at me as if they were bringing back a smuggler instead of a set designer.

"Ach," I said trying to set their minds at ease, "it was just a little accident. Bumped into a car with my bike. They just don't make cars the way they used to. Anyway it wasn't even my fault."

They didn't quite believe me. Not that I gave a shit. I was off to a new adventure.

267

By the time we got to Kwammerschlagen we were all buddies again and Krappsalaten eagerly asked me if I wanted "a little something" to eat? When I said, "No thanks," his chubby face fell. He almost burst into tears. So I quickly said, "Ja," and his face cleared up, the clouds disappeared, and out came the sun again.

Puffing and beaming he hurried me into a restaurant across from the station because "the pea soup it is sehr gut here." Meanwhile Beinkrampf had gone over to the theater to make an appointment for me to meet the director that evening. I'd already put away two warm meals that day. I had a hard enough time finishing off the first bowl of thick green stuff with its big chunks of fat and bony meat. Then Krappsalaten insisted I have a second. Just to keep him company. The thought of starting in all over again was too much for me. I raced off to the can and—*Braack*—up came another free meal.

268

The set-up in Kwammerschlagen looked good. The director turned out to be a charming gray-haired guy with thick glasses. A real old-school Prussian-type heel clicker like they don't make any more. He found my work "very interesting indeed" and told me I could start right in designing sets for two important productions: Audiberti's *Die Frauen des Ochsen* and *Der Kaiser*.

I told him I'd designed sets for the Living Theater in Spain and for some Brecht plays. (I'd worked for the municipal theatre in The Hague, helped out in return for paint and used canvas which I reused for my own paintings. I advised and assisted an Israeli designer. We worked around the clock together for days. Though most of the scenery was based on ideas I'd given him, the Israeli got all the fame + fortune. Besides which he started imitating my style of painting.) I said I was deeply honored to have been chosen to decorate this great stage in this great theater in this greatest of all great towns. The playwright, he said, would give me further instructions. I would start off with five thousand marks (after taxes) for the two plays. Insurance, bed, and board would be deducted, and how long I would be kept on would depend on how well they liked my work.

"Many, many thanks," I said. "Thank you, Herr Doktor Direktor. Danke, danke!" Then, standing stiff as a ramrod, I clicked my heels together so hard I was sure I'd broken both ankles. Then I bowed so low that when I jerked my head up again, I practically fainted from dizziness. The director was speechless with delight as I stalked out of the room.

I'd made a good impression on him, that was one thing for sure. A stiff spine, a deep bow, and a pair of exploding heels—a surefire hit in Germany. The only way to get to the top. Ach ja, Deutschland, Deutschland Über Ahahahalles!

269

Cheers and applause greeted me as I sailed into the canteen. I was the new sensation. Tubby old Krappsalaten was standing up on a wooden bench excitedly telling them all about The Adventure at the Border.

"So then I said to the police, don't you dare, you stupid Schweinhund, or I'll report you to the Kommandant. And that'll be the end of you! Who the hell do you think you are? We may not be at war right now but just you wait! Now let this young man go or, by Schickelgruber, you'll wish you had!" Even Beinkrampf, shy as he was, chimed in. "Ja Ja. Those damn Dutchmen at the border, they're crazy all right."

The actors, actresses, and dancers almost hoisted me up and carried me around the room on their shoulders. But I thought, cool it, Krauts. Krappsalaten ordered some sausages and I asked for a stein and the three of us sat down at a table to discuss the final details of the contract. I'd have a ball here, I could see that. There were a couple of fine pieces standing around. The girl behind the bar was something to keep in mind. The first time I saw her all I could see were her tits. Two real blockbusters. When she brought me another mug of beer she bent over and hung around to give me a nice long look of the soft pink flesh bulging out of her bra. It looked a lot more appetizing than the big shiny reddish-brown sausage she set down in front of me. Plenty of work to be done around here, I thought, particularly with the Special Brush.

Krappsalaten and Beinkrampf were obviously big wheels in Kwammerschlagen. I'd seen that by the treatment they got when we entered the restaurant the night before. After we'd finished our sausages, the girl with the blockbuster bust served us real fresh-ground coffee and big slices of cheesecake. It wasn't half bad. The waitress, Tooti was her name, had baked it herself. Have to have another piece of that sometime.

I had to start first thing Monday morning. The opening was only two weeks off. I had a big studio to work in. Six assistants. As for supplies, anything I wanted. If I brought this off I knew I could look forward to plenty more work. I decided I'd design and make the costumes too. When the director asked if I knew how to actually make costumes, I looked as insulted as I could and haughtily informed him it was my specialty. (As far as theoretical background was concerned, I could tell the difference between dungarees and a gray flannel suit, and as for practical experience, I'd darned a sock once.) I figured it would be a nice job for Claudia. At least we could keep the money in the family that way.

There was one problem. They'd already noticed my German wasn't exactly flawless and that I might have a rough time understanding a difficult play, so they gave me three hundred marks to get a Dutch translation made.

It was time for my train back to Holland. Krapp and Krampf brought me to the station. Everybody was convinced I was one of the world's top set designers. Especially since my slides were mixed up when I was showing my work and included shots of some really fine female landscape. Including Claudia in a bikini. Made a great hit.

"Excuse me," I said. "A little technical difficulty."

Proving once again that you can mix sex with business after all.

I got home late that night. By taxi, because I'd already picked up a small advance. Claudia was still up. I told her the whole story and that I'd do the sets and she'd make the costumes.

"But I don't know how," she said. As a matter of fact I knew Claudia's knowledge of costumes didn't go any further than panties and bras, and that even sewing on a button was hard work for her.

"Don't be silly," I said. "Just think of all the girls who'd give an arm for the chance to work with me, and you, you get the chance and all you say is you don't know how. What the hell! Just think of it—the two of us, the famous team of Cremer & Cremer, Experts in Costumes and Stage Design. We could work our way all over the world. Interviews in all the papers, pictures of the two of us. Our names in big letters in all the programs. Credits in movies, names on TV. Reputations in Berlin, in Paris, in London, Vienna—even in Holland. We'd make a fortune. All the big directors would invite us over. A weekend in Palma. A weekend in Ibiza . . . or, well, maybe Corsica. We, the two of us, the theater experts. Don't you see what it could mean? No more fights, just lots of hard work. We'll be able to hire a governess to take care of the baby. A sweet black chick. Then when I get home at night she can scratch my back. I can already see our names up in lights on the marquee: *Jan & Claudia Cremer, Sets and Costumes*. We'll open a boutique where you can sell all the dresses you design on the side. All that money—just think of it. Otherwise I'll have to start hiring all kinds of characters who won't do what I want anyway. No, it's got to be you and me."

251

I went on for hours but she just kept saying she didn't know how to make costumes.

"Like hell you don't," I said, "and you're going to."

270

The train early Monday morning was packed with commuters. They all got out at the last stop in Holland, leaving me behind in a thick cloud of Van Nelle's Strong Shag smoke. Since I had the compartment all to myself now, I stretched out, put my feet up. The conductor had already been around twice to punch the tickets. I wasn't feeling too good—a result of the farewell drinking bout we'd had with a few friends the night before. Claudia and I decided it would be better if I went first. If everything went well I'd come back and pick her up. She was expecting the baby any day now. Also, I couldn't have anything distracting me from my work.

At the border I had to show my receipt for the fine. The bright M.P. had spotted my name on the top of his Black Book list. Actually he was a nice enough guy with a pimply face who knew about me from the papers as a revolutionary artist and stunt man. I went back to work on my translation of *Die Frauen des Ochsen,* the first play they were going to do. I'd bought a German-Dutch pocket dictionary and, after all, I had a gift for languages. (Or was it arithmetic?) And the three hundred marks would come in handy. For a genius like me it was a breeze. I was already more than half done.

The door opened and a German border official came in wearing a hat that looked like a flying saucer.

"Passport," he snapped. I handed it to him. "Anything to declare?" he asked when he'd examined my passport.

"No," I said.

"Open that suitcase," he barked. I dragged myself to my feet. I'd been stretched out very comfortably. When I'd opened my suitcase, he began rummaging through it with his gloved claws, messing all the clothes Claudia had neatly folded up.

"Easy, Gramps," I said. "The war's over, remember?"

"What what what?! What did you say??"

"I said the floor's clover and if your wife's a pickled pepper you better peck a bale of horse, right?"

I thought that would give him something to work on. But maybe he never got paid his overtime for the war and still had a chip on his shoulder because suddenly he exploded.

"Where are you going?" he screamed.

I told him I was going to Kwammerschlagen to work in the theater.

"Do you have an official Working Permit? Nein? Then it's strictly verboten for you to work there. You just stay here in Holland where you belong and keep out of Germany!"

I was slowly losing my cool. These Krauts really had their nerve. They were the ones who lost the war, not us. So I screamed right back at him, "Listen, Heinz! It's none of your fucking business where I'm going or what I do. You got any complaints, you take them to the director of the theater in Kwammerschlagen. In the meantime, bugger off."

He was a really mean-looking bastard, the kind that always plays the SS officer in American war films. The one who kicks wounded soldiers and twists out his cigar butt in a blind Yank's eyesocket. Then he roars with laughter. He also tortures prisoners, pulls out their fingernails. He had a sharp expressionless face, mouse ears, and light blue eyes. The typical Teuton. He stood with his legs spread in a pair of tight green riding breeches and big black boots, his jacket buttoned up to his chin, his silver buttons brightly polished, my passport in his hand.

"I'm going to report this," he said. "You have no right to do work that should be done by a German!"

"Come off it, Adolf," I laughed. "Give me back my passport or *I'll* report *you.*"

"Come with me," he commanded.

It had been fun for a while but now I was really getting mad. What was the bastard picking on me like this for? What did he have against me?

"Come with who, where? I want your name and number. I've had enough of your shit and it's your ass that's going to be in a sling, not mine, Jack!"

At that moment another customs official came by. Just as big as my pal. Bigger. He looked in, saw his comrade, and opened the door.

"What's going on?" he asked. My Kraut didn't look so happy now. All his fierceness drained away. Very calmly he explained that I didn't have a Working Permit for Kwammerschlagen. The other man, obviously his superior, took my passport, leafed through it, said something like "Ach, forget about it," and told me to see the Arbeitsamt in Kwammerschlagen about getting a permit. Very polite. Very friendly.

"But . . ." my man in green stammered.

"But nothing," the friendly one said. "Everything's in order. Now come on!"

They left the compartment together after the Blond Beast had handed me back my passport with a sour look on his face. When he looked back through the window I saluted him with my middle finger—stiff as a ramrod—and grinned in his sadistic face. Poor Adolf, it just wasn't his day.

271

Downtown Kwammerschlagen looked like a ghost town. A thick dirty mist hung over the streets. Everybody was hard at work in this prosperous German industrial dump. At work on the Wirtschaftswunder. Hundreds of towering chimneys spat smoke and fire into the gray air. The only traffic on the streets was clanging streetcars and farting buses. The taxi stands were deserted. I walked to the theater.

The Städtische Bühnen was next to a big well-kept park. I wandered around under the bare trees. Alone, except for a few old men shuffling down the graveled paths. Across from the theater was a big gray bunker. A square box. The walls, chipped and nicked by thousands of bullets, were camouflaged now by a twenty-year growth of vines and weeds. It stood there—a silent monument to the war.

I looked at the bunker and felt the walls and thought of all the soldiers who'd been lined up against them. How many Americans, Tommies, or Germans? How many times had open wounds been ripped open again? How many times had the words "Mama" or "Mutti" rung out? How many times had the bunker itself writhed in pain? The walls of the gigantic bunker looked cold on this chilly autumn morning. They reminded me of battered flesh. The bunker brought back long-forgotten memories of the war.

272

The factory town was heavily bombed. Me and my friends spent days rummaging through the rubble. Sometimes the junk was still smoldering. We poked our sticks under bricks, wallpaper, and smashed china looking for something we could either eat or sell or use for fuel. Sometimes we found other things, too, under the bricks, like a dead dog, a dead cat, or a dead bird in a crushed cage. That was usually about all that was left by the time we got there.

As soon as the walls had caved in and the screams turned to silence, the looters started in on the place. They cleaned out everything that was worth anything. If you were a kid and came across a real find the others had missed, like a soot-covered sack of potatoes, you had to watch out. Carrying a prize like that could cost you your life.

One of the rich streets near the hospital was bombed. Houses collapsed. The dead were dragged out and taken off in hearses. Neighbors and vultures, black market men and thieves picked the place clean and bare as a bone. You weren't allowed to go into bombed-out houses. But we were bored and we liked adventure, so we slipped in anyway. "Rich" houses were our favorite hunting grounds. Sometimes there was still an expensive toy or two lying around.

One afternoon after a bunch of us had poked our way through one ruin without turning up anything worth saving (but had had fun looking), my friends took off for home. I sat down on a pile of stones and was just fiddling my stick around in the rubbish when suddenly I uncovered a burlap bag. I pulled it out. It was filled with potatoes. Big round spuds. The greatest treasure I'd ever found in my life. Now my mother and I wouldn't have to go hungry any more. I was so happy I did a war dance around and around the burlap bag. I waited till it got dark, then started dragging that incredibly heavy bag foot by foot along the ground. I'd drag it, then stop, take a look around to see if anybody was watching, then when the coast was clear, drag it on a little bit farther. Night came and I could already see my mother's happy face in front of me. She'd be proud of me!

To get to our back yard I had to go through an empty bombed-out, cleared-off lot. I was too impatient to wait until later that night and I didn't dare leave the bag there. Besides, if I got home too late, my mother would be worried. So I risked it. Some people passed by but nobody pays much attention to a five-year-old kid. I had almost made it into our back yard when a man rode up on a bike. The hard wooden tires thumped against the stones. I'd seen him looking at me a couple of minutes before. He got off his bike—a tall wreck of a man in a suit two sizes too small for him. I didn't pay any attention to him until suddenly he blocked my way.

"Whatcha got there?" he asked.

"Sand," I said in a trembling voice.

I was so close to home I couldn't stand the idea of anything going wrong now. I said a quick prayer. "Our Lord Jesus Christ, please help me with the potatoes, amen."

"Where do you live, little boy?" the man asked.

When I let go of the bag to point out our house, the guy grabbed for it and tried to sling it on the back of the bike. I started screaming, "Mother, mother, come here quick!" and tried to hold onto the sack. I didn't even see him swing but suddenly a punch practically went through my skull. I fell and he kicked me hard. When I got up again I saw my mother running toward me armed with a frying pan and the man disap-

255

pearing into the dark night. The bag of potatoes on the back of his bike. I still felt like a hero, even though I cried my eyes out because, once again, I'd come home empty-handed.

273

Sienie lived on our block. A tall, skinny girl, sixteen. She did "dirty things" for money. She used to go around with a bunch of older women. "Painted witches," my mother used to call them, or "sluts," when they came by to pick up Sienie on their way downtown. Sometimes they even rode up in a real car, with soldiers who cracked jokes and laughed a lot and sang while they were waiting for Sienie to come out wearing lipstick and rouge and high-heeled shoes and jauntily swinging her little umbrella. Sienie was my girlfriend. She asked me to deliver messages to a café or the barracks for her. She gave me cigarettes or candy wrapped in shiny red paper. None of the kids were allowed to have anything to do with her. But I liked Sienie. Wanted to marry her someday. One afternoon I followed her to the ruins without her knowing it. I stayed outside. I wanted to surprise her when I came in. After a few minutes I tiptoed in the door and got the shock of my life. Sienie was lying on her back naked, a German soldier on top of her ramming away. I wanted to hit him because Sienie was cry-ing—sometimes really screaming. But I was so scared I ran away. Sienie saw me and a few days later I had to promise I wouldn't tell anybody about what I'd seen. I promised. Then I gulped down some piss from a rusty can as a Sign of Secret Union that I would never tell on her.

274

One night a terrifying noise wakes me up. The sound of boots kicking at our back door.

"Open the door! Open up! Polizei!"

I come out of the bedroom frightened and see mother in the glaring light of the kitchen lamp, trying to hold the door shut. The door swings open. Mother falls. Six German soldiers—loud and insolent—stand in our kitchen.

"We need food!" they yell. "You got any jewelry? Any gold? Any-body hiding out here? Any bread? Meat? Schnapps? Come on! Give us whatever you've got or we'll smash the whole place—and goddammit, get a move on!"

Mother says we don't have anything.

"We don't even have any food for ourselves!" she says and shows her bony wrists to the soldiers. They storm and swear and finally leave.

The next morning a noise at the back door. Somebody knocking. When mother opens the door, nobody's there. Just a big wooden crate. Full of food—bacon, meat, cheese, bread, flour, soap, salt, oatmeal, and sugar. A note with "Sorry about last night" scribbled on it.*

> Hitler's kaput
> Stalin's dead
> & I still don't feel any better.

275

The grumpy doorman at the theater didn't want to let me in. A crusty old fart with a big droopy mustache and a peg leg. Half walrus, half pirate. By the time he finally let me pass, I'd filled him in on my past history from the Year One, listed the capitals of every Dutch province, and sung the national anthem three times over from start to finish. And he still looked suspicious.

Krappsalaten wasn't there yet and Beinkrampf was in conference. I went to the canteen and ordered a big mug of beer, which I finished off in giant gulps. Tooti, the piece with the whopper-knockers, wasn't there. Probably just worked the night shift. So I had another big mug of cold lager. I left a note with the doorman saying I'd be in the canteen. By the time Krappsalaten finally blew in I was pleasantly plastered. Naturally we had a little bite to eat together. Then he introduced me to my assistants. My chief assistant was a nice Polish kid, Olov. The first thing I had him do was bring a crate of beer up to my new studio. The studio was a big square room with neon lights, drafting tables, couches, a refrigerator, and a telephone. Super Deluxe. Actually it belonged to the guy who generally designed all their sets but who had gone off to Switzerland for an international convention.

"Away with this junk," I said to Olov, and everything that belonged to the other set designer vanished. Down to the cellar. An hour later I asked a painter to take the other name off the door and put mine on. In gold letters, please. When I got back from the canteen the words JAN CREMER BÜHNENBILDNER stood out against the black door in sparkling gold.

---

* A few days after the war was over Mother and I were arrested by the Dutch Police—for collaborating with the Germans.

I got down to work. Made sketches of the scenery the way I thought I'd like it to look. Then Olov drew my sketches to scale and constructed three dimensional models. He was a very gifted boy. Since he wanted to be a Bühnenbildner when he grew up, he was eager to show what he could do while the big boss took on a few more beers down in the canteen. It takes time for me to wake up in the morning. At least two hours.

276

I'd finished my translation of *Die Frau des Ochsen*. A snap. A breeze. For instance, it starts off in German like this: "Der ganze Akt spielt in einem Dorf des Languedoc, im Erdgeschoss des sehr weitläufigen Metzgerhauses, und läuft ohne Unterbrechung ab." I played it by ear and in no time at all came up with: "The guns-act spiels in a turf that's along a dock in Erdgeschoss." Which seemed pretty clear to me. It got a bit rougher as I went on, though. What did "This sour wide-loafed mixed your houses and loafs on in under [the] breaking ape" mean? Or wasn't it supposed to mean anything?

I'd heard that Audiberti was avant-garde, but this seemed pretty far out to me. I'll settle for Bert Schierbeek s brand of nonsense any day. It may not make much sense but at least you can understand it:

> *cow near well*
> *says moo moo*
> *catches fly and*
> *car says beep*
> *shirt on fence*

Or something like that.

It was a good thing the scenery was supposed to be abstract anyway, otherwise I would have really been lost. We got down to work. At least Olov did because I was mostly in the canteen waiting for Inspiration. With Tooti with the Titan tits. She was a doll. Not pretty and not all that young either. But she looked like a good piece and she could make great cheesecake. If she was behind the bar she always served me first. Gave me an extra big mug with a big head of foam.

The first few days I slept at a Gasthof, in a dark German alley. An actors' hangout. The dominant color in the bar downstairs was a somber dark brown. They drank beer out of boot-shaped mugs. In the morning you got dry bread and bitter jelly for breakfast.

I had a big dark room that looked out onto a deserted street. On the bed was a big fluffy feather-stuffed plumeau. The kind that flops on the floor as soon as you turn in bed. It was very cozy. The trouble was you had to be in by one o'clock every night. I never could get used to that. Of course they went on drinking after the place was locked up, but not for long.

One night (I'd gone to bed early with a good Raymond Chandler mystery and dozed off, probably because of the healthy German air—if you took a deep breath of that Kwammerschlagen smog you felt like you'd just smoked a pack of cheap cigarettes on an empty stomach!) a tattoo of thumps against my wall woke me up. The wall was about a foot thick—wood. Whoever it was, they must have been fucking away like mad. Then I heard footsteps in the hall, somebody banging on the door next to mine, then the door must have caved in because the next thing I heard was two voices screaming bloody murder. A woman's voice and a man's.

"What are you doing with my wife?" I heard somebody scream. "Heinz, Heinz, Heinz, don't!" howled the woman.

"We were just warming up, sir," I heard a young man's voice say.

"Well, your engine looks hot enough to me. You're ready for take off. Now fly!" bellowed the other man.

Yelps from the young man, yowls from the woman, the tinkle of glass and a solid thud on the street outside. I rushed to the window and saw somebody lying on the street, stark naked.

Since I was up now anyway I put on my watch, dressed, and went downstairs to the bierstube. I bought a pack of cigarettes and a bunch of actors who were all completely stoned by this time invited me to come over. They were up to their armpits in deep conversation.

I heard "Braunenschwanzen gruterfeintjedermann vereinschlingert-jchenkaputt menschfleishig." After a few more beers the conversation turned to Holland.

"But," said a fat Kraut who always got cast as the villain, "we're not Germans or Dutchmen. We're all Europeans. Europeans!!" He gurgled, spun, and slowly slid under the table.

It was all a lot of bullshit so I went back upstairs, curled up in my nest, and visions of Deutsche Mädel sugarplums danced in my head.

Kwammerschlagen was an unbelievably dull town. I worked hard on the sets. I was very popular with the guys who had to make the sets, because I always started the day off with beer and sausages for all. Which fosters good will. The scenery was a huge supercinemascopic panorama. One big screen in back with an abstract landscape that changed every time a different spotlight picked it up. In front of that there were three welded steel structures, and in front of them the actors. One of the critics wrote: "Jan Cremer's sets and constructions were fantastic and grandiose. The pity was that the actors had to stand in front of them!"

People from the theater often invited me over to their houses for supper, but their parties always broke up around midnight, which is just when I start to come alive. That's why I moved into a hotel that was open all night. Right across from the station. A big impersonal pseudo-American hotel with neon lights, plush carpets, elevators, modern mosaics on the walls with cute little birds and fish, stuck-up receptionists, stuck-up chambermaids, and a stuck-up asshole of a manager. In short, one big stuck-up hell of a hole.

I had a cubby hole of a room with a view of the back of the police station. First thing I did when I moved in was take the fruit out of the bowl and pitch it at a few cops standing out in the yard. I only hit one of them. But I hit him good. A soft pear smack in his flying-saucer hat.

Very early the next morning big knuckles knocked on my door. Still half asleep I opened the door. Two of the Boys in Green. I was scared shitless. Thought they'd found out who threw the fruit. I was just going to slam the door in their faces and try to escape over the rooftops when they handed me a note saying I had to report to the police station before noon with my passport to get a Working Permit. That crazy Kraut on the train hadn't forgotten me.

I said thank you, but that I wouldn't be dropping over to the police station. I was too tired (it was only ten and I never started work until after lunch). And I didn't like police stations, and furthermore I was here as a guest of their city, so if they needed any papers signed they should see the guy who ran the theater.

Kwammerschlagen was a dead town after midnight. The one place still kicking was the Amerika-Keller. A big nightclub under an apartment building close to the hotel. I dropped in every once in a while. It was very German, very dark. Broads behind the bar with hard permanents and banana tits. All dolled up for the trade. In the halls a scrawny pack of teenyboppers out cruising for the night.

The prices were sky high. The only thing you could do was pick up a bopper and take her back to bed. Or get lushed out of your nut. Which was what I chose to do. I was in a rotten mood. I'd lost a bet. Two hundred marks down the drain.

It was the night of the Patterson-Liston match. I bet on Patterson. Besides, I just felt like tanking up on beer. But in the Amerika-Keller every time you order a beer you also had to have a glass of brandy. House rule. It was a syrupy sort of rotgut. Paint remover with grape juice.

There wasn't a single cute chick around. Plenty of bleached hair, pimply faces, skinny legs, and fat asses. I sat at the bar. A glassy-eyed B-girl noticed my wallet was bulging and began giving me a soft-eye massage. Drop dead, I thought, you're a dog. You've got corns on your cunt and they screwed your tits on backward.

But I said, "You're beautiful. You look just like a girl I used to know back home. I wanted to marry her, but," I sighed, "she committed suicide, poor sap."

I was starting to feel pretty weird. From mixing all those drinks. The more I drank, the noisier I got. I said I was an American pilot (I spoke German with a strong American accent, like Chris Howland used to on Radio Luxemburg when I'd settle down with my girl every Thursday night between seven and eight and we'd eat potato chips and I'd show her how to smoke and we'd listen to E. Presley, B. Haley, and Little Richard) stationed in Germany and wasn't it a bloody shame the war was over because I'd like to put all those years of training to use and bomb Germany flat again. Which led to a bit of trouble, of course.

I got into a fist fight with a fat Kraut sitting next to me at the bar. He had a mean face. I thought maybe a little cognac would wash it off, so— slosh—off it went. One way to get rid of the stuff. They all jumped me at the same time. I fought like a madman, made confetti out of one guy's jacket, socked a woman right up and over the bar—a nice short leggy flight. But in no time they had me pinned on the floor with a waiter on each side to hold my hands. I lay there on the blue carpet in front of a juke box that kept changing colors. Until the police arrived and arrested me for disturbing the peace.

"Kommjetzt! Schnell!" they said, grabbing my elbows.

"Get your fucking paws off, you lousy Kraut!" I said. "Don't you know who I am? You wanna start an international scandal or something?"

At the police station they told me to sit on a bench, but I jumped right up and started making trouble all over again. I demanded they call the director of the theater, which took a lot of wind out of their sails. A complaint was filed and they told me I could go now but would be hearing from them soon. A smart-assed bunch of bulls. I gave them an F in Conduct and beat it.

The next morning I had to report to the director. I was the black sheep of the theater. Every day there was something new about me in the *Zeitung*. Usually not exactly favorable. Just one damn scandal after the other. That the well-known Dutch set designer Jan Cremer, invited to Germany to work for the Stadtische Buhnen, had been involved in a fist fight in a notorious nightspot. Or had resisted arrest and shouted anti-German slogans at anybody who cared to listen and at more who didn't.

True, it was the third time a complaint had been filed against me for disturbing the peace. The director had also gotten a veritable flood of

261

unofficial complaints. Once I threw up out of my hotel window onto a police car. Insulted the help. The chambermaid for instance had gotten an awful shock when I opened the door stark naked. Refused to pay the bill in a big-deal restaurant because the prices were too high. Every time anything happened the director wanted to see me.

He tried to use psychology on me, pointing out that I was a guest in a foreign country and ought to behave myself. He didn't care what I did when I was off duty as long as I kept the name of the theater out of the papers. He was all for publicity but not this kind. We'd been all through this a dozen times already. They couldn't fire me because I worked like a horse till late every night, was keenly interested in their programs (actually only in the ballet chicks), and did my best in every way. If the reporters felt like writing nasty articles about me, it wasn't my fault.

I told the good man what Oscar Wilde always used to say, that bad publicity is always better than no publicity. He said yes, yes, of course, but the only trouble was that he wasn't the only member of the board. The mayor, the Oberveranstaltungsführer, was a member of the board too. Everyone was impressed by my talent and good will, but I must leave the name of the theater untarnished.

That particular morning, after a little heart-to-heart dad-son speech, he tried out a new angle: "You must leave the name of *Holland* untarnished! Holland! Untarnished!"

He was a phony old fart. With his perfumed suits, manicured hands and dyed locks. He could speak a bit of Dutch since he'd been in Holland during the Krieg.

After listening to his fake chuckles long enough, I promised him it wouldn't happen again and thought, Up yours, Jack. Twenty years ago you were smiling on top of a tank and your face hasn't improved since.

He advised me to send for Claudia.

"Not a bad idea," I said.

I promised him I'd think about it. Of course, he thought, once Cremer's got his woman he'll calm down.

The director's room was in a different building and I had to go past the dancers' dressing rooms on my way back. There was actually just one interesting female in the whole troupe. Her name was Ingrid. A big blonde piece with a nice hard German face. The Hildegard Neff type. I had my eye on her even though she was engaged. To the regular set designer, the one who was off in Switzerland for that convention. When I walked down the hall peeping into the dressing rooms, I accidentally bumped into her. She was on her way back from a rehearsal of *Der Bettelstudent*. She looked very appetizing. All she had on was tights and a leotard, if that's what those things are called. Anyhow, I could see she wasn't wearing a bra because her nipples showed through the thin black material. Trim round tits with big buttons in the middle.

"Hello," I said, pretending to be very surprised. "Want to have some coffee when you're through?"

I knew a good coffee shop where they had good cheesecake and strudel. The chocolate-covered cream puffs were fantastic, likewise the whipped cream. She wanted to, but since she couldn't just say yes right away she said no.

"Too bad," I said, "because I know a great place where we can sit and. . . ."

I'd pick her up in an hour. The tea was good—rosehip tea, bright red and slightly bitter. Constipated anybody, try rosehip.

277

Ingrid had a room in a big townhouse. Furnished like the rooms of actresses, ballerinas, folk singers, fashion designers, painters, sculptresses, women writers, and poets all over the world: Toulouse Lautrec posters on the walls, expensive framed etchings of flowers, a picture of Bertolt Brecht, books about The Theater scattered all over the floor, dried flowers in cute little vases, colorful strings of beads hanging on the walls, dolls, bedspread from India, brightly-colored corduroy pillows, hand-painted porcelain cups and saucers, droopy plants, old-fashioned tasseled lamp shades, colored bottles on a shelf, abstract paintings, Miles Davis and John Coltrane records, and, of course, *The Threepenny Opera*.

She was a sweet kid. We talked about the theater for hours. After a few drinks from the bottle we took along when we left the bar, we decided I'd sleep there. Not much sleep but a very pleasant night. And as my father always used to say, "If you haven't laid a Deutsche Mädel, you won't know Deutschland."

278

The police called the theater. To find out what the score was with my residence permit and Working Permit. They notified me three times to report to the police station. But I never showed up. I was asking for trouble, arrest, and a fine. Beinkrampf made an appointment for me for the next morning. There was no getting out of it. I'd have to go. Tell them I worked for the theater. Show them the letter Beinkrampf wrote saying I was working there. All I had to do was get a stamp in my passport. Nothing to it.

The next afternoon, as soon as I woke up, I went to the police station. A big squat cool building with marble steps, light green walls (same as in jails, police stations, and government offices everywhere in Europe), and a uniformed guard at the door. I showed him the note and he told me where to go, a few flights up. On the staircase I could hear the clack of heavy boots on hard floor as cops stomped around the halls. The foreign police office was filled with desks littered with typewriters and stacks of paper. Behind the desks, clerks in shirt sleeves. The clerk I showed the note to pointed to another desk.

"Herr Schweinarsch ist over derrr!" he said.

I strolled over to Schweinarsch and handed him my letter. He was a typical sauerkraut veteran. A scar zigzagging down one side of his face, the regulation ugly mug, and one arm (probably left the other behind in Stalingrad). His sleeve was sewed up just under the elbow.

"Cremer!" he roared, rolling the R way back in his throat. Then his voice rose a few octaves and he snapped, "Who do you think you are? Here," and he crashed his one fist down on his desk, "it says eleven o'clock. What time is it now? It's one o clock. Come back tomorrow! At nine o'clock!"

Nine is no hour for me to be anywhere except in bed. I was astounded that anybody—even a cop—could be up at that hour. I gave him Beinkrampf's letter, which he glanced at briefly. He wanted my passport. "Heil Hitler!" I said clicking my heels.

"Wass?!" he yipped. "Wass wass dass?'

"I said, handle with care!" I said. "Why?"

"Be back tomorrow at nine," he repeated.

I said I was afraid nine was a bad time for me since I always slept until noon. Which maybe I shouldn't have said. Schweinarsch probably liked to sleep late too, but since he could only swing it on weekends—in peacetime anyway—he was touchy on the subject. Very touchy. So was I. Also, I was in a hurry. Besides I hate bureaucracy. Now that I was there I wanted to get it taken care of once and for all.

So I said, "Do it now. Just put your stamp on and let's be done with it. Otherwise I won't ever come back! I've got better things to do than take a lot of lip from a two-bit clerk!"

"We'll just see about that!" he boomed (all the other clerks looking up from their bulging files or comic books).

"Ach, Herr Schweinhund," I said, "skip the shit. Just give me my passport and make it fast. Before I start losing my temper. I don't even know you. Why should we fight? The war's over. Too bad, huh? Still, you don't hear me giving you hell about that bike of mine you stole, do you? So why don't you just ram it, Charlie—you lousy SS-er, you dumb Kraut! Who do you think you are anyway? Hitler's been kaput for a long time, Heinie."

I was really getting mad now. It took me a while but I was getting there.

"A pity all they got was your arm. It's your head they should have blown off!"

He was hysterical now. He screamed that he'd show me who was boss around here. He dialed a number. He was going to have me arrested. I thought, in a pig's ass you are. I've a rehearsal at two o'clock and Beinkrampf knows I'm here. Two uniforms clumped in. I was escorted out to a waiting room. In came a big bull. He shot me a dirty look. I shot back. A draw so far.

"Could I please have something to drink?" I very politely asked the cops who were playing cards in the waiting room. I got a cup of coffee from a Thermos bottle. They told me the top cop was upstairs and that they were trying to figure out what to do with me. The door opened again and big bad bull came in with my passport.

"You have to be out of Germany no later than noon tomorrow," he said. "Otherwise we'll escort you to the border ourselves. And you know what that means? You can go now." I thought, I wouldn't bet on that if I were you, Buster. He who laughs last laughs best!

Beinkrampf was furious. Furious with the police, of course. They were waiting for me to tell my assistants how to complete the sets. I pretended I was terribly upset, a broken man. Beinkrampf went with me to talk to the director. I had already told Krappsalaten I'd be leaving that night. He suffered a mild nervous breakdown. The premiere was just a week off. I was the only one who could finish the sets. Besides, Beinkrampf and Krappsalaten refused to work with anyone but me. I told the director I wanted to leave, that I wasn't used to being treated this way.

"Papa kaput! Mama kaput! Okay! But for a great artist to be hampered in his creativity? That's going too far. I can't understand it. The Germans used to like art, love art, take as much of it as they could lay hands on. Why I remember, not so long ago. . . ."

They tried to console me. But no, I had been wounded too deeply.

"I don't even *want* to stay here any longer!" I said. "My whole family gone. And now this!"

The director started going off his rocker now, too. Raging mad, at the police. He called a few people and I heard a lot of "Donnerwetter jammerknapfen!" crackling through the receiver. Then I was asked to please go back to the police station. To be so kind as to take Beinkrampf along with me this time. He told me that the Kwammerschlagen Establishment, including the mayor, had been alerted. The police chief was going to regret having started anything with me. Beinkrampf spoke to the guy at the door, who quickly phoned ahead to announce our arrival, and a few minutes later the chief himself came striding down the hall. With a friendly smile and outstretched hand. It had all been a most regrettable misunderstanding and if I would kindly be so kind as to come upstairs I could have as many stamps as I wanted. He walked us all the way to the office where, he said, Herr Schweinarsch would be delighted to be of service.

279

Since Claudia didn't want to make the costumes, I had to do them myself. So far, we'd spent all our time on the sets, me and my assistants. Besides my personal assistant Olov, I had three more men: a carpenter, a painter, and a welder, plus two girls for the costumes. Between management and those of us who did the actual work, contact was sometimes strained by the fact that socially they belonged to one class and we belonged to another. One week before the premiere, Beinkrampf and Krappsalaten were pacing the floor and wringing their chubby hands because they were sure the sets couldn't possibly be finished on time. Just because in the past the crew had always refused to work overtime.

"Leave it to me," I said. I knew I could get my crew to do the work. All I would need was beer, sausages, and wine. One afternoon there was a meeting—the last full-dress meeting of the entire staff, including me. To discuss the supplies that still had to be bought and the costumes. Olov reminded me of the meeting when I walked into the studio that morning. It had completely slipped my mind. The meeting was at two o'clock and it was now twelve. I told Olov to go to the library and get me a book about costumes, since all I knew was that pants have a fly and brassieres have hooks. After spending an hour reading through *Knaurs-Kostume-Lexicon,* I knew all I wanted to know about costumes and their history.

All the heads of the various departments were there at the meeting: the chief lighting technician, the costume mistress, the director, the producer, and the dramaturg. Olov and I were the last to arrive. Me in my best suit, Olov with a huge stack of papers under his arm. Because you had to make an impression. Show that you'd been working hard. There were only a few quick sketches in Olov's impressive pile. The rest was just blank sheets. About twenty people were seated around a round table. After the usual chat, cigars, tea, a cigarette, soccer scores, the budget, and Krappsalaten, it was finally my turn.

I gave a terribly intellectual little speech, throwing out lots of words like "creativity," "the history of the theatah," and "existentiality." Once I got going on the topic of costumes I was cruising along so nicely that I gave a detailed survey of their development from Eve's fig leaf all the way up to the Theater of the Nude. I must have talked for twenty minutes about costumes in the Reconnaissance before a lady corrected my German.

"Mr. Cremer means the Renaissance," she said.

So there was no problem about the costumes and the tea was delicious.

280

After finishing up at night I sometimes went over to the canteen where Tooti worked. I got into violent discussions with the theater people about Shakespeare and Stravinsky. In the meantime I'd feast my eyes on Tooti and my stomach on beer, schnapps, and sausages.

Management reprimanded me gently for spending so much time in the canteen and getting too chummy with the work crews. Screw that. After all, we weren't living in South Africa.

I went to the premiere of *Der Bettelstudent,* a hilarious operetta with almost 564 acts of hoopla. I was sitting in the front row getting a steady shower of spit and sweat from the actors. The lady next to me, a society dame with her neckline cut down to her navel, kept mopping at the river running down between her dugs. Ingrid danced in an embroidered peasant costume, her tits popping over the top like a couple of honey dew melons.

Our relationship had come to an end. There'd been too much gossip about it at the theater and she'd had a mad phone call from Switzerland. She wanted to stay with me, but then we'd have to get engaged, I'd have to meet her parents, etc. That turned me off fast. Look before you leap, I always say. Before you know it, you're all dolled up in a peasant blouse, a little cap and knickers, dancing around with your hands on your hips singing Heylala in German. I didn't feel like spending the rest of my life in a real-life production of *Der Bettelstudent.*

281

After the show I went over to the canteen. To have another beer and see what was up with Tooti. I was in the mood for love. I'd fooled around with her once in the kitchen. She asked me if I could help her get something out of the ice box, then suddenly grabbed for my crotch and there I was inside her dress. "Ich liebe dich," she sighed. I had it made.

Tooti had been married to an East German Vopo who'd fallen off the Berlin Wall. She had a baby and lived with her parents in Kwammerschlagen. Which was why she couldn't take me home with her. I couldn't take her to my hotel either, because two-bit provincial German hotels give you a harder time even than the Hiltons.

The canteen wasn't in the same building as the theater itself. Stage hands, Bettelstudents and prospective ballerinas stood around drinking beer or coffee. I sat down at the table near the counter. Tooti came over with a beer and I said, "Cold out, isn't it?" Just to have something to say.

When the canteen closed at twelve, I left with Tooti. She knew a hotel in town where we could spend the night together. It was on the top floor of a third-rate dump on a bleak mean street. Tooti knew the owner. After we'd had some beer and wine in the bierstube downstairs, we went up to our room.

It was one of those same-all-over-Europe hotel rooms, dimly lit by a weak bulb behind a yellowish thick-skinned lampshade, rose-patterned wallpaper faded to a sort of turd brown, two little lamps on the two shaky night tables, a sink with luke warm and cold running water, a bidet, a big sturdy bed with a crocheted bedspread, a poor reproduction of a pastoral landscape hanging at the head of the bed. I'd brought along a bottle of Eisbrandt and a few glasses. I poured us a drink. We lay down on the bed.

Tooti was a dark well-rounded woman with slim legs and arms, a small waist, but an enormous pair of knockers. She was wearing a tight-fitting shiny black dress and when she lay down on the bed she kicked off her pumps, lifted her skirt, and rolled the nylons off her legs.

We talked for a while. She talked about the Vopos and how she'd been raped by the Russians in the war, when she was only sixteen. The Bolsheviks knew how to pick them all right. She looked good to me now. At sixteen she must have been a real knockout!

We necked and when she slipped out of her dress I was thrilled. Her skin was a nice mellow brown and her chubby buttocks bulged out from under her black garter belt. But what really caught and held me were her magnificent tits. Now that she had her dress off, they'd suddenly became enormously real. They were deliciously soft and her bra was colossal. It took some doing to get it open.

Why the hell can't they make one kind of standard bra all over the world, with the same sort of button or snap or hook? Of the 589 different kinds of bras, I've been able to open maybe sixty-two of them on the first try. But every time I get used to one kind, they start wearing another. Just think of how much precious time is lost that way!

When the bra was finally open—Tooti had to help me out a little—her terrific boobs came spilling out in waves (when the Niagara Falls first fell they must have come out in a gush like that). Her nipples were big light brown discs, and where her bathing suit started her skin was a delicate pale white. Her enormous breasts sagged a little * which made them all the more appetizing. She could easily compete in a Miss Fantastic contest and maybe even win. She was in the Jayne Mansfield 38-22-38 class. Her nipples smelled sweet and I licked off the sweat between her breasts.

I stripped and before long we were lying there in a "neun-und-sexig." Her twat lips were strong and sturdy and when I took a good bite of her spicy tulip, Tooti writhed with delight. She purred and meowed like a cat in heat. I kept licking until I got a cramp in my tongue. She wasn't exactly the intellectual type, although she did pant and say, "Play me a tune on your magic flute," which showed, I thought, a pretty keen interest in opera.

I stuck my Schwanz † between her delicious soft warm buttocks and she murmured "Komm in meinen Fotze,‡ Liebling, komm." Little Jan didn't have to be told twice. Like a leopard I leaped for the meat.

Like a U.S. Marine I landed on the soft underbelly of Germany and like a starving man I devoured the German steak garnished with sperm sauce and a dash of garlic. Together we celebrated the rise of Naked Lust. I got my share of the "Wiedergutmachung" while it lasted. Before my closed blue eyes visions flitted by of swastikas and Blitzmäädel, German girls in shiny black uniforms lifting tight skirts up to their hips, girls in sexy knee-high boots. My boneless bazooka destroying innumerable Messerschmitts between her thighs. She sighed and groaned and moaned all through my Hot War offensive. With my flesh-colored machine gun I fired on all the enemy emplacements deep inside her. Time and time again I tangled with the enemy. After complicated tactics not given in any infantry manual, I emerged triumphant.

I wished I had an orange cock—orange for the House of Orange—then I could show her who had carried the day. This was war! I subdued one vital area after the other. I kept coming back up to the line of fire. With all my might. At zero hour I fired all my remaining ammunition into her soft white buttocks which split open emitting the stuffy perfume of human munitions. We celebrated victory by resuming hostilities.

Under the bridge there lay a maid.
Her wide-spread legs spread wider.

---

* Critics throughout the world commented that all the women in my first book were Super Women, e.g., endowed with fine firm full and upstanding well-pointed breasts. That's why I'm letting them sag a bit now. Maybe the critics wouldn't be so critical if they'd look at their wives.

† Low German for dick; prick; cock; meat-flute; sword, etc.

‡ Low German for cunt; nooky; quim; twat, etc.

Jan Cremer *Deutschland Über Alles*

> *When up came a soldier with a naked blade*
> *Which he buried to the hilt inside her.*

It was dawn by the time our tempestuous battle ended. Tooti got dressed. She had to take her kid to school, otherwise the teacher got mad. German chicks are the finest Europe has to offer. The only trouble is they get a little too Mütterlich. They remind me of the counselors in the camp in the Harz Mountains the Welfare people sent me off to for two months when I was ten.

282

A big villa in the mountains where poor kids and orphans are sent for their summer vacation. I was with the Dutch delegation. A handful of kids. Poor. Parents killed in the air raids or in bad physical condition. An awful bunch of brats. The Welfare people dressed us all up for our big trip abroad. Clothes dating back to the First World War. We looked like a bunch of pint-sized bums.

Even in those days I had a thing about good clothes. I always wore a big checkered flashy cap. My mother didn't appreciate my exquisite taste, said I always picked out the wrong clothes. Right after the war, for instance, I wore short pants all through the winter, either short pants or jodhpurs, awful green jodhpurs with black leather patches on the knees and seat. Which soon got me the nickname "Black Ass."

About a hundred kids—German, Dutch, Danish, and Belgian—lived there in the villa. There to recover from the aftereffects of the war. We smeared Harzer cheese in each other's hair, did "dirty things" with the girls, who loved every minute of it, and in the afternoon went for long walks with the counselors. But as soon as they turned their backs we were gone.

On one of our private expeditions, three German kids and me came to a barn lined with cages. There were all kinds of animals in the cages: squirrels, weasels, woodchucks, hamsters, and ferrets. Naturally we let them all out.

In his eagerness to escape, a weasel bit me. A tiny scratch, but that afternoon police cars with sirens and big ambulances came tear-assing up to the villa. The animals had been injected with poisonous chemicals for laboratory research. I spent three of the eight weeks in a hospital in Hannover. Every three hours another shot in the butt. Pasteur treatment. The four of us in one room. Drinking apple juice and devouring Kim and Tarzan comics, watching emergency cases come in. Or peeking under the blankets in the morgue.

Sometimes me and Herbert, my German buddy who was a little older than me, climbed over the high fence and went into the city. Both his parents had been killed in the war. He knew Hannover since that's where he came from. Just one big wreck. Ruins, houses with only a fireplace left and steps leading nowhere. The Wirtschaftswunder was already in full swing—new houses and office buildings going up day and night. Herbert came from the red light district and sometimes we went to visit his aunt, a good-looking big-titted hard-working whore. She always had a glass of beer and some cheesecake for us. She also gave us money. She really liked me and used to kiss and hug me a lot, which made me feel pretty silly. I was embarrassed every time Herbert mentioned how much his aunt liked me.

As long as we got back to the hospital by three, everything was okay. Herbert knew an awful lot of people. Mostly girls on display in the windows. Wherever we went, we were welcome. We got comic books, candy, and a little handout. Everybody looked at me and touched me affectionately. Herbert described me as a poor war victim from the Lowlands. I couldn't care less. As long as there was plenty of chow any story was fine with me.

Germany was a good country then. A country with character, filled with people who knew firsthand what war was. It had left its mark on their faces. Old grannies walked the streets pushing baby carriages loaded with junk. Every third person was short either an arm or a leg. The wheezing overweight money men weren't there yet, the ones with the big rings on their greedy fat fingers who seem to be running and ruling Germany now. In the Harz we greeted each other with "Glück Auf" and sang German songs.

One of the counselors, a dark pretty girl with a Polish name, terribly tall and sweet, with enormous breasts and dark hair under her armpits (I was madly in love with her and worked for a week on a beautiful crayon drawing for her), said yes on the last day when I burst out in tears and begged her to marry me as soon as I was old enough.

283

When Tooti left after a big hug and a mouthful of kisses, I closed the door and dove back into the warm bed. Loud German marching music from the radio two floors below woke me up later. I got dressed and had breakfast in the Gaststube. After all, I'd paid for breakfast for two. I spread a double portion of the delicious strawberry jelly on the crisp fresh buns and washed it down with good German kaffee. Life can be schöniful!

284

The costumes had to be fitted. I designed a gorgeous gown for the female lead, a prima donna. In the play Audiberti described her as "Madame Gontron, mistress of the house, devoted much of her time to domestic chores, good-natured but awkward." I immediately added "voluptuous" to the description when I saw the actress in question. An affected broad who always wanted to be the center of attention.

(A type you sometimes see on the Dutch stage, too. They talk like they've got a hot potato in their mouth and their shiny faces beam at you as if they've been eating cheese and washing themselves with Sunlight soap all day. The only interesting thing about these older actresses is that they usually have a good pair up front. I don't go to plays very often, but when I do I like to get my money's worth.)

The costume I'd designed for her was something Napoleon would have got his hand out of his jacket for. A long flowing gown with silk sleeves and a low cut neckline, my own interpretation of the Renaissance style. The kind of thing you always see in movies about Napoleon or the Count of Monte Cristo. Tits spilling out all over the place. The actress put on the dress, but where were her tits? Carefully concealed in her bra. I saw my creation destroyed before my very eyes.

I unzipped her quickly under a withering look from the lady, then grabbed her breasts and pulled them out in the open.

"Out with the knockers!" I said.

She clucked and turned purple with rage. Wham! A nasty slap on my wrist. I still held on to her whoppers though.

"What do you think you're doing, young man?" she shrieked.

"Come off it," I said, "art is art, baby, and these things belong out front."

285

I wrote to Claudia telling her the coast was clear; she should take Provo to the vet and have him vaccinated and I'd pick him up. I got to Amsterdam at six in the afternoon and we'd take the last train back. Claudia was packed and ready to go and Provo was wagging his tail.

At the station I bought some magazines for Claudia—*Harper's Bazaar, Twen, Vogue,* and *De Lach* (*The Laugh*). Her favorite, *Piccolo,* had gone out of business. I chose an exciting literary masterpiece for myself. After I'd bought three books, then changed my mind and returned them all, I finally ended up with the latest book by Harry Mulisch,

a talented Dutch kid who'd already written a couple of books. After struggling through the first two pages, I came to the conclusion that this was
way beyond me, opened the window, and tossed the book out into the dark
Dutch countryside. Finders keepers. Plenty of toilet paper on the train.

Traveling was a big experience for Claudia. The baby would be
coming any day now and for the next few months she'd be tied to the
cradle and the diapers. At the border I had to show them my certificate to
prove I'd paid my fine and then we were barreling through Germany. The
German customs inspector came in.

"Haben Sie etwas anzugeben?" he asked me.

I said "No."

"Haben Sie etwas anzugeben?" he asked Claudia.

"What?" she asked.

"Haben Sie etwas anzugeben?" the man repeated.

"Jawohl!" Claudia said, the only German she knew.

"Wass denn?"

"Jawohl," she repeated.

"Kaffee? Butter? Schnapps?"

"Jawohl," she said obligingly.

He didn't leave until I'd explained the whole situation to him, and
even then he left reluctantly. The three of us had the compartment to
ourselves. Provo stretched out on two seats. Claudia plunged into her
magazines and I peered out the window into the dark German countryside, enjoying my Van Nelle Strong Shag. Couldn't be had in Kwammerschlagen. I'd had to go without it for a whole week.

286

The clerk in my hotel, the Ruhrland, didn't want to let us in when we
arrived that night. The town looked like a ghost town, everybody already
sound asleep though it was only midnight. The clerk was a clean-cut young
type working his way up in the hotel trade and he refused to let Claudia
come up to my room. To say nothing of the dog.

"Cut the shit, Heinz," I said, because I'd taken about all I could take
of the joint. It was a fake outfit, complete with fake good manners, and the
staff hated my guts. It was one of those hotels with built-in radios in every
room that automatically stop working at midnight, where the chambermaids
pound on your door every five minutes all morning from nine o'clock on.

They must have thought I had something to do with the Mysterious
Disappearance of all the right shoes on the third floor. Some drunkard
took all the right shoes of the pairs left outside the doors to be shined and

273

dumped them in the incinerator. All except mine. Suspicious coincidence! And mine were brand new!

A couple of times they complained about the way I dressed—in a manner unsuited to such a high-class hotel. But that was their problem, not mine. I always walked around in dungarees. I told the manager that if something was bothering him he should scratch where it itches because I was paying forty marks a day for a closet-sized room and what more did he want?

So there I was. In the middle of the night in the wilds of Germany with a pregnant woman and a dog. The clerk said he couldn't let us in because we weren't married. Besides, no dogs allowed, though the night watchman had a gigantic German shepherd that lay growling in a corner of the lobby.

I made such a racket the clerk threatened to call the Polizei. We decided to look for another place. On our way out we saw "Welcome" written in big fat letters on the doormat in front of the hotel.

287

Out in the fog again we finally managed to find a taxi, then a hotel. A first-class hotel with prices to match. At any rate we had a bed for the night and Provo had a rug.

Early in the morning Provo started yelping, tugging the blanket off the bed, and scratching at the door. We let him shit in the bidet and went back to sleep. Until it was time for me to go to the theater. I took him along.

Everything was going fine and the sets were finished. I went to the Bookkeeping Department to ask for an advance because I'd spent all my money. The bookkeeper, a grouch with an old-fashioned duck's ass haircut, handed me a paper showing what I had coming *vs.* what I had to pay out. I had to pay more for German theater insurance and taxes than I could normally scrape together in a whole year. Who the fuck did they think they were? Out of every thousand marks I had coming to me they wanted eight hundred.

"Keep your figures to yourself, Groucho," I said. "Just give me my money."

A bit too gleefully he explained that if I didn't pay my taxes and insurance, I wouldn't get any money at all.

"Like hell I won't," I said. "Stuff your taxes, jam your taxes, and just cough up the money!"

"Bitte?" he said.

"Cough," I answered. And he did, and up came the money.

288

Germany has the reputation of being a country built up from rubble, a country full of bloodthirsty men marching around on endless parades with, preferably, some hair on their upper lip (Wilhelm had a lot and Adolf a little), insatiable gluttons who snarl and panic at the drop of a pin. American television programs keep the image fresh, always showing the Kraut as greedily stuffing himself on "Sauerkraut mit Eisbein," or humming a sentimental tune as he squeezes his accordion.

A normal conversation in a normal tone of voice is completely impossible for the Kraut. Just growling, snapping, barking, bawling, grunting, screaming, and squawking. True. If you go into a bar or a hotel in Germany and talk to the waiter in a normal way, he's liable to treat you like dirt, and not even German dirt at that. If he's good enough to bring whatever it was you ordered inside an hour, you're lucky. If you forget his full title and just call him "waiter" he'll either (*a*) not hear you or (*b*) screech "*Herrrr* Waiter!" at you. I got the point soon enough. In the beginning I used to walk into a bar and order a drink in a normal human tone of voice, but after I'd been barked at long enough I tried out another method, a method that was a lot more fun. I came in, slammed the door behind me, made a lot of noise, sat down, stared furiously at anybody who wanted to make something of it, grabbed the menu like it was the neck of an enemy, clapped my hands, and yelled "Hey you! Come here!" snapping my fingers impatiently.

"Hey Adolf," my voice boomed as soon as the waiter started rushing off to get my drink. "Did I tell you you could go? Well then, beer and sausages and make it fast, bitte!" Using this method I got what I ordered within three minutes. The waiter was polite and obliging. It wasn't all that long ago that they were used to being screamed at like that. Though in the more civilized restaurants there was always a chance Herr Waiter would ignore me completely. Or slip a printed note on the table saying "You are kindly requested to leave."

Ja, ja, Deutschland über alles.

289

We didn't hang around long in that first-class overpriced hotel. In the first place, at nine on the dot every morning march music started up in the halls. A kind of military Muzak. The chambermaids, two bossy dykes, kept time by banging their mops against their pails or their brooms against the wastepaper baskets. Every morning we gave our breakfast to Provo who soon got wise and refused to touch it. It was one of those hotels with thick

carpets, genuine silver silverware, lousy soup, closing time, watery coffee, and a lot of brown varnished wood. Besides we had an electric bath and if there's one thing I'm scared of it's an electric bath.

The hotel owner called the director of the theater to complain about me. Said we were "dirty people." Claudia always slept until two and then went down in her dressing gown to have lunch in the dining room. Furthermore, he said, I came home drunk every night, made a hell of a racket, had insulted the night watchman and even challenged him to a duel. Had thrown out the two beautiful paintings that were hanging in my room (two sloppily painted purplish landscapes with windmills). Had let my monster of a dog sleep on the expensive couch and defecate in the bathroom—now soiled beyond repair. And the chambermaids refused to clean up after a dog. Human shit was one thing, but dog shit, no!

The bastard, the cheap little ass-licker. Wasn't I paying him more per day than I'd be paying in Amsterdam for a whole house for month? I thought I ought to have a word with this guy. I was raging mad when I got back to the hotel in the afternoon. Olov said goodby to me at the door in a hurry. He had noticed I was carrying the big Luger he'd bought for me on the black market. I usually kept it in the studio. Not that I had any intention of shooting anybody. I just thought if the good man wouldn't listen to reason, I'll let him have a look at my Luger. Just a look.

At the desk in the lobby I asked if I could please see the owner. He wasn't in, his wife said. Up in the room I found Claudia sobbing her eyes out. She was miserable. Somebody had been rude to her on the phone and when she'd gone down to the dining room they refused to serve her and the boss had cussed her out in front of all the other guests.

"Pack your bags," I said, "and smash all the mirrors!"

I grabbed a fat vaseful of flowers and smashed it on the expensive rug. With a few well-aimed kicks I turned the sides of the four-poster bed into kindling. I slung the fluffy feather-stuffed plumeau at Provo, who took a bite out of it and went on biting until the whole room was littered with feathers. Claudia stared at me astonished and quickly started packing. I went downstairs with Provo and demanded once more to see the owner. I was coming on so strong that the woman retreated behind the curtain into the private office. A few seconds later out came the owner himself, a round little butterball with gray bebop hair. He obviously knew what I was there for because he was white as a sheet. Nevertheless he asked in his slimy subservient way if there was anything he could do for me.

"You cheap freak, you poor swinemouthed fartfaced mothering pig," I said. "Just exactly what the fuck did you think you were doing giving my wife a hard time anyway?"

He looked a shade paler and said he didn't know what I was talking about. Which threw me for a second because I knew from long experience that Claudia sometimes made up the weirdest stories if life was getting too dull. But when I remembered the scene I'd had that morning with the director, considered the situation from all angles, and come to a conclusion, I grabbed the pig by his lovely tweed jacket and pulled him right over the counter. He tried to get loose and I heard howls and moans from behind the curtain where his wife was following the action. I hissed between my teeth the way they do in American gangster films. He was spread out on the desk like a blotter.

"The gentleman got any complaints? Tell me your troubles, Buster. Maybe I can help you out." I glared at him through half-shut eyes. The way Bogart used to do.

"Nein, nein, nein," he whined. "I didn't say a word, didn't do a thing. I have nothing against you, you know that!"

I thought how nice it would be to tuck the big Luger into the rolls of fat on his belly. I let him go. He quickly straightened his jacket and said if I didn't leave the hotel at once he'd call the police. His wife came out from behind the curtain and stood heroically at his side with a brass letter opener clenched in her fist. I leaped over the desk and grabbed Fats by the lapels.

Grabbing one of his hands, I pressed it down against my pocket so he could have a good feel of the hard steel of the revolver. Little drops of sweat popped out on his forehead and he stammered, "Aber bitte, Herr Cremer!"

"If you're eager to join Uncle Adolf," I whispered, "just say the word, Fats. Now just take it easy or something may go off."

In the meantime a crowd had gathered in the lobby to gape at the rare things going on at the desk. When I saw them I smiled my friendliest smile and gave the trembling hotel owner a hearty slap on the back. He shrank back in terror. Alarming cries from the office: "Polizei" and "Help bitte!"

"Mommy's calling," I said and dragged him behind the curtain. His broad was on the phone. When she saw us she let out a yelp, dropped the phone and backed up to the wall, without dropping the brass blade though. She still kept it pointed at me.

I hung up for her and said, "Calm down, Granny. Nothing to get excited about."

"But," she stammered, "you can't get away with this. Beating my husband. Terrorizing us like this! This is a matter for the police! We're going to have you arrested."

I told them to cool it. I said if they cared anything about their hotel's reputation, and if they didn't want the whole place torn apart, they'd better shut up fast. If they wanted to call the police, that was fine with me. I'd have some good publicity and so would the hotel. Plenty. Nationwide. On the front pages of all the big papers. I'd be delighted to tell the reporters that Dutchmen weren't welcome in this hotel and that the owner had abused my wife. Abused a pregnant woman! And tried to poison my dog. That all the trouble started when I refused to pay an extra month's rent for the room and that I checked out because I couldn't live in this lousy pig sty any longer.

"So go ahead," I said, and pointed to the phone. "Go ahead and call the papers!"

That got to them. They looked whipped.

Claudia had packed the suitcases but had forgotten to take care of the mirrors. It wasn't easy. First I tried swinging a lamp, then a chair against the big sheets of glass. No luck. With the handle of the Luger I finally managed to smash the bathroom mirrors to smithereens. A fantastic sound, all that tinkling glass. I turned the faucet on full blast, put my thumb under it, spurting the water in all directions. Provo thought it was a new kind of game, climbed up the curtains, then cheerfully leaped on the bed, ripping the bedspread to shreds and spreading bits of it all over the room.

While we were walking down the hall with Provo and our suitcases, I saw a fire extinguisher. Which gave me a bright idea. My passion for destruction knew no bounds. I set down our suitcases, pulled the thing out of its clamp, went back to the room and—*thump!*—the red fire extinguisher was upside down, just like the instructions said. The white jet that spurted out looked like the column of smoke that bursts out of the booster engines at Cape Canaveral, and it soon covered all the furniture including the lampshade. A beautiful sight. A few flames might add to the glory. But you can't have everything. With a feeling of deep satisfaction I closed the door behind me. Once again I had created a work of art.

The hotel owner and his wife glowered at us from behind the reception desk when I came up and told Claudia to sit down on a couch. I asked them to call me a taxi and whether I still owed them anything. They had the bill all made out. I was supposed to pay for another four days.

"What?" I shouted as loud as I could so that everybody within five hundred yards could hear me.

"Forty marks a day for this pig sty? You gone right out of your nut? For *that* room? That broom closet? This is highway robbery. Know what I'm going to do? I'm going to call the police. *And* the papers. And every broadcaster—radio *and* TV—in the goddamn district."

That little message got through to them and they started stammering. "Ach nein, nein, bitte nein."

Just then Provo saw a nightmare walk by in the shape of the owner's chihuahua. The little demon yelped and yapped every time he saw Provo and teased the hell out of him—at least when Provo was on the leash. Now all Provo's hate and aggression homed in on that miserable dog. Eagerly licking his chops, he looked first up at me, then down at the chihuahua haughtily prancing past us, its nose in the air.

Provo's turn for a few kicks now, I thought, and said, "Sic 'em, Provo! Quick! Get him!" That's all it took. He was off like a shot after the yappy little frankfurter—down the hall, into the dining room, under the tables, through people's legs. You could follow his course through the dining room just by watching people jump up from their lunches. I whistled to him. The owner's wife went into the dining room on a hysterical hunt for her hairless wonder. The taxi drove up, the driver picked up our luggage, and Claudia took Provo in her arms. I leaned over the counter to say goodby to the owner.

"Look," I said, "if and when you take a bath, wash off that SS tattoo under your armpit, why don't you? And one more piece of advice: next time you plan to bug my wife on the phone or give her any more of your lip—don't."

And off we went. Leaving our hosts dazed, demoralized, and dancing with rage. Which is what you get for fooling around with little Jan Cremer. Their own fucking fault.

That afternoon we found still another place to stay. A big room on top of a Chinese restaurant. The only hotel left in Kwammerschlagen. In the middle of the night Claudia started having labor pains and woke me up.

"It's started," she said. "I've got to get to a hospital."

I was afraid of this, even though the doctor had said the baby wasn't due for at least another month. Otherwise I wouldn't have asked Claudia to come to Kwammerschlagen. I was willing to do anything to keep the baby from being born in Germany. Not that I had anything against Überallesland. But who wants their baby born there?

"You sure?" I asked Claudia.

It was very late and to use the phone I'd have to wake up the Chinaman.

"Yes, I can feel it coming."

"Can't it wait till tomorrow?"

"No, of course not, stupid!"

"Godamitgodamitgodamitmygodgodamitmygodmygodohlordylordy!"

I got dressed and tiptoed through the dark house, down one staircase and up another. I banged on the Chinaman's door. His mistress opened the door, a cute German chick with a pointed pair poking out through her nightgown. I asked if I could please use the phone because my wife was going to have a baby. She went downstairs with me to open up the restaurant where the phone was.

She was some piece. She and the Chinaman ran the restaurant together and I couldn't make out what her game was with the old bastard. When she swished down the stairs in her filmy nightgown, her cheap perfume tickled my nostrils. I felt like grabbing her. Kneeling and in from behind. Position 45. I called the taxi company, ordered a chauffeured limousine, and said I was in a hurry. In the meantime Claudia had already gotten dressed.

I told the driver not to slow down until he was on Dutch soil. We raced through the pitch black German night. Stretched out nice and comfy in the big limousine. A race against time. Every minute meant a mile closer to the Fatherland. The baby had to be born in Holland. Even if only for the tax deductions. The closer we got to the border the less pain she felt. It didn't look as if the baby was coming after all.

When we were finally within sight of the border and could see the lights blinking, I told the driver to turn around. Claudia had made a mistake. The baby wasn't coming yet. Two hours later we were back in bed on top of the Chinese restaurant. Me ranting and raving because the trip cost me two hundred marks. It happened three times in two weeks! And every time—no baby. Still, you couldn't take any chances. I got to know that road very well—all the curves, bushes, roadside cafés. I could have driven that road with my eyes shut.

290

The day of the premiere came. My sets had got lots of publicity. Management, actors, and crew all very happy with my art work. Me too. Two big abstract sets with massive iron structures. "Mobiles" I called them. There was a beautiful program with a good picture of me (photogenic bastard, aren't I?) and my iron statues.

Since it was one of the most important premieres of the German theater season, directors and producers from all over Germany had come. In dark tuxedos with their wives in evening gowns with low-cut necklines giving you a good view of a bad scene: shriveled bananas. There were even some interested parties from Holland.

Not that they'd ever give me a chance to design any scenery in Holland. Oh, no. I didn't have enough experience, lacked the proper training, didn't come from an artistic family, and didn't lick ass. Still a couple of directors and theater people made the trip over to see the show. There was a lot of back slapping (my back) and vague talk like, "Drop over some time and we'll see what we can do for you."

Up yours, I thought.

I got a few telegrams from good friends back home. I had to go on television and radio and mumble a few words about art, etc., and Audiberti.

Before the intermission there was a play by Beckett without any stage sets. *Krapp's Last Tape,* a story about a little old man who always recorded everything that happened on a tape recorder. All his life he's been talking into this tape recorder and now he's playing it back, talking about it, etc. And who did they pick to play that part? The star of the company. A whining narcissus type, a slippery male-model type. All beauty and no balls. The sort the Dutch Theataah world is loaded with.

Claudia and I sat in the front row with all the big shots. Right next to the stage with the table and the tape recorder and the star. When the lights went out and the spotlights zeroed in on the leading man you could have heard a pin drop. The play demanded concentration and silence. The monologue droned on monotonously. The audience hanging on every word.

"I've got to go to the toilet," Claudia suddenly whispered in my ear, loud enough for everyone to hear it.

"Quiet," I said.

"Ssshhh," from all sides.

"Shut up!" I said. "There's a play going on."

A little later she whispered she couldn't wait any longer, she really had to go. Lord, I thought, what a mess. Whatever made me want to bring her here anyway? That woman has absolutely no taste for the arts. I should have left her puttering around back home.

After a lot of noise, squeaking, puffing, and panting, Claudia got up and started up the aisle. I stared straight ahead of me. I've never been so embarrassed in my life. She was unbelievably heavy with child and looked like a baby elephant tottering around on high heels. The star of the show knitted his false eyebrows and glared at her furiously. When she was safely out of the auditorium, he went on with the play again. A little while later back came Claudia. Bonk bonk bonk bonk bonk.

When she'd finally sat down after making a racket that lasted a full two minutes, I was so mad I hissed at her, "Goddammit, couldn't you have made a little *more* noise?"

"Oh, don't get so worked up," she said, almost out loud. I winced.

"Quiet!" I hissed. "This isn't a fish market, you know!"

I cursed myself because she hadn't wanted to come in the first place—I was the one who'd insisted on it.

"Look," she said so loud that this time the *sssh* came all the way from the back of the house, "don't you talk that way to me or I'll get right up and go!"

Mamma mia, oi oi oi, I thought, why the hell can't she shut up? I'll be the laughingstock of the whole town! The whole country! The actor was glaring at Claudia now and spitting hairs out between clenched teeth.

"Oh," she cried suddenly. "*Now* I recognize him! That weirdo we met the other day. That fake beard and those glasses threw me. He really looks like some kind of freak, doesn't he?"

I almost fell through the floor. I would have loved ⸱ ⸱t keep sinking. The whole audience was acting up now, mumbling a⸱ ⸱spering to each other. The poor actor was having a hell of a time conc⸱ ⸱ting on his part. Sweat was streaming down his forehead onto his beard, ⸱hich slipped off on one side. If looks could kill, we would have been rip⸱ for the morgue.

To top things off, Provo, whom I'd left with the doorman because we couldn't leave him alone in our hotel room, suddenly started barking like mad. I was afraid the actor would have a complete nervous breakdown right then and there. I couldn't hold it in any more and burst out laughing. It's like in church when suddenly you have to laugh at some little thing you wouldn't even smile at otherwise just because you're not supposed to laugh in church. Fortunately for the actor he was near the end. The curtain came down and the audience applauded more out of duty than anything else. When he came out for his curtain call, he looked finished. He's probably a tax collector now.

When the curtain came down after the Audiberti th⸱ applause was deafening. One curtain call, two curtain calls, and at the third the actors pointed down to me. Krappsalaten came over to where I was sitting and led me up onto the stage. We'd rehearsed it all before but when I actually found myself there in the spotlight, looking out at those thousands of people clapping for us, I got stage fright. The bow I made looked like a cross between a ballet step and a stripper slipping on a banana peel. I jumped down off the stage fast and sat there staring straight ahead until the house was practically empty. There was a reception afterward in an expensive restaurant. Plenty of steak, beer, and whisky.

I could look forward to a promising career as a set designer. I could go to Berlin and work in the Brecht theater. There were plenty of jobs. I could take my pick—until during a performance of *Thomas More* (a serious drama with lots of old-fashioned costumes, fake beards, capes, and tights) I ambled on stage stoned and flopped right at the feet of a flabbergasted Swiss guard. Grim looks on stage, loud laughter from the audience.

I was sitting in the canteen afterward, letting Tooti bring me one cup of hot black coffee after another, when in came the director foaming at the mouth and wearing a raincoat over a pair of rumpled pajamas. Well, if I'd busted up his show it wasn't really my fault. I'd had to wait out the costume drama before I could get on stage to try out my sets for the next production, *Draussen vor der Tür, a* good antiwar play by Wolfgang Borchert. So I'd had a few beers and some wine on top of the beer and every once in a while I'd slip over to the theater, tiptoe into the wings, and see how much longer I had to wait. Then I got dizzy and there I was flat out on the stage.

Though Krapp and Krampf fought to keep me on at the theater, the director had had all he could take of his Dutch set designer. There goes another good job, I thought. Not that I cared much. I was getting pretty sick of chow mein and chop suey (we always ate downstairs in the Chink restaurant and nights we either watched TV down there, or if I had to work I gave Claudia free tickets to the opera). I didn't have any money left. Just enough to pick up an old motorcycle, a discarded heap of scrap metal. With the help of a few stage hands I fixed it up like new and used the walks and grounds around the theater as proving grounds.

291

On the train back to Holland two customs men stepped into our compartment at the border. After carefully examining our papers one of them asked if we had anything to declare.

"No," I said.

"What's that then?" the other asked and took a shiny blue black Luger out of my raincoat, which I'd purposely hung way back in the corner. That bitter-faced broad sitting across from us must have ratted on me. The Luger had fallen out of my coat pocket when I was taking it off.

"Oh that," I said casually. "That's just a toy for my little kid. Says he wants to be a Texan when he grows up."

292

After my German period I had to start bringing in the bread because Claudia really would be having the baby any day now. I still had a studio in The Hague. Two big rooms. There were still a lot of paintings there. I could sell them. We needed money badly.

I'd had a good time in Germany, but now that I'd decided to stick with Claudia I wanted to get down to some serious work. Maybe I could have another exhibition. I had a couple of pictures stored away in the studio that I knew I could sell in two minutes. If I asked for a lot less than I knew they were worth.

1000 guilders reward

1000 GUILDERS REWARD

293

Wednesday afternoon I went down to The Hague for the first time since I'd gotten back from Spain. I'd been too busy with my theater work to go before. Claudia had been there a couple of times while I was still in Spain. I didn't use the studio anymore, but all my things and paintings were stored there. I wanted to look things over, take a few paintings back to sell. I got a ride down with a photographer friend. There was a new lock on the front door, which I'd painted bright red, and my key didn't fit. I had to go see the landlord. He owned a restaurant behind the studio and lived two houses away.

While I was abroad I hadn't been able to keep up on the rent and the landlord had written me in Spain telling me I'd either have to pay or vacate the premises. A friend of mine got hold of a lawyer who said he'd take charge of the matter. Since I was broke I could hardly send any money from Spain. But I knew why he wanted me out. The place had been a wreck when I first moved in. I'd fixed it up and made it livable. I paid next to nothing in rent—which figured, since the place wasn't worth any more. A big roomy dump in the center of town, that was about all you could say for it.

The landlord wasn't there so his bookkeeper got down the key and came back with me to open the door. As soon as I walked in, I saw all my things in one big pile—furniture, clothing, paintings, and supplies. All mixed up like a tornado had dropped them there.

Two of my favorite paintings, "Self-Portrait" and "Birth of a God," both done in 1956, had been badly mutilated. Somebody had slashed them right down the middle with a knife or some other sharp instrument, then either stamped on them or kicked them in. A lot of lithographs and water colors were ripped in two.

I went back to the landlord's office and demanded an explanation. They claimed they didn't know anything about it. With them as witnesses I called the police who promised to send somebody over right away. Then I called the photographer who was going to drive me back to Amsterdam. He was in conference but advised me to notify the press, so I called the papers and a few syndicated news agencies. My photographer friend made a few calls too. When I filed an official complaint two days later the police tried to get me to say I'd called the papers first and informed the police afterward. In their press release they insinuated the whole thing was just a publicity stunt, and of course a few papers took their word for it.

Before the police got there I walked over to a gallery on Molenstraat where I'd had a few exhibitions. I told the owner what had happened. He came back with me to my studio. In the meantime reporters and photographers had already arrived. Sergeant Visser from the police department was there too. The sergeant, the gallery owner, and I went upstairs. Sergeant Visser took notes.

I showed him the lock that had been forced and the mutilated pictures. Ten minutes later he left. In their official press release the police claimed there was no evidence whatsoever that anyone had broken into the house. The landlord told the police that a couple of months ago he'd noticed six windows were broken, that there was cause to suspect burglary, and that just three weeks ago he'd noticed more windows had been smashed and had seen a number of partly burned books lying on the table.

(I pointed out the remains of the burned books as well as a number of burned paintings to Sergeant Visser while he was there.)

The landlord also stated that a week ago he'd told his cleaning women to clean up the studio and they said they'd seen the pile of torn sheets of paper (lithographs, guaches, sketches) but hadn't paid any special attention to it. I went on to say that the big cardboard portfolio, in which I'd put most of my work before taking off for Spain, was gone. At that point, with all my furniture, clothes, suitcases, etc., all stacked on top of each other, regardless of whether they were breakable or not, it was impossible to say exactly how many things were missing, mutilated, or destroyed.

After the sergeant had left and I'd said my say to the reporters and showed them the evidence and the photographers had taken a lot of pictures, I went back to Amsterdam with the photographer. There I read in the papers that I hadn't filed an official complaint, so I had to go all the way back to The Hague to see the police. The official police statement referred to me as the "alleged victim." A number of papers made very broad hints that I'd broken into the studio and torn up my pictures myself just to get the publicity.

I filed an "official complaint" two days later. Sergeant Visser was put in charge. For two hours he interrogated me as if he was the judge and I was the criminal. He pointed out the consequences of making a false statement and cited contradictions in my story (Sergeant Visser said there were witnesses who'd seen me in The Hague when I was "supposedly" in

Spain), and brought up "the fact" that I'd called the papers before informing the police. I gave him a list of facts and conclusions. (Claudia had gone to the studio twice while I was in Spain. She hadn't noticed anything suspicious, had found things just the way I'd left them.)

Sergeant Visser wanted me to write out a complete list of everything missing or mutilated. I told him I couldn't until I'd had more time to look things over. He took down my official statement, I signed it, and that was it. Except that he said he'd keep in touch with me at my Amsterdam address and inform me if any progress was made. That was four years ago. I still haven't heard from him.

The main reason I'd alerted the papers was that a year before (November, 1961) I'd reported a theft to the police—art supplies and paintings stolen, my mail tampered with—and they hadn't done a thing. At that time I was subletting the top floor to B.N., a student who called himself a sculptor. We'd agreed that he would forward my mail on to Spain, swab the studio once in a while, and keep an eye on the things I'd stored there. Some agreement. He stole my property, opened my mail, and neglected to pay the rent. When I came back from Spain I saw that all my closets had been broken open and my oils used up. He used my canvases and used my frames. But that wasn't all. He also copied my paintings.

I locked up and got in touch with B.N. and tried to reach some kind of settlement with him, but he wouldn't even pay me back for the supplies he'd used. After I left The Hague he broke in, later claiming the police had advised him to (off the record, of course), and walked off with more supplies plus some of my personal belongings. This time I notified the police. Sergeant De Gilde claimed I had only myself to blame; by locking the door to the house, I'd more or less forced B.N. to break in. (B.N. forced the lock and broke two windows.) So the police wouldn't do anything until I could actually prove that B.N. had stolen property in his possession. In a few weeks I was planning to take off for Spain. If I got involved with the cops the thing could drag on for months. I dropped the charges.

But I wasn't going to let the whole thing—burglary, mutilation, and pure destruction—just sink out of sight as if I didn't mind. That's why I notified the papers, hoping that would force the police to clear up the whole miserable business.

I told Sergeant Visser I had good reason to believe B.N. had done what he did just to get back at me. Not for gain, just for revenge. The paintings that had been destroyed were worth more than anything else to me. They dated back to 1956, my figurative period. In spite of several offers from prospective buyers, I wanted to hold onto those paintings and had refused to sell them. Their value couldn't be expressed in terms of money. The mutilated lithographs and drawings were worth about two hundred guilders apiece (that was in 1962, J.C.). Prints of the graphic works were in numerous art collections all over the world, including the Municipal Museum of Amsterdam, the Dutch Art Foundation, the Municipal Museum of The Hague, and the National Collection. The pictures weren't insured. Neither was my personal property. As far as I know the police have never made any attempt to investigate the affair.

Four years later. I've had a lot of other things on my mind. The newspapers and the police authorities led most people to believe the whole thing was just a big publicity stunt. Advance publicity for my first book. And to let everybody know I was back in the country. In spite of repeated requests for an investigation of the matter, nothing has ever been done about it. Obviously the police decided it was easier to just forget about it.

From an art-historical point of view, this was a great loss. They were my very first paintings. I'd been attached to them ever since the beginning of my career in 1956. They were mementoes of a phase of life gone in a flash. As a Dutch citizen and tax payer I feel I've been screwed pretty bad. A scratch on the frame of a Rembrandt and the whole country boils over. But when some maniac mutilates or destroys the entire oeuvre of a gifted artist who's now world famous, the authorities couldn't care less. Which is why I'm taking this opportunity—via my American publisher—to announce

1000 GUILDERS REWARD

to anyone who can supply clues leading to the apprehension of the criminal(s).

the little black soul

294

I climbed the rickety staircase up to our room.

"I've had it with this hole," I said to Claudia. "We've got to find another pad fast."

The place was a madhouse. Kotshut, that half-assed queer, was milking his house for all it was worth. He'd rented it not only to us, but then gone and rented it again to the medical student Bart and his wife, who somehow happened to have some money and were looking for a place to stay.

"Oh," said Antoon Kotshut to them in Spain, "you can move into my place in Amsterdam. Jan and Claudia are staying upstars but they'll be leaving any day now."

I cursed the prick but there wasn't much I could do about it since he was off in another part of the world freeloading off his middle-aged American lady friend. The little money I had left I had to spend paying off Kotshut's creditors.

Bart and Barbara moved in downstairs. All day long a steady flow of junkies and assorted hopheads. When Claudia had to go shopping she tripped over the reefer smokers sprawled out in the hall. In the middle of the night the noise of people vomiting all over the staircase woke us up. Or we'd both get splitting headaches from the smell of piss and sweat. Half-naked broads wandered around in a daze and Bart's guests stole our food. That was "hip."

Tanya was there too, a girl who later married a promising young writer and Master of Radio Chats, a boy from Brabant. I knew her from when I was studying art in Arnhem. She told Claudia the weirdest stories about me. About how I tied her to a chair and burned a hole in her twat once when her parents weren't home. About how I'd reamed her with beer bottles, carrots, broomsticks, and burning cigarettes. All wishful thinking. All I'd ever done to her was maybe say hello twice. She used to live next door to a former girlfriend of mine and that's all there was to it. But try explaining that to your wife.

The house looked like a hurricane had hit it, but Bart thought that was "hip." Mixed-up teenyboppers who'd run away from home or escaped from institutions were always welcome. When I found out the whole house was infested with lice, I'd had it. Claudia almost had a nervous breakdown and I was suffering from a bad case of paranoia. We had as little to do with hippie cubs as possible. Still, we didn't want to risk getting involved if the police raided the place. Even out on the street, the smell of ether and grass was so strong people would stop and sniff suspiciously.

We didn't know anybody in Amsterdam who could help us out. Even if we had known somebody, I was too proud to ask. The only possibility for Claudia was to sleep at her mother's house. As for me, I'd manage somehow. Claudia needed a good warm bed. The baby was due any day now. I always managed to find someone who'd let me sleep on the floor near the stove and early every morning I picked Claudia up at her mother's house. 1 had to promise I'd do that before she would agree to go there. We couldn't allow her mother to get a hold on her again. It was hard on her to even spend the night there. But there was no choice.

What else could we do? Even though we went to the Housing Department every day and they promised us they'd "do their best," we were still homeless and penniless. I wasn't an artist the government cared to subsidize. They still didn't think of me as a serious artist. There was plenty of work for me at the post office or down on the docks. But when I applied for a job at the post office they didn't even want me there. Claudia and I visited people morning, noon, and night. Or went for walks in the park. Exercise was good for her. That's why the baby came early.

Leading a respectable life isn't easy.

295

One evening Claudia and I were at the Grijplings' house. People I'd known for a long time. He had a doctor's degree in Art History. She came from a rich family and had a degree in something or other too. Their house was a meeting place for artists.

I knew him because when I was just starting out he used to send me long letters praising my work. He'd even bought a few lithographs at a "special price for friends." They found it stimulating to have lots of artists around the house. He painted, too. His wife made him. A la mode.

They'd been in Ibiza, lured south by the success of my exhibition, and I'd let them stay in my studio. For nothing. Good-hearted bastard that I am, I couldn't let them sleep outside in the tent they'd schlepped along all the way from Holland. People who have a lot of money are usually misers. They're thrifty and try to live as cheaply as possible without realizing that you don't get anything for nothing.

The Grijplings were very respectable, very refined. The kind of people who never call anything by its right name. If you said "cunt" or "fuck" she got all itchy and wanted you to tell her all about it. He had a castration complex, she had an orgasm complex. She could go on for hours telling Claudia how big my prick was. Every time she met a man she wondered how big his prick was. The milkman had a crooked one and the baker's was tiny. She had it all figured out.

Claudia and I visited them a lot because they had a good stove. In exchange for artistic conversation we got a meal and coffee and cake. We couldn't come too often and we weren't welcome when people from their own milieu were there. Jan had such a crude vocabulary.

Claudia's labor pains started. The baby was coming. Panic. We were at the Grijplings' house but they were out. Claudia could feel the baby coming. What should we do? Keep calm. We didn't have any money. The hospital wouldn't admit her because we couldn't pay. They told her to go to the clinic when the time came. We scraped together the money for the doctor. A fortune.

"Quick," Claudia shouted. "I've got to go now. The pain's getting worse."

We didn't even have a guilder. Claudia and I had been walking around for more than a week with a big bag of baby clothes and a night-gown for her. We took it with us wherever we went so we could go straight to the hospital when the pains started. Days of waiting. The Grijplings lived right near Claudia's mother's house where Claudia spent her nights on the sofa. I wasn't allowed in the house.

"You think we'll make it with the streetcar?" I asked. "What should we do?"

The Grijplings were out. They could have taken us to the hospital in their car or at least lent us the money for a taxi.

"No," Claudia panted, doubling over from the pains. "I've got to lie down because I feel it coming. Let's go to my mother's and ask if she'll take us to the hospital!"

We hurried down the ice cold street to her mother's house a block away. Claudia leaned on me with all her weight.

"Hold on, honey," I said. "Everything's going to be all right. We'll be in the hospital in no time."

I rang the bell. Her mother opened the door.

"Good evening," I said. "Claudia has to go to the hospital. Could you take her in the car?"

"What?" she snapped. "I thought I told you never to come here."

"Forget about me. Your daughter needs your help," I said. "She has to get to a hospital. The baby's coming."

"Can't she go by herself? With a taxi or something?" she asked glancing disdainfully at Claudia. "We're watching a good program on TV."

I said it was urgent. Reluctantly she went inside to talk to her boyfriend.

She came back and said, "No, Dirk will take Claudia but he won't take you. He doesn't want you in the car."

I looked at Claudia desperately.

"You want to go with him?" I asked. I didn't mind being humiliated if it would help Claudia and the baby.

"No," she said proudly. "We'll manage somehow."

"Come on in," her mother said. "We want to talk to you."

"I have nothing to say to you," Claudia said loyally.

She was writhing with pain while I was desperately trying to make it clear to her mother that we didn't have any money.

"It was your bright idea to go live with him, wasn't it?" she snarled at Claudia. "Well, now you see what you get for it. Not a cent to your name, just misery. Oh, all right then," she sighed, "I'll give you two and a half guilders. Not that I ever expect to see it again!"

She went inside and came back with a crumpled two-and-a-half guilder bill.

"You can call a taxi from the bar across the street," she said when Claudia asked if she could drive us to the taxi stand.

"You know we don't want to have anything to do with you any more since you decided to carry on with Jan," she said and slammed the door—after asking us to let her know whether it was a boy or a girl.

There was no time to be lost. Claudia was afraid to walk, afraid it would make the baby come faster. The nearest taxi stand was a quarter mile away, by the Museum.

I tried to wave down a passing car. I didn't know what to do. Claudia burst into tears, panic stricken. A police car drove past but I was afraid it would lead to too many complications. A red Volkswagen pulled up. The driver asked what the trouble was. I explained the situation. He rushed us to the maternity clinic of the hospital. A Catholic hospital.

296

Claudia was admitted by two nurses.

"Who are you?" the nurse in charge snapped at me. "You're not married to her so you'll have to leave."

Claudia held onto my hand and said "This is my husband, Sister. Please let him stay with me."

"Well, all right," she said. "As long as you don't get in the way and the doctor doesn't have any objections."

I had called the doctor who was supposed to deliver the baby as soon as the pains started coming. He came half an hour later. In the meantime they washed Claudia and shaved off the hair under her big belly. He put a kind of wooden horn against her belly and said, "Push, that's the girl. I'm going to have a bowl of soup in the canteen." He told the nurse, a skinny kid with carrot-colored hair, she could reach him there.

He called me out into the hall and said, "What's with the money? You still owe me two hundred guilders. If you can pay me now, we'll call it quits."

I had the money on me but had to go to the men's room to get at it. I opened my shirt and took out the hundred guilder bills I had taped to my chest. To make sure I wouldn't lose them or spend them. I gave him the money. He unfolded the bills and tucked them away in his wallet. I went back into the room.

A light green room with naked light bulbs that cast a cold light on Claudia's pale face. Between the pains she looked up at me sweetly. I sat in a chair near the head of the bed and held her hand. I found the whole process very exciting. When the nurse left she asked me to write down how long the intervals between the pains were. They kept getting shorter, which meant the baby was on its way.

The big clock above the door went on ticking off the seconds. That was the only sound in the room. It suddenly hit me that every time the clock ticked it meant one more second we could never go back to and which would never come again.

The pains got sharper. Claudia squeezed my hand harder. She started groaning. Panic. The nurse came in and gave word to interrupt the doctor's third bowl of soup. She put rubber gloves on and handed a pair to the doctor when he rushed in. I held Claudia's hand tight. I've heard so many stories about men who go to pieces when their wife has a baby and I thought, that's not going to happen to me. In Malacca the men groan while the baby's coming. Not me. I decided to think about thrilling movies.

Blood started streaming out of Claudia.

The stream got bigger and bigger.

The doctor pressed on her belly.

"Good girl," the nurses shouted. "Push, push!"

Suddenly a tiny head emerged and The Baby came sliding out into the doctor's rubber gloves.

The nurses threw towels on the bed and the doctor cut the umbilical cord. The baby was covered with slime, a gory mess, kind of purplish. The

293

doctor picked it up by the feet like a chicken and slapped it on the behind. The kid started bawling. Good strong bawling. Jan-Cremer bawling that filled the room. Everybody laughed. So did I. I was a proud father and kissed Claudia with tears in my eyes.

Claudia opened her eyes and stared at the table where the baby was being washed.

"What is it, Doctor?" she asked, still panting.

"A girl," the doctor said. "A beautiful girl, a fine healthy girl. Eight pounds worth of daughter born in five minutes."

"A daughter," Claudia said and smiled at me.

"Yeah, fantastic!" I exclaimed, with more enthusiasm than I really felt. I'd been counting on a son. A sturdy little guy who'd take off with me someday to roam the seven seas. I could hardly ask them to put it back. A girl was okay, too, though I could already hear what people would be saying to the backs of their hands when I was an old man shuffling into a bar with a cute chick I claimed was my daughter.

Birth is beautiful, I thought, but it sure is a mess. Bloody sheets, bloody everything. The afterbirth was the worst part. When the doctor started inspecting it I thought, Oho, so that's your hang-up, you slimy bastard. I thought about all the poets and writers who'd written odes to birth and how beautiful it was, new life on earth. I thought it was beautiful, too, but not the kind of beauty I'd care to write an ode about. It was nature. That's all. The same as dying, eating, taking a crap.

"What did you think of it?" the head nurse asked, a nun in black and glasses.

"Beautiful, Sister," I said, "it was a beautiful birth."

"Don't you think it's miraculous? The new life, the new soul entering God's world."

"Yes," I said, "except it's Mother Nature and not God that created this baby. It's nature, like taking a leak or a crap, or farting or belching. Nature."

"Yes," she agreed pensively, "but this is something different. This creates something new. A new soul, a baby."

"Still," I said, "don't forget that this sweet little baby will toss the first handful of sand on my coffin some day."

"You mustn't look at it like that," she said, shocked. "Shall I call the priest and have him baptize the child? Its soul is still black and neither of you are believers."

"No priest is going to lay hands on my baby!" I said roughly. "My daughter's soul isn't black. It doesn't have to be whitewashed."

297

The baby was washed and cleaned and looked beautiful. Just like a purple little old bald-headed man. A couple hours later you could see what a masterpiece she was. I smelled her. She smelled delicious. Like an angel, like the blue sky, I thought. She had a few tufts of black hair on her head and bright blue eyes.

My Claudia finally dozed off and fell asleep. After they'd moved her onto another bed, a wheeled bed. Out in the hall.

A nurse came with a pad and pencil.

"Where shall we take Claudia and the baby tomorrow morning?" she asked.

I didn't know what to say. We didn't have a house. No address. I'd hoped she'd be able to stay in the hospital for a few days. But that was out of the question. The head nurse had done her a favor letting her stay overnight, even if it was on a bed in the hall. There was no room in the hospital for paupers. The two hundred guilders covered just the delivery. We didn't have any health insurance.

"But you can't just put her out on the street in the middle of the winter, can you?" I asked desperately.

"Isn't there anybody you can stay with? You don't have a place of your own? No relatives? No friends? No acquaintances?"

We didn't have any.

"If you bring the money early tomorrow morning she can stay here."

I didn't have any money and I told her so.

"Shall we call the Welfare Department tomorrow morning?" the Sister asked. "Maybe there's room in the Shelter for the Homeless."

298

Ever since I'd gotten back from Spain, Claudia and I had gone down to City Hall practically every day. To see a special clerk in charge of finding housing for artists. Every day the same old song and dance: We'll see, terrible problem, we're looking into it, etc. It was always perhaps tomorrow. Bullshit. There simply weren't any houses for people like us. In spite of the scandalous housing shortage in Amsterdam, though, a number of artists do have enormous houses. Bachelor actors have whole town houses all to themselves. Actresses have luxurious apartments. Theater people come first, that's obvious. All you need is a good reputation and a tongue of honey. Or lots of money.

The Municipal Housing Department had us filed away as an "emergency case." All we had to show for it though was a so-called "priority card." Not that it got us anywhere. The fact was that if you had money enough to bribe some. flunky your problems were over. All the clerks had their price. They kept us dangling.

"Come back next week," was the answer we got. Or, "Don't call us. We'll call you."

And the government's always surprised when a man who's out of work and living with his wife and eight kids in one room stuffs his head in the gas stove. Or when marriages break up. Surprised there's a booming black market in houses, that landlords never had it so good.

They had me filed away as an Artist, which more or less meant an asocial individual. Rent a house to an Artist and watch the real estate value drop. When things had really come to a crisis and we were out on the street and the baby was due any minute, the clerk at City Hall advised us to wait until the baby was born, then have the Welfare Department find us a place in the Shelter for the Homeless. "After you've been there for two weeks they'll have to find something else for you; two weeks is the limit there. And you can live together there because the father belongs with the mother and the child. Even though you aren't married, they'll let you do it. And it's not so bad in the Shelter. Three meals a day and a bath. All paid for by the Welfare Department. They'll have to give you a place when the two weeks are up. So now that's what I'd do if I were you."

Why didn't he just tell us to poison each other in the hospital as soon as the baby was born? At least then the Welfare Department or the state or god knows who could have brought her up as a good respectable taxpaying citizen.

In retrospect I understand now why I toyed around with the idea of murdering somebody. Maybe the mother of my child would have the right to a house if I split somebody's skull? There wasn't a jail in Holland that wasn't better than the Shelter for the Homeless. I knew that. Why the hell had we ever come back here anyway?

What Holland needs is another war. A revolution. And all the "rulers" beheaded in public. I'll be the first to volunteer for the job. The big brute with the sharp ax.

299

"Think it over tonight," the nurse said. "As long as you come for her before noon tomorrow. And don't forget to bring the money. You'll have to pay downstairs and bring us the receipt. Otherwise," she said with a nasty smile, "we won't let you have her."

I kissed Claudia goodnight and said, "Don't worry, honey. I'll come up with something."

The doctor drove me back to town in his big American car. He dropped me at the Grijplings.

"I have a daughter," I said enthusiastically as I walked in.

They offered to let us stay at their house for a few days. Claudia could have the guest room, just big enough for a single bed, and I could sleep on the couch in the living room. As long as I was up by nine because friends often dropped in in the morning. Though I could feel that we were unwanted, that the Grijplings were only making the offer because they felt it was some kind of moral duty, I swallowed my pride and said we'd be delighted.

The next morning I went to get Claudia. She was still too weak to walk so we carried her up the two steep flights of stairs on a stretcher and put her in the narrow bed. I took care of her, sat next to her bed like a faithful watchdog. I had to take Provo to a kennel. The Grijplings didn't want him around. He was too big and they didn't trust dogs. She'd read a story once about a blind man who'd been attacked by his seeing-eye dog. She just couldn't believe that blind people aren't necessarily good to their dogs. In the kennel they fed him well, let him run around as much as he wanted. I called the people who ran the kennel and they told me he had a girl-friend and was having a ball. As soon as things started looking up, we'd come and get him. Provo understood.

Claudia smiled at me as I was sitting there by her bed telling her jokes.

"You know," she said suddenly, "you look just like a wolf. A bit like Provo. When you laugh you have a wolf face. And big long teeth, fangs. You tear everyone and everything around you to pieces. And you've got sweet little wolf ears."

"Grrrrrroouuuuwww!" I growled. "Better watch out or I'll gobble you up!"

300

I had to go to Claudia's mother. To pick up the baby clothes and sheets Claudia had left there. I went over there the next day. A short walk from the Grijplings' house.

"Well," she said, still chewing her food, "what is it?"

"A daughter," I said coldly. "I came to get the sheets and clothes."

"Come on in. I'll get the stuff out of the closet," she said. "First let me finish my meal."

I came into her room, full of plush and fake Persian tapestries hanging on the walls. She snatched up off a chair a sweat-stained bra that easily could have held two udders of a good-sized cow and told me to sit down. She sat down at the table and, hunching over a big bowl and whipping the spoon into her mouth again and again at a fantastic tempo, bolted down her pea soup. Then she pushed her chair back, stood up, burped, and farted like a ruffle of drums.

"How'd the delivery go?" she asked without any show of interest.

"Good," I said. "It was over in five minutes and there was this beautiful little girl. Fantastically beautiful."

"Beautiful babies make ugly brides," she said sardonically.

She took the clothes out of the closet and put them in the big bag I had with me. Goddamn bitch, I thought, you old whore, when she needs your help you don't give a shit and now you ask how she is.

"Where is she?" she asked.

"Staying with friends of mine," I answered coolly.

"I'll come over and see her sometime this week," she said. "Give her my best regards."

"I don't think Claudia cares much about your regards at this point," I said.

"Just how the hell would you know that?" she asked fiercely. "I don't know what she sees in you anyway. She had such a good future before she met you."

"You mean whoring for that old American? You think that's what she wanted to do? She can lead her own life."

We started really letting each other have it then. I told her a few things I'd been dying to tell her ever since she sent that first nasty-assed letter off to Claudia when we were still in Ibiza.

"You dumb old whore, you call yourself Claudia's mother?" I yelled. "Just what the fuck did you ever do for her, you money-mad Judas of a howling bitch, except make her life hell for her?"

She turned white with rage. "Get out of here, get the hell out of my house!" she snapped at me. "I'll get even with you. I'll go straight to the police. I happen to know more about you than you think I do. You and your nice friends."

"What are you driving at?" I asked.

"I keep my eyes open. *And* my ears. I know a thing or two about you. I can have you thrown in jail right this minute!"

"Oh yeah?" I said. "What for?"

"Just you watch out!" she threatened. "Because I happen to know that any more trouble with the law and you'll *really* be in trouble. Claudia told me about some of those tricks you pull."

"What tricks? I don't have to try any tricks," I said.

"All I have to do," she said with a grin that made my skin crawl, "is tell the police you stole some money or smoke marijuana and they'll hold you for questioning long enough to keep you away from my daughter for a good long time."

"And when they find out you're just lying?" I said. "You can't fool the Dutch cops and you can't buy them either. They know what people like you are like. I wouldn't try it if I were you, because I know a few things about you, too—like quite a lot of abortions you had a hand in, you worn-out hooker."

"Get out! Out!" she screeched.

It seemed like a good time to go.

"I'll get even with you," she screamed, "even if it costs me a thousand guilders. I'll make sure they do a good job on you, too. They'll club your head in. Just you wait!"

"Know what you'll get?" I laughed. "Beware the 20th of April. That's when the cancer's going to really break loose."

I left, glad I'd let her have it at last.

"Pimp!" she shrieked after me from the door. "Just you wait! My time will come! I'll get you yet."

301

Our welcome at the Grijplings' wore thin pretty quick. All kinds of people came in to look at Claudia like she was some kind of circus freak. The poor beautiful little woman who'd just had a baby and didn't have a house and, to really top things off, belonged to the Beast. The Little Match Girl hadn't had it half so bad. I could have made a fortune selling tickets. Our hosts made it pretty clear it was time for us to clear out.

Where to go? I didn't know. I called all our friends and acquaintances. We got an offer from the Zweeters, a photographer with a photographer-wife, three kids, and a three-story house on one of the canals. We could stay there for a while. Katja had just had a baby herself and her husband Beertje took enough pictures of it to publish a whole book, which he did.

We slept in the studio. A big bare room. We slept in between the big cameras, rolls of colored paper, and spotlights.

I decided to get back into training as a writer. Took notes and started in again on my book.

My daughter shot up in no time to become a beautiful little girl. I named her Claudia Caramella.

("Oh," a Catholic nurse exclaimed in surprise when I came to pick up Claudia and she asked what the baby's name was, "named after the Holy Mother Claudia Esmeralda?"

"No," I replied laconically, "after Claudia Cardinale!")

We had a cozy life there. Three kids tearing around screaming all day long. One baby crying when the other stopped. Or both together. Beertje stomping through the house whenever things threatened to quiet down.

Plenty of bare boobs there, too. I was always just sitting down to start reading a book when Katja would bring in her baby, flop out a tit and start nursing. Her enormous Balkan boobs were quite an eyeful. So were Claudia's. But I was used to hers. Nipples are beautiful. I'm crazy about them, in all different flavors and various shades: pink, light brown, dark brown, crimson. I could write a whole book about nothing but nipples.

They knew a real estate agent, a slippery little guy with a booze-red nose and a chuckle that came from midway between his crotch and his asshole. He helped us into a house in the old part of town, the part they were going to tear down soon anyway. First, though, we had to get a note from the Housing Department saying we were an emergency case. We also had to put down a hundred guilders security. Our new home was in what used to be the Jewish quarter. One room about 10′ x 12′ with a tiny little alcove on the side and a midget kitchen. A great view out onto a junk yard. Still we had our own place now.

the existentialist
murder case & the
amsterdam happening

302

A rumor started spreading around Amsterdam that there'd been a murder in Ibiza. According to this rumor, the same day I made my legendary exit somebody on the island was planning to bump off a rich Spaniard. Who? A couple of broke friends of mine. Barry was implicated because he suddenly appeared on the island right after I took off. Even Nollie was supposed to have played a big part in the whole thing.

The last time I'd seen Nollie was that morning in Barcelona when I had coffee with her and was in such a rush to catch my train. She was working at the Jamboree, the Music Bar on the Plaza Real.

I sniffed a good story and wanted to find out what had really happened. One afternoon Claudia heard Nollie was back. Deported from Spain. Put on the plane involuntarily by the Dutch consul himself. I started scouting around and found her that evening. She looked pale and exhausted. Skinny and nervous. She told me the whole story. I smelled a scoop. Barry had been arrested, though he couldn't possibly have had anything to do with it since he'd been off in America chasing Barbara at the time of the murder. He was in a bad fix and nobody was around to help him out. I could kill two birds with one stone. Get my scoop and, at the same time, help a friend.

I called *Vrij Nederland*. Yes, they were very interested. We'd talk about what they would pay for the article later.

"If you can have it in by the day after tomorrow, we can print it in this week's issue," one of the editors said, and I got down to work.

I worked all that night and straight on through the next day. Claudia helped by tiptoeing around the room and picking up the baby every time it threatened to start crying.

Late that night I fell asleep, but when Claudia lay down next to me in bed I felt driven to get back to work again. So out of the nest and back to the table. Until early the next morning. On a diet of coffee and hand-rolled cigarettes. The article had to be well documented. My main concern was to make it a good piece of journalism. Of course the fee was important, too. Claudia and I were in our usual financial shape. We needed milk, bread, and oil for the stove. The baby had to have baby food.

At around dawn the piece looked in pretty good shape to me. Objective. Unemotional. Down the icy streets, I walked through the early morning winter air to the building on the canal where the *Vrij Nederland* offices were. People were just coming in, just starting to thaw out. The editors said they would read it, that I should call back in an hour for their decision.

When I called back they were very enthusiastic. Said they'd already sent the article off to the printer. They'd pay me thirty guilders for it. Not even ten dollars. What could I do? For me every guilder meant a bottle of milk, a loaf of bread, a pack of cigarettes, oil to keep us warm. Maybe I could even buy some coal. I knew that this particular progressive left-wing weekly paid at least a hundred and fifty guilders for an ordinary dull run-of-the-mill article (for example, "The Drifting Dunes of the Veluwe" or "So You Want to Raise Hogs in Drente?"). My article was an international scoop packed with firsthand information. An article that would be the talk of the town for a long time to come. That's what you get for working for the left. Any respectable right-wing paper would have paid at least a thousand guilders for the story.

After a long hassle they finally raised my pay to thirty-five guilders. I could pick it up any time. I walked from the phone booth over to the office where they tossed their dog his bone.

I came home. Claudia asked enthusiastically if they'd taken the piece. "Yes," I said.

"Can we afford to go out to a movie tonight?" she asked cheerfully. "It'll be great to go out. It's been such a long time. We'll hire a babysitter and afterward we'll go dancing. We'll have a ball."

I had to disappoint her.

"I only got thirty-five guilders," I said.

"Thirty-five guilders?" she repeated incredulously. "For three days' work? I thought you'd get at least two hundred. The cheap bastards. Well, who wants to go to the movies anyway?" she said sweetly. "We'll have a good time right here. Can't you get the article back? Give them their money back. We'll do without it."

Something was better than nothing, I said, and besides it was a good piece of journalism. Maybe they'd pay me some more later.

"I can't believe it," she sobbed. "All that work for nothing. Let me go to work. I can get a part-time job. Then you can stay home and do your own work. I don't have to go out. Really I don't. We'll have a good time. Right here. The two of us."

Two days later I bought a copy of *Vrij Nederland* at the newsstand.

My cold hands shook as I opened it. My article was given a full double-page spread. The headline was big and black:

THE CRIME OF THE EXISTENTIALISTS

"By a Special Correspondent" was the by-line I'd asked them to use for safety's sake. My name wasn't all that well known as a journalist yet. This was my first big professional contribution to the Dutch press. Proud of myself, I rushed home to show it to Claudia. I read it over her shoulder.

It was early in the morning of October 14, 1962, when the twenty-one-year-old American James Wagner stepped off the boat from Barcelona and onto the Balearic Island of Ibiza. A deserter from the U.S. Army, Wagner hoped to lay low on the island for at least six months. He had, however, no money and no passport.

(According to various writers and journalists who've spent some time on the island, Ibiza is a veritable paradise for junkies and dope smugglers, an isle of vice, a sort of tourist resort for outlaws only. Their articles, plus movies and TV documentaries deploring the "disgraceful state of affairs" on the island, succeeded in rousing the interest not only of the national Spanish police and Interpol but also of the F.B.I. Vice, these lawmen decided, should be exiled and righteousness restored. People were, and still are, deported without regard for either their innocence or guilt. Artists, beatniks, beach bums, and other obvious misfits are no longer welcome.)

Shortly after arriving in Ibiza, Wagner meets Steve, an American English teacher, and Steve's Spanish girlfriend Pillie, runaway wife of a rich Barcelona businessman. After telling Steve and Pillie about the fix he's in, Wagner tries to borrow enough money to buy a false passport. He fails. For the next weeks, however, he stays with the American and his Spanish playmate until, in mid-November, he decides to go to Barcelona to try to pick up some money.

Jokingly (at first anyway), Pillie suggests that Wagner might try robbing her husband, the tycoon Francisco Robirosa Closas—a good target since he has plenty of money and contributes nothing to Pillie's support. (In Spain, there is no divorce and consequently no alimony either.) The idea appeals to Wagner, who asks Steve for further details, which Steve gets from Pillie and passes on to Wagner. The penniless deserter now has the address, a sketch of the house, and he knows where the businessman keeps his money. At this point —when Wagner is already seriously thinking of going ahead with the plan—the American teacher and his girlfriend start getting worried. They tell him to drop it. He promises he will. No more is said about the matter. Steve takes the precaution of tucking his sketch away in what he considers a safe place.

On Saturday, November 17, accompanied by a Dutch girl, Wagner arrives in Barcelona on the boat from Ibiza. He looks up a friend of Steve's, Jack H.—an American who runs a nightclub on the Plaza Real—and tells him his troubles. Wagner has found out where he can pick up a false passport, but he's also discovered it will cost him five thousand pesetas (around eighty dollars). Remembering the businessman's address, Wagner asks Jack H. if he would mind taking him there since he doesn't know his way around Barcelona. He also asks for a gun (though only to use as a threat), but Jack H. doesn't have one. Wagner then asks him if he has a hammer he can use (to hide under a newspaper and make it look like a gun). Jack H. asks his sister-in-law Nancy, who works in his nightclub, to bring a hammer over from his apartment. She asks no questions and returns later with a hammer wrapped up in a copy of *Time*. Wagner and Jack H. then take off for the sedate section of Barcelona where Robirosa lives. It is siesta time.

While Wagner goes into the house, Jack H. waits outside. Half an hour later Wagner comes back. There is blood on his hands and clothes (the victim defended himself with a knife, cutting three of Wagner's fingers), but all he says is, "I knocked him down and tied him up." He has stolen a grand total of only two thousand pesetas. Giving Jack H. his hammer back, Wagner steps into a drugstore to have his hand bandaged. He seems very cool, shows no signs of panic. Jack H. then lends Wagner some of his own clothes and arranges for an English girl, due to take the boat to Ibiza leaving at seven that night, to throw a parcel containing Wagner's bloodstained clothes overboard once the boat is safely out to sea. The girl, who asks no questions about the parcel's contents, throws it overboard late that night. "Jimmy" Wagner, apparently calm but perhaps unusually shy, hangs around the nightclub until, on Monday, the 19th, he boards the ten o'clock nightboat leaving for Palma de Majorca.

That same evening, Robirosa's father enters his son's room and finds his son has been savagely murdered. His throat has been cut, his body stabbed in eighty-five different places; he has also been suffocated; his face is covered with a tied-on cloth. Next to his body the police find a pair of scissors marked "United States Army Germany," a bloodstained glove with three ripped fingers, and a copy of *Time*. On the floor lies a cashbox stuffed with a fortune in bills. The police also discover a recent letter from Robirosa's wife in which she begs him to send her some money. Swiftly hunting Pillie down, the police arrest her and her American boyfriend the following day in Ibiza. In Steve's wallet they come on a sketch of Robirosa's house. In Barcelona, Spanish plainclothesmen start investigating Americans and all habitués of the two nightclubs on the Plaza Real.

On Tuesday, November 20, at about four in the morning, just about closing time, national and local police barge into the Blue Note and make a mass arrest. The manager, the bartender, the waiters, and about fifteen American and English customers are hauled off to police headquarters. None is aware a murder has been committed. The nightclub, however, has long been suspected of being involved in the drug-smuggling racket, has been raided repeatedly but never with any success; after lengthy interrogations, the police have always had to let everyone go because of lack of sufficient evidence. Thus the raid appears to be simply a face-saving show of police power.

At headquarters, Pillie and Steve have been sitting for some time handcuffed to their chairs.

Later that morning, Spanish newspapers come out with shocking headlines: AMERICAN EXISTENTIALIST GANG ARRESTED FOR ROBIROSA MURDER. One paper publishes a big picture of two girls arrested that morning (but completely innocent) captioned: "Beneath their masks of sweetness lie hatred and the face of Satan."

First the police chief himself, then day and night shifts of police inspectors, grill the suspects. Since none of the suspects knows anything about the murder, however, the police get nowhere. By radio, television, and the papers, the police appeal to all druggists, doctors, and hospitals to notify them if any person has recently received treatment for injuries to three fingers. All suspects rounded up by this appeal are locked up and, like Steve and Pillie, handcuffed to their chairs. Given neither food nor water, they are treated to almost constant police brutality during the three days they are held for questioning. Hard blows with the edge of the hand to the throat are the usual treatment. Time and again, suspects are told the treatment will stop if only they will name the murderer or admit they were accessories to the crime.

Pillie receives the same very effective handling. Blows against the larynx leave no recognizable marks but are extremely painful and make breathing difficult. Steve wears a beard and a hair is pulled out as each question is put to him. Jack H. gets the roughest treatment. His jaw is broken in three different places. (Questioned by the Spanish police three years before—he had been suspected of dealing in drugs but had been let off for lack of sufficient evidence— he had had his jaw broken in five different places.)

The Barcelona druggist who bandaged Wagner's hand notifies the police and provides a description, which is immediately circulated throughout the Spanish mainland, the Canary Islands, the Balearics, and, with the help of Interpol, all over Europe. The American Army in Germany concludes from the description that the person they are looking for is probably the deserter James Wagner. Police informers, who infest every café, hotel, restaurant, and other public places in Spain, recall having seen Wagner in the company of various suspects. Checking a travel bureau's passenger list, Wagner is traced to Palma de Majorca and found working on the galley crew of a yacht scheduled to leave on cruise the next day.

In a state of complete apathy, Wagner is brought to Barcelona where he confesses everything and implicates everybody: Pillie and Steve thought up the plan, Jack H. gave him the hammer and brought him to Robirosa's house, Nancy dyed his hair, and Joan took his bundle of bloodstained clothes and threw them into the sea. He answers all questions in great detail and in his so-called confession mentions all the suspects. Later all he will say is, "I don't remember any more," but for the moment the police have enough information to justify keeping their suspects locked up.

One of these suspects is an American Negro singer named Gloria —a soloist at the Blue Note and, according to the police, James Wagner's "concubine." Though anyone and everyone is willing to swear under oath that Gloria does not know and never has known the murderer—much less ever lived with him or heard anything about his plans—and though Gloria's first glimpse of him is at police headquarters, the police claim they have their "proof" and won't listen to anyone.

Among the imprisoned suspects are four Americans who had dropped into the Blue Note for their first or, in some cases, second time. On vacation, they had only recently arrived in Barcelona and had never met Wagner. In spite of this, they are being threatened with deportation. Gloria, the mother of two children, and an English woman, the mother of a four-year-old daughter, are both locked up without being allowed to make arrangements to have their children looked after. The police do nothing about the children. For days the English woman's daughter wanders the streets until at last a Spanish hotel keeper takes her in. Without his help, the child would have been left to fend for herself in a country known for its great love of children. Joan, the girl who got rid of the bloodstained clothes, is arrested in Ibiza and shipped back to police headquarters in Barcelona.

Now that the murderer and his so-called accomplices have been arrested and have "confessed" (Wagner alone has confessed), some have been taken off to the courthouse, others to jail. One of the jailed is a twenty-one-year-old Dutch girl who worked at the nightclub. She shares her cell with five other girls. The cell is six feet wide and nine feet long. It has one small barred window. Unheated and in the basement of the building, the cell is damp and ice cold. There are no beds and no blankets and, in their thin summer dresses, the only way they can sleep at night on the cold concrete floor is by lying close to—practically on top of—each other. Conditions in the women's jail are unbelievably primitive. Medieval barbarity and tyranny reign and the entire staff is corrupt. Food and cigarettes cost a fortune. A pack of cigarettes that normally costs sixty pesetas cost almost three hundred pesetas in jail. Contact with the outside world can be arranged only via the nuns, and the nuns are as corrupt as the rest of the staff.

Only for a stiff fee will they smuggle notes in and out of jail or bring in a paper with news about the murder.

The murder has made news in America and both English and American journalists are eager to speak to the prisoners, but the Spanish police have turned down all their requests. Though consuls from the various countries are allowed to visit their respective countrymen, they are unable to provide much assistance. The Dutch consul, informed about the Dutch girl "suspect" from the very start, waits twelve days before visiting her, by which time she has already been transferred to the women's prison. After giving her a long sermon, he asks if her parents can pay her flight back to Holland. Three days later, she is released. Four policemen escort her to the airport and give her passport to the plane's pilot. At Schiphol she is welcomed back to Holland by two detectives who have come to check that she has actually returned.

The interrogation lasts about three weeks. In the course of the interrogation, suspects are shown pictures of the brutally murdered man. It would seem that, before going to Robirosa's house, Wagner took three tubes of centramine or benzedrine; that the businessman fought back with a knife, wounding Wagner badly; that Wagner then lost his head and, under the influence of so much benzedrine, butchered him. He had brought the scissors along intending to cut the telephone wires after stealing the money.

One of the many peculiar aspects of this affair is that none of the foreigners involved is permitted any legal assistance. (Journalists from abroad say they would gladly arrange to find lawyers but, as previously mentioned, they are not allowed access to the prisoners.) Pillie, the Spanish woman, is the only one granted a lawyer. Though Spanish papers refer to her as "a sinful woman" (she abandoned her two children), and though she is more closely implicated than many others, her wealthy family will quite probably be able to buy her freedom with the help of the best available counsel. For the others, no such help is available. The Spanish police don't consider it essential. Spanish lawyers refuse to touch the case. Consulates and embassies who have attempted to hire lawyers have been consistently rebuffed. Only one lawyer has indicated any willingness to represent a defendant but then only for a minimum fee of $30,000.

The American Army, meanwhile, is requesting extradition for James Wagner—the only chance he stands of escaping Spain's ancient and horrible death sentence: death by strangulation. There is no doubt whatsoever that, should the Army's efforts fail, he will be condemned to death. As for his hiring a lawyer, the police say, "Not necessary."

Other sentences, according to reports from reliable sources, have already been decided upon. For the American teacher Steve, the "brains behind the plot" who also lured a Spanish mother away from her children, twelve years. For Jack H., long wanted by the Spanish police, also twelve years. For his sister-in-law Nancy, as an accessory to the crime, six years. For Joan, who pitched the bundle of clothes overboard, three years. For ten others—Americans, Australians, South Africans, Canadians, and Dutch—deportation, for being, according to the Spanish police, either friends or acquaintances of a murderer and/or his accomplices.

A trial, open to the public, will be held some time next year. But "open to the public" has a special meaning in Spain. Hours in advance, the government sees to it that the courtroom is packed with a picked crowd of plainclothesmen and Falange party regulars so that there is, unfortunately, no room for anyone else when the trial begins. Meanwhile, in Ibiza—where, the police say, the murder plot was hatched—the police are already busily tracking down new "suspects" for a new sweep. Tourists judged to be lacking "sufficient means of support," and young people found lacking almost anything the police care to name, are being systematically driven off the island. Sometimes they are even forced to leave what money and property they do have behind. Ibiza is being purged very effectively, in order to "prevent a new outrage." Early one December morning, the police raided a large apartment in the island's capital in which a number of Americans, Englishmen, and Germans were living together. At police headquarters they were informed they must leave the island at once. Reasons for deportation: "unseemly behavior, inadequate funds, associating with Spaniards, and using drugs."

On the morning of December 1, a twenty-eight-year-old Dutchman named Barry N. was arrested in Ibiza for "possessing marijuana." Barry N., who had spent half a year in America, was vacationing in Ibiza before coming back to Holland. His arrest is obviously a direct result of the Barcelona "crimen de los existencialistas" and its attendant Ibizan purge. There is reason to believe that he will be given an unduly severe sentence (he is one of the first to be arrested on the charge of possessing marijuana) to serve as an example. It is now the end of December and the Dutch consul has not yet so much as visited the prisoner. Food is not provided in Ibizan jails; the prisoner is left to his own devices. The Dutch vice-consul in Ibiza, Don Pineda, is a Spanish businessman who does not speak Dutch (and speaks only a few words of French), and to Dutchmen in difficulties he has never been of any assistance whatsoever. Don Pineda refuses to step in and the nearest consul, Mr. Raemakers in Barcelona, refers frustrated Dutchmen from Ibiza back to his do-nothing colleague.

The article made an impression all right. The editors said they'd already had dozens of calls about it. I'd promised Nollie I'd split whatever they gave me for my piece because it was her tip that got me going. But I had to disappoint her. Claudia and I had already spent the money.

"Forget it," she said. "As long as it helps those people there who didn't have anything to do with the murder. Nobody does a thing for them."

I wondered what I could do to help Barry. I didn't have any money and I couldn't see any point in going to Spain myself. I was really worried about him. Then suddenly the ball started rolling. A week after my article came out, I heard about it on the radio and read in the papers:

QUESTIONS IN PARLIAMENT
ABOUT ARREST OF DUTCHMAN

The Hague, Thursday (ANP)—"Is it true that in December a Dutch citizen vacationing on the island of Ibiza (Spain) was arrested on suspicion of a misdemeanor and is being held in the Ibiza jail where food is not provided for prisoners?" This question was raised in a letter written by Member of Parliament Mr. M. Van der Goes van Naters (Labor Party) to the Minister of Foreign Affairs, Mr. J. M. A. H. Luns. He wants to know if it is true that neither the Dutch consul at Palma de Majorca (who exercises jurisdiction over Ibiza) nor the vice-consul in Ibiza, though aware of the above-mentioned facts, have sought contact with the Dutchman or provided him with food and legal aid.

303

My article started things moving. At least it got the authorities thinking. And, I thought, it's not every journalist whose first article gets questions raised in Parliament.

One evening an Irish girl came by with a letter from Barry. She was on her way home from Spain. Barry was in bad shape—a physical wreck. I hadn't seen him in more than a year and, according to the girl, he was now very nervous and thin. Barbara had been deported from the island and was forbidden all communication with him. Barry was released from jail as soon as my article penetrated through to the island authorities. They confiscated his passport, leaving him a prisoner who could walk around freely, but with no money and under constant surveillance. His lawyer advised him to get off the island even if he had to swim. But he was afraid to risk crossing the border without a passport. He was damned right. They shoot first and ask questions later. He needed money. I had to help him somehow, even though we weren't exactly rolling in money ourselves. At any rate Barry could count on plenty of publicity. The papers were on his trail. In *Het Vrije Volk* the following article appeared:

Jan Cremer *The Existentialist Murder Case*

BARRY N.—RELEASED FROM SPANISH CELL—
LIVES IN MORTAL FEAR

Businessman says: "Gestapo methods."

The twenty-eight-year-old Dutchman Barry N. was released on bail from the Ibiza jail but is forbidden to leave Spain. His passport has been confiscated. According to a Dutch businessman recently returned from Ibiza, Barry N. is suspected of smuggling marijuana from Morocco to the United States.

A Member of Parliament, Mr. Van der Goes van Naters (Labor Party) addressed a number of written questions relating to Barry N.'s arrest to the Minister of Foreign Affairs. He wants to know if it is true that Barry N. is in a jail on Ibiza where no food is provided for the prisoners.

The businessman, who wishes to remain anonymous because of his business interests in Spain, has informed us that Barry N. is still in Ibiza. The police follow his every move. He shuns contact with fellow Dutchmen and is letting his beard grow so he will be less easily recognized.

Barry N. comes from Amsterdam. He is well known in Leidseplein circles. On December first he was arrested in Ibiza after having spent half a year in America. According to the police he had his girlfriend Barbara try to smuggle five pounds of marijuana from Morocco in a package to friends of his in California.

According to the businessman, Barry N. spent a number of weeks in the dismal jail of Ibiza. In this jail, prisoners are left to fend for themselves. No food is provided for them. They are completely dependent on outside friends for their food.

A sensational article appeared in *Vrij Nederland* describing a purge in Ibiza following the murder of a Spanish businessman by a U.S. Army deserter. It was in this article that mention was first made of the arrest of Barry N. His arrest was supposedly a consequence of the murder. After the murder the police rounded up foreigners who had no visible means of support. It is said that the police used Gestapo methods. A number of these young people were deported. Those suspected of having any connection with the murder were placed under arrest.

One of them was a twenty-one-year-old Dutch girl. She was held in a women's jail in a crowded cell only nine feet long and six feet wide. A grim system of tyranny prevailed in this jail. Exorbitant prices were charged for food and cigarettes.

The article in *Vrij Nederland* accused the Dutch vice-consul in Ibiza, Don Pineda, and the consul in Barcelona, Mr. Raemakers, of having done nothing whatsoever to assist the two Dutch nationals arrested. It is alleged that, in the case of Barry N., neither vice-consul nor consul made any attempt to contact him during his stay in jail. Mr. Van der Goes has requested information on this matter as well. The Dutch businessman generally confirmed the story as reported in *Vrij Nederland*. "Before the murder, the Spanish police treated the beat-niks, who had more or less cut themselves off from society, extremely tolerantly. I have, though, occasionally seen young people taken off the island in strait jackets. They had pumped themselves full of benzedrine. They smoked marijuana as if it was ordinary tobacco. After the murder everything was different. The police from Madrid and even Interpol started keeping a close watch on the kids and the Spanish police are anything but gentle," the businessman said. He felt it only right, how-ever, to emphasize the fact that the rest of the Dutchmen and foreigners on the island have never had any difficulties with the police.

According to the businessman, Barry N.'s attempt to smuggle marijuana to California was extremely amateurish. As soon as his girlfriend Barbara walked into the post office it was obvious that something was wrong. "I am glad the affair is coming out into the open here in Holland," the businessman said. "It's a shame the way they're keeping this Amsterdam boy there on the island without any legal aid whatsoever. The impression he made on me was that of a man living in mortal terror."

That very same day the "other side of the story" appeared in our favorite patriotic freedom-loving daily *De Telegraaf*. Their Spanish cor-respondent presented the story as follows:

BAREND N. TREATED FAIRLY

Madrid, Tuesday—Barend Niekamp (29) the Dutch author who, according to the questions addressed by Mr. Van der Goes van Naters to Minister J. M. A. H. Luns, is supposedly pining away in a gloomy Spanish jail, was found to be in good health on a boat headed from Barcelona to Majorca last night.

Barend is no longer confined to jail and has never complained to the Dutch vice-consul on Ibiza about the quantity or quality of the food during the time he spent in jail as a result of "possessing marijuana."

And now for a short summary of the Spanish adventures—or as much as we know of them—of this unfortunate and rather reckless young man. We first heard of Barend in a small news item in a Spanish paper informing us that he and a girl named "Barbara" were suspected of being involved in smuggling narcotics. He had been ar-rested in Ibiza and was awaiting trail. The charges brought against Barend on December 3 were that on November 28 he had attempted to mail a newspaper at the post office with a small quantity of marijuana concealed between the pages. It was, Barend stated, addressed to a friend in the United States.

On the tenth of December, the Dutch Embassy received a letter from the consul in Ibiza informing them that Niekamp had been appointed a lawyer who would be able to get him out on bail for the sum of fifteen thousand pesetas. The consul in Ibiza and Niekamp's lawyer managed to get the bail reduced to four thousand pesetas. Niekamp's friends paid the sum. Barend was released from jail on January 7 after turning in his passport and agreeing to report to the Ibiza police every three days. Some time later, however, he disappeared without leaving a trace. Yesterday he reported to the consul in Barcelona to request a "laisser-passer" which would serve as a passport and enable him to return to Holland. The consul advised him to go back to Majorca where he could stay with some German friends of his and to report to the police as soon as possible.

304

The next morning *Het Vrije Volk* chickened out, repeating the story in *De Telegraaf* almost word for word. Also some Dutch Man of Letters, a resident of Ibiza, felt called upon to come to the defense of his island. Probably pressured by the Spanish authorities and worried about his own sunny future there. In a long emotional letter to the editor in *Vrij Nederland* he went into detail about how great things were on this island where freedom reigned and the police showed no signs of fascistic or Gestapo behavior. He'd lived there for years and never noticed any police brutality. Of course he was aware that the police sometimes took harsh measures against beatniks, artists, etc., but they were just asking for it. Besides, he wrote, the author of the *Vrij Nederland* article had got his facts all wrong. The body had not been stabbed eighty-five times. Only eighty-three times. The editors of *Vrij Nederland* washed their hands cleaner than Pontius Pilate. After all, the Dutch Man of Letters was on very cozy terms with several members of the editorial board, even deigned to pen little articles for their sheet every once in a while. They apologized for any inaccuracies. They hadn't had time to check all the facts.

One fact there can be no doubt about is that a large number of Spaniards lead pretty rough lives on Ibiza. Some are invalids because they fought on the losing side in the Civil War. It's said that on the nearby island of Formentera prisoners from Civil War days are still working in the salt mines—a ball and chain on their ankles and armed guards to make sure there's no loafing. The owner of the Fonda Pedro in Formentera—a mecca for tourists and longtime residents alike, a bar, café, restaurant, and hotel all in one—is said to have been the public executioner who, after the Civil War, executed more than twelve hundred people.

In Ibiza there are also a few guys who, they say, were pretty big heroes back in the thirties. They fought on the wrong side, no matter which side you pick. Caught, beaten up, their bones broken, they were usually either crippled or blinded by the Security men. Until a businesslike agreement was reached. In exchange for names, ranks, and hiding places of their still-uncaptured comrades they were freed. The Spanish Government rewarded them generously, granting them leases on cafés or hotels in exchange for information. The Civil War ended a long time ago. But the Spanish police are still interested in rounding up enemies. The task of these "reformed traitors" is to keep a close watch on tourists and non-Spanish residents. While sipping a glass of good Spanish wine and listening to the thrum of a guitar, the tourist is only too glad to give his opinion of Franco and the government. And who can ask for a better audience than a charming old Spaniard who's picked up a few "utterly charming" words of French, English, German, and Dutch? And who always agrees with you.

Ibiza, land of milk and honey. And of Dutch Men of Letters. A favorite resort for tourists.

305

Early in the morning the loud ring of the doorbell, making itself heard over the clang of scrap iron and steel out back, woke me up. I opened the door and there was Barry. Pale, skinny, with a mangy beard, a wool cap pulled down over his ears—but with the same old smile. "Well, here I am," he said. We laughed.

I gave him some winter clothes to put on since he was wearing a thin pair of pants and a light denim jacket. All he had with him was a blue army satchel with a Moroccan peace pipe in it, a copy of the *Bhagavad Gita,* a notebook, and a cigarette lighter, souvenir of Ibiza. He hadn't had anything to eat yet. We had lots to talk about and went off to the market to buy a big sack of mussels. Barry brewed up a delicious mussel soup while Claudia and I listened to his stories and adventures and I took notes for an article—an epilogue for *Vrij Nederland* just to prove my first article was one hundred per cent true, contrary to all the letters to the editor and miscellaneous gossip.

Editor Rinus, a cigar-smoking dwarf from Zeeland who stuffs his weekly sheet with articles about politics, the nouvellest vague in movies, the cultivation of newer and better potatoes, and who force-feeds his poor readers with a list of his own dull and undaring opinions on literature and music, crams his columns with cocktail chatter and so-called "popular humor," a man who labors under the delusion that every cab driver, whore, ragpicker, stevedore, and senile old lady has nothing better to do than wait for him to stroll into a restaurant or bar or a waiting room so they can pour their quaint humorous hearts out to him—Editor Rinus, who slips away with his silent cigar whenever he's supposed to appear on a "controversial" television program, informed me that he and his staff had decided upon a fee of thirty-five guilders for my second exclusive firsthand scoop. A better price than the first article because this one was only half a page long. When I saw it in print, I thought I'd done a pretty good job. It went as follows:

BARRY N.: THREE WEEKS IN IBIZA JAIL

Nervous, exhausted and gaunt, Barry Niekamp returned to his native city of Amsterdam last month after a rough trip back from Spain.

Painter-author-musician Barry Niekamp (29), arrested by the Spanish police early in December for attempting to smuggle half an ounce of marijuana out of the country, spent three weeks in the Ibiza jail.

In the January 19 issue of *Vrij Nederland,* mention was made for the first time of the arrest of this Amsterdamer in an article about the recent "purge" in Ibiza following the murder of a Spanish businessman, Robirosa Closas, by James Wagner, a deserter from the U.S. Army.

The article pointed out that B.N. was being held in an extremely primitive jail without food or legal assistance of any kind and that the Dutch consulate had not even made any attempt to contact him during his stay in jail.

As a result of this article Mr. Van der Goes, van Naters, a Member of Parliament, addressed a number of written questions to the Minister of Foreign Affairs. Mr. Luns did not see any reason to take measures against the consular representatives in Ibiza. *De Telegraaf* contradicted the report that B.N. had been without food. It claimed that B.N. received seventy-two cents a day for food, besides the food which his friends were said to have given him. It further reported that the vice-consul had spoken to B.N.'s lawyer on a number of occasions.

First, a short summary of the facts: B.N. spends a year in the U.S., spends some time in Morocco, travels through Spain, and plans to take a short vacation in Ibiza before returning to Holland.

At the end of November he brings a copy of *La Vanguardia* (a fascist magazine) to the Ibiza post office to be sent off to America. Between the pages is a small quantity of marijuana, a gift for a friend in California.

As a result of the recent murder in Barcelona all outgoing mail is being censored and, upon inspection, the marijuana is discovered. B.N. is apprehended at an outdoor café and taken to the police station. The post office clerk identifies him and he is taken to a cell. The next morning he is brought before the public prosecutor. He confesses and is officially placed under arrest. He remains in his cell for three weeks without being brought before a judge or the public prosecutor. During this time not once is he contacted by any representative of the Dutch consulate!

It is true that he received seventy-two Dutch cents a day for food, but this was only enough, he says, to get "a bread sandwich with sometimes a little bread in between." By chipping in whatever they had, he and his fellow prisoners ("often people who didn't even know why they'd been arrested") managed to buy one warm meal a day. The food supposedly provided by friends was, he says, purely imaginary.

On the second day of his imprisonment he writes a detailed letter to the Dutch consul in Barcelona requesting legal aid and financial assistance. He receives no reply. The only person who can do anything to help him is his American wife. She is forbidden to see him.

The interpreter present at the questioning turns out to be a "lawyer." Through his efforts, and after turning in his passport and promising to report to the police every three days, B.N. is released on eight thousand pesetas bail. Afterward it is evident that one of the preconditions to his release is that his wife was threatened and forced to leave the island without being given an opportunity to get in touch with her husband. During his imprisonment B.N. sent a number of letters and messages to the Dutch consul, to which he never once received a reply. Neither did the vice-consul on Ibiza ever visit him or offer him any help. Every three days B.N. reports to the police station where he is assured that his passport will be returned as soon as the investigation of the "Existentialist Murder" is completed and there is clear proof that he is not implicated. For weeks on end they keep him waiting for his passport. His lawyer (who charges one hundred dollars for two one-hour consultations) advises him to leave the island as quickly as possible, "even if you have to swim." Desperate, without a peseta to his name, hungry and overwrought, B.N. goes to the Dutch consulate in Palma de Majorca in the hope of getting a "laisser-passer" enabling him to return to Holland. He gets a cool reception and, after explaining his problem, is told, "But, sir, we can't possibly give you a laisser-passer. It's against the law in Spain. You'll have to go to the vice-consul in Ibiza. Perhaps he can help you. Or to Barcelona. They'll be sure to help you there."

B.N. replies that he doesn't have enough money to go back to Ibiza or to Barcelona. A call is put through to "Madrid." A few hours later, when the call has supposedly been made, B.N. is informed that in Madrid they refuse to give him a laisser-passer or help him in any way.

After B.N. has made it clear that he has no money at all, the Dutch consul says, "Well, you can always pick up some kind of job, can't you? Washing dishes in a hotel. Or you can even get a job on a foreign yacht. Tell them the position you're in and they can get you out of Spain illegally. But we really can't do anything for you."

For days B.N. roams the island, homeless and hungry. Returning to the consul, he is advised to go straight to Barcelona—where they tell him to go back to Palma. In the meantime, things begin to happen back in Holland. Mr. Van der Goes van Naters asks questions in Parliament and in *Het Vrije Volk* an article about B.N. appears in which a Dutch businessman describes him as "living in mortal terror" and verifies the fact that B.N. had been held on the island without any legal aid and has spent a number of weeks in the Ibiza jail where the prisoners are indeed left to fend for themselves.

In *De Telegraaf* a scrambled account of fabulous facts appeared under the headline: *"Barend N. Treated Fairly."* The author of the article claimed that B.N. had never approached the vice-consul on Ibiza for help. The article opened with the following sentence: "Barend Niekamp (29), the Dutch author who, according to the questions addressed by Mr. Van der Goes van Naters to Minister J. M. A. H. Luns, is supposedly pining away in a gloomy Spanish jail, was found to be in good health on a boat headed from Barcelona to Majorca last night."

In the meantime B.N. was close to a nervous breakdown. Sent off on one wild goose chase after the other, he made two trips from Barcelona to Majorca and back and two trips from Majorca to Ibiza and back. All that trouble just to get back home. In Barcelona he made one last desperate attempt and went to the consul, who again said there was nothing he could do to help him. "We can't risk getting into any more trouble with the police for the time being." He refused to say anything more helpful than, "You'll have to get a job or try to make your own way over the border, but really there is nothing I can do to help you."

In *Het Vrije Volk,* this consul, Mr. Raemakers, stated (under the headline '*Barry N. didn't come to me for help*') that he had given Barry N. all the help and advice he could wish for. According to Mr. Raemakers, Barry N. didn't seem "to have had such a bad time in the Ibiza jail."

After having read the article in *Vrij Nederland,* the consul said to Barry N. scornfully: "It says here you didn't get any food. Then how did you manage to stay alive?" Barry N. explained that if he had been dependent on the Dutch Embassy all that time, he undoubtedly would have starved to death and wouldn't have been able to drop in at the consulate at all.

The following comment was printed in *Het Vrije Volk*: "Until the day before yesterday Barry N. had not requested my help. Until that moment, I knew about his case only from what I had read in the Spanish newspapers." It is reassuring to know that the consul is aware of the imprisonment of Dutch prisoners without letting it disturb him in any way.

In the end the consul advised Barry N. to return to Ibiza and report to the local police so as not to antagonize them. The consul refused to offer him financial assistance, but thanks to a number of old acquaintances whom Barry N. happened to meet, he was able to finance the trip to Ibiza. Upon his arrival at the police station he was informed that the public prosecutor had decided not to prosecute him. Barry N. was now officially a free man and wanted to go back to Holland. He sold all his earthly possessions, except for a small bundle of clothes, to pick up enough money to get back to Barcelona. This time he went to the consul there to ask for a loan to pay his fare back home. For two full hours he spoke to the consul, but the consul refused to lend him thirty guilders. "You can hitchhike," said the consul. Barry N. explained that he didn't have enough money to even buy himself a meal. Finally the consul agreed to call Madrid. The Embassy advised against lending Barry N. the money. "Let him hitchhike. After all he's been through, this won't make much difference."

Barry pleaded with the consul, told him he hadn't eaten for the past few days and that hitchhiking at that time of the year (early February) was nearly impossible, but the consul simply said: "Of course we are willing to grant financial assistance to Dutchmen in need. But only a small percentage of the Dutchmen abroad are in a position to qualify for this assistance. Unfortunately you are not one of them. Thus I see no reason at all why we should help you."

Wearing the only clothes he had—summer clothes—Barry N. hitchhiked up through Europe in bitterly cold winter weather and finally reached Holland. At the moment he is working on a book about his recent experiences. Let us hope that other Dutchmen who unexpectedly find themselves in a difficult situation in Spain will be "in a position to qualify for financial assistance." Apparently those who least need it can always depend on help from the official representatives of their Fatherland.

A footnote was added to the article without my knowledge. Busy Body Simon up to his usual tricks again. He asked the editors of *Vrij Nederland* to notify their readers that he, the Noodle, had not written those articles about the Spanish murder. As if he could have!

My first article had been a journalistic coup. People wondered who the "Special Correspondent" could be. Simon, who'd spent a few weeks on Ibiza and had been running his mouth off about it ever since, slyly insinuated he knew. Which, of course, he didn't. He'd even suggested maybe he himself was the mysterious correspondent. Since he was such a renowned Ibiza expert, he couldn't understand how anyone could have written the articles without first consulting him.

306

The Happening came to Holland. It's practically a law of nature that the latest fad in America has to blow over to Holland sooner or later. So, too, the Happening. Naturally the Soggy Noodle had a limp hand in the affair. I let them print my name along with all the others on the posters and wrote an article blasting the whole thing in advance for the mimeographed catalogue handed out at the Happening. Why not?

My interest in the whole business was strictly professional: I was a journalist. I took Claudia, mainly to give her a chance to get out of the house for an evening. The Happening was a big fiasco (Friday nights at the Salvation Army are a lot more fun) and everybody lost money on it. Except for me, Jan Cremer with the Golden Fingers. What I was after was a scoop and I wrote articles for *Vrij Nederland* and *Het Toneel* and a complete account of the whole thing, illustrated with Beertje's pictures, for *De Post*:

Open the Grave
May the Happening Rest in Peace

That mad, antitheatrical, all-out, new art form, the Happening—sprung from the loins of Greenwich Village where the so-called Beat Generation first bared its body and soul in front of a generally uncritical audience—has finally, after touching down in Paris, London, Rome, and Milan, arrived in Amsterdam.

Crowds of people headed for the condemned house in a sleazy working-class section of Amsterdam where the Big Happening was scheduled to happen. According to the organizers—Melvin Clay, ex-Living Theater actor; Frank Stern, American businessman and film producer; and the Dutch author Simon Vinkenoog—"something very beautiful" was going to occur that evening, something they had been working hard for days to prepare: the World Premiere of "Bilingual Multinational Happening 1962."

"A beautiful thing is going to happen: a Happening. A reminder of the past which is still to come. And what a beautiful future it is! In the little time still left to us, plenty can still happen!" writes Simon Vinkenoog pseudodramatically in the mimeographed brochure offered to all comers—for a guilder a copy.

Painters, authors, beatniks, the Leyden Square crowd, plus a bevy of assorted chicks worked for days to provide the ramshackle house with the proper "atmosphere." Posters, paintings by would-be painters, paper streamers, photographs and pictures from children's books, dirty bones, hunks of rotten meat, mobiles made out of horse and cow gut—all this and much more was lugged in and hung up. The notorious publishing firm, De Bezige Bij, generously provided big black-rimmed posters to emphasize the name of the game—"Open the Grave."

The posters were smuggled out around town to keep the police from starting a little Happening of their own. If the police found out, the show probably wouldn't go on, meaning a great loss of Face, Time, Money, and Effort.

The select crowd, hip to the "importance" of the Happening and who knew where and when it would get off the ground, braved the cold winter wind and patiently waited for the doors to open.

Among the Happeners, famed in Holland if nowhere else, were: Louis van Gasteren, the sculptor Tajiri, film stars Yoka Berretty (who howled "I'm staying right by the door, this scene gives me the creeps," when bones started flying through the air), and Ingrid Valerius, who'd agreed to honor the occasion with a short act but couldn't make her way up to the stage.

The only quiet moment of the evening came when the bean-pole figure of Simon Vinkenoog mounted the rickety stage to tell the uninitiated what the Happening was all about. ("Each word here quivers with acrophobia. Each word is its own Happening. Each name, every reaction to an action creates a new situation!") He also introduced the first act.

Jean-Jacques Lebel—a pro at these things, "the ambassador of catastrophe," who'd come all the way up from Paris with his side-kick, the actor Jean-Pierre Moulin, just to do his bit—went ahead and did it. He came on stage dressed up in a cardboard box cut out to look like a TV screen and holding two sticks. His performance consisted of a rhythmical repetition of two names—Jackie Kennedy and Khrushchev —during which he waved his arms up and down. His little number, a jab at how simple TV is, got such a terrific reception that he had to do an encore. For the encore, he stuck to his old material but this time his face was inside the TV screen and he kept trying to bite at a bone hanging down from the ceiling.

The crowd also went wild when Gerrit—a well-known Leyden Square type—whirled on stage and made his own personal contribution to the evening by hurling the props for his dramatic work "Ode to Ether" out the window and, instead, delivered a ten-minute sermon on the pros and cons of Christmas. Gerrit and his gang were, without a doubt, the (unexpected and unscheduled) high point of the evening. They were always wherever anything really Happened. Wherever they went, glass broke, the air grew fuzzy with ether and incense, innocent bystanders burst out in flames, and everything that could be broken broke up. During the evening, every chair in the house was smashed and the Mobile Art Group created—with the help of an axe and a can of red paint—a quick work of art. "A new statue for the city museum!" they shouted in triumph when it was done, then started going for a bunch of life-size cardboard film stars with bloody bones in their hands and howling like mad.

In fact, the spectacular event got out of hand almost as soon as it started. The organizers were pacing the floor trying to cool the scene. All they wanted was to get things back on the rails, to get the Happening back on schedule. Impossible. Vinkenoog finally managed to break out of a circle of fans and fight his way up to the stage again, leading a bashful boy with curly locks, a turtle neck sweater, sandals, etc. "That's Johnny!" the crowd murmured in awe. Johnny, "the animated phenomenon," stared out at the mob with his beady little eyes and smiled shyly when they started shouting for him to do his thing. This was the famous "Johnny the Self-Kicker*—nineteen years old, veteran of many asylums and reform schools as a consequence of trying to poison off various members of his family—who'd been discovered by a young medical student with a sharp eye for new talent who'd seen the kid perform in a hick town and had brought him to Amsterdam to put some life into wedding parties and other cultural get-togethers.

"Electric-Jesus-Johnny," better known as "the Self-Kicker," refused to perform until there was absolute quiet. (Generally, "the phenomenon" needs at least half an hour of silent meditation to warm up.) All Vinkenoog's begging and tears were in vain; Johnny wouldn't start. Until his manager (a budding headshrinker) and the movie cameras moved in on him, that is. Then, suddenly, he was ready to go. The audience heaved a sigh of relief. Johnny started off by having himself tied to a chair and thrown on stage. Then he was off—screaming, yelling, bleeding, sweating, weeping, then howling out a short collection of poems, then shadow-boxing with himself, then starting off on a long rant like Goering after too many beers. The sweat was pouring off his head, the audience was cheering like mad.

But as soon as the cameramen decided they'd gotten enough of him and started shooting the other side of the room, Johnny's act screeched to a halt. He was up and off after them, trying to yank them

---

* I coined the name that evening when I thought to myself, "That's no ordinary kicker. That nut's a self-kicker." Johann van Doorn has used it for his stage name ever since.

back, when Tania—the famous Tania—calmed him down and then, since she was already on stage, started reciting "The Kiss of Death." When she'd kissed death off, big clouds of smoke, small explosions, and a barrage of fireworks announced the arrival of Robert Jasper— the Antismoke-God, the living nightmare of all cigarette manufacturers and antidrug police. Dressed as Santa's helper ("Santa is the big connection, the Man, I saw him in a vision once and have become his humble helper") he handed out crackerbarrel bits of advice plus bags of black market Mariwho—a blend of Mariwhat and Mariwhere. People were pushing to get the bags and biting each other to get ahead while he went on droning two words: Publicity and Cancer.

In the meantime, a nearly naked Miss Danielle (French, a former dancer in Jean-Louis Barrault's company) did a rhythmic pantomime to the music of Charlie Mingus—hardly audible above the whooping.

Meanwhile, too, that suave M.C. Simon Vinkenoog was elbowing his way through the room yelling and selling programs and handing out matches ("You can either eat them here or save them for breakfast") and magazines. The magazines were meant to be ripped up and stamped on—very symbolic. Then he sat down on stage with his portable typewriter "to take detailed notes" and, between bursts of typing, recited a number of his own works.

According to the poster, the purpose of this Happening was to mourn the past or future deaths of Henry Miller, Karel Appel, Lumumba, Ben Gurion, Joe Stalin, Sandberg, Chinese food, Humanism, etc.

Due to the racket and confusion, a number of the stars who'd been advertised to appear failed to. Brigitte Bardot, for instance, suddenly disappeared. Also Rotterdam's noted poet Cornelis Bastiaan Vaandrager, who was going to do "a violent, bloodthirsty, astonishing" act in which he would tear his friend and idol Vance Taylor to shreds, then kick him to death and shoot him with a cap gun. Enviously watching lesser poets hog the spotlight, he couldn't seem to attract any attention. Finally, he retreated to the men's room, stripped off his leather Vance Taylor costume, folded it up in his suitcase, and took off for Rotterdam—a beaten man, a neglected artist.

The Happening swelled into full-scale carnival. You could throw meat if you felt like it, or make "action-paintings" with blood or erasers, tear down the pictures, get up, or stay and recite anything that came into your head, or pick up the "soul phone" and talk to the souls of the late Chessman, Hitler, Billie Holiday, or Adolf Eichmann. An altar was erected for the recently deceased Marilyn Monroe and decorated with hundreds of pictures.

Johnny the Self-Kicker was winding up his act by kicking everything off the stage, throwing out slabs of meat or strings of gut to the audience ("Oh," the chicks yipped, "all that blood! It's the greatest!"), and finally collapsing unconscious on the dirty wood floor.

When the floor started to look as if it might cave in under all the stamping feet, the Action Committee announced the Grand Finale.

All the invited performers were called up to the stage, all the uninvited shoved off. With their backs to the audience, they then expressed "their respect for the dead" and recited a small ode to the living.

When the room was emptied of people, all that was left was a huge pile of garbage and a mongrel pup. One of the insiders commented, "It started off as nothing, ended up nothing, and signified nothing. A poor imitation of all those mad, antitheatrical, all-out Happenings in New York and Paris."

The next day Simon Vinkenoog declared (in a slightly hoarse voice): "It was fantastic! Not all it should have been, but then we're just starting. It'll get better. The next one—in the Museum—will be bigger and better!"

the new horatio alger

307

Claudia and I settled down to being Respectable Members of Society. We furnished our love nest as best we could. Some Sanitation Department barges were tied up on the other side of the canal. That's where we got our furniture—a few wooden chairs and a table which I sanded down and then painted blue. At the flea market I bought some black net curtains and a couch. Claudia still had her old bed. We were going to get a stove from an architect friend of ours, Zeeuwse Bas, an admirer of my paintings. In the meantime we had to make do with the awful kerosene stove. I hate them. They give off the smell of poverty.

We lived cheaply and happily and ate what Dutch artists are famous for eating: Brussels sprouts, string beans, endives, peas, kale, spinach, scarlet runner beans, cauliflower, sauerkraut, onions, carrots, leeks, beets, red cabbage, white cabbage, Chinese cabbage, green cabbage, savoy cabbage, and turnips. We bet on the soccer scores and at night played cards or Stratego. That usually led to out and out warfare because Claudia didn't want to say "Boom!" when I bumped into one of her bombs. Or she cheated.

"Kaput," she said when I bumped into a bomb.

"Damn it, you have to say Boom!" I said. "It's in the rules. Say Boom!" I commanded.

"No," she said.

"Now are you going to say Boom or not?" I asked. "Otherwise I'm not going to play any more."

She finally gave in and said "Boom" but very softly. Usually I couldn't even hear it. "I said it, honest I did," she said.

"Yeah," I said, "sure you did."

"Aw, kiss my ass," Claudia replied.

We got Provo out of the kennel as soon as we moved into the house. We had to put a muzzle on him because there was a rabies epidemic. People were bitten in the hand by other people and the Little White Puppy was front page news. Everybody was looking for it. The true nature of the animal lovers came to the surface. Hundreds of faithful dogs

323

were abandoned in the woods or tossed out of cars on the highway because people didn't want to pay a guilder for a rabies shot.

One morning we found a pregnant dog on the ice near the garbage cans. Her belly was open and four puppies were lying there, still in the fetal sac. Somebody had stuck a cane in her belly.

308

Right in front of our door there was an enormous scrap-iron yard. Tons of steel were welded, cut, and flattened there every day. An unbelievable din that started up at seven in the morning. We pulled the blankets up over our ears. A tremendous racket of cranes, welding machines, oxy-acetylene cutters, and hammers. Trucks piled high with scrap iron dumped their loads there to be reshaped for further use. The place had atmosphere all right.

Vincent lived under us with his wife. A painter who strummed on a guitar in the evenings, a good friend of mine. He and his wife played cards with us a lot. While the ladies chatted about baby powder and instant coffee, we discussed art and war.

One Saturday night Vincent and I went to the Film League. When I saw the old John Ford movie *The Grapes of Wrath* with the young Henry Fonda for the second time, my mind was made up. I knew I'd go to America sometime. Had to. That was my Paradise. My Valhalla. I'd come through over there. Hard work for hard money.

309

Christmas came. The Zweeters invited us to come over Christmas Eve. The kerosene stove stank, our bellies were empty, we could just about afford food every day for Provo. Caramella grew, feasting on Claudia's big hard nipples.

On Christmas Eve we asked the neighbors to watch Caramella for a few hours and walked through the snow to the Zweeters' house with Provo. Their house was decorated for the occasion. At least two hundred guilders' worth of stuff on the table, big stuffed turkeys, cherry pies, and champagne. And about a thousand guilders' worth of Christmas decorations, green and gold balls all over the walls and ceiling. A simple Christmas meal in the true Christmas spirit.

We went reluctantly. We didn't like leaving our home, even for a short time. Claudia and I didn't believe in the Savior. All we were interested in was the food. The Zweeters were furious because we got there late. An hour late because of a little family warfare about whether or not we should spend Christmas Eve in somebody else's house.

As soon as Provo came in he smelled turkey and jumped up on the table. The kids got the shock of their lives, howling hysterically about the Big Bad Wolf. Beertje charged around the room ferociously with a big knife in his hand and Katja lost her cool and started cussing me out.

"Everything's ruined!" she screamed. "Get that damn dog out of here!"

"Calm down," Beertje roared.

Katja whined like a hyena with a bad tooth.

"You ought to be glad I invited you at all, you bastard!" and her shrill voice cracked. "Nobody else would even want you in their house. You ought to be thankful we let you in here. And then you have to bring that goddamn dog and can't even get here on time. I just did it for her," she said, pointing at Claudia. "That poor wife of yours."

What a generous holy gesture, I thought. "Who the hell do you think you are?" I said. "Putting on a goddamn act like you're the queen of some bloody ball. You and your fucking money! Trying to show off with this ton of crap here. Well, who needs it? Kiss my ass. You can't lend us any money because you say you don't have any. But when you want to show off, the whole house is full of money. It makes me puke, the whole charity bit. Just because you're sick of each other you want other people around. Well, we've got better things to do. Don't try to snow us, sister. We can see right through you. You can ram the whole table up your ass for all I care!"

Meanwhile Provo was having a feast. When Beertje tried to get him off the big turkey, he bared his sharp white teeth for the first time in his life, then quickly snapped off another mouthful.

"Come on," I said to Claudia. "Let them choke on their Christmas dinner. We don't need it."

I took Provo off the table spread with a special Christmas table cloth, now a big dump of chewed up bones, the gutted remains of two turkeys, scraps of lettuce, pastries, slops of caviar, whipped cream, mashed potatoes, and candle grease.

Katja screamed after us on the stairs, "Bastard, idiot, cretin, fool, shithead! I hate you, I hate you, I hate you!"

Crying hysterically, she finally let Beertje drag her away from the door and the door slammed shut.

Claudia and I smiled at each other.

"They'll have a lovely Christmas dinner." I laughed heartily now that I was rid of that awful ashamed feeling I had before we came.

"They'll be giving each other hell and throwing things and they'll punish the kids and send them off to bed early, all because Provo had a ball." I laughed. "He's the only one with a full belly. Provo's learning. He's not as dumb as he used to be."

I admired Claudia's fidelity. We belonged to each other and didn't give a shit about anybody else. Nobody had to put on a show for us. We weren't interested. All the money we had was seven and a half guilders. We had a few whisky sodas at the Cotton Club where it was nice and cozy, with a few candles on the bar, red crepe paper on the lamps, and some mistletoe on the table. On the way home I bought a chicken, a little bottle of rum, and a double portion of French fries at Tante Jopie's snack bar.

We celebrated the birth of the Messiah at home. We put on the radio and danced a polka to accordion music. There's no place like home.

310

Claudia's family wouldn't leave her alone. They wanted her to spend the holidays with them. All her brothers and sisters were going to be there. They said I couldn't come. So Claudia didn't go either.

On New Year's Eve I advised her to go anyway. She could have a good meal and a chance to talk to her youngest sister Tonia. She was very fond of Tonia. The only one in the whole family who looked like Claudia. She was married to Tim, a nice guy from The Hague whom I'd known for years. He was the best guy a woman could wish for and they were happily married, as they say. A pleasant guy with an ordinary job who knew what was going on. A nice guy to have a few beers with. Plenty of common sense. She'd married Tim even though she would have preferred an artist with a beard.

Tim realized quick enough that his wife shouldn't spend too much time with her darling mother and did his best to keep her away from her. If Tonia got nervous she stuttered. Her mother had given her such a beating once when she was a kid that ever since she'd been a little paranoid and stuttered. The mother and Lena—Claudia's older sister who in the meantime had married an American professional Negro—weren't willing to let her get away that easy. Every once in a while they'd take off for The Hague to try to turn Tonia against her husband who was off at work. As a result the poor girl had a nervous breakdown and started seeing the weirdest things.

Claudia did that too, sometimes. Suddenly she'd ask the craziest questions. Or she'd say, "The kitchen is full of nails. Millions of nails!"

311

Though we were flat broke, we had a good life. For the first time in my life I had a woman and a house of my own. We rented a TV set. Within two months I'd smashed it.

One evening after supper I stretched out in bed to read the paper, the TV set about two inches away from my feet. The big gray eye. I was in a lousy mood. I'd just spent a few hours at the karate school where a night-club bouncer had accidentally jammed his finger in my right eye.

Claudia ironed the only good shirt I had left and naturally she scorched it. Then a man came to bring some kerosene. The last straw was when Rens, a cabaret star, poked his scrubby little head in the door. With a karate trick I'd just learned that afternoon I flipped him out the door, at the same time smashing in the TV screen. When the inspector came from the store I'd rented it from, I said, "My daughter, you know. She's just a kid. Doesn't know her own strength. She threw her bottle at it."

Finally the Advisory Board of the Fine Arts Subsidy Committee came to pay me a visit. Take a look at my pictures. A bunch of old farts. I could hear their joints creaking as they panted up the narrow stairs. I even thought I spied Santa Claus among the art lovers. I quickly hung a dirty palette on the wall and Claudia put on a sexy low-cut dress.

312

I worked. Caramella babbled in the play pen and I wrote. And I made paintings on thick pieces of cardboard I spread out on the floor. Caramella was a beauty. A pretty, sweet, sensitive little girl. What do you expect with a beautiful father and a beautiful mother?

One afternoon when Claudia went shopping and I was playing with Caramella (I made funny faces and stood on my head against the door, and she stared at me with her enormous eyes, wondering if her daddy was trying to be funny or had gone completely out of his mind) Claudia came back with Skinny Suzie.

An old girlfriend of mine. A pretty girl who'd been at a window with a red light for years. After an intellectual Negro made an unsuccessful attempt to reform her, she hurried back to her warm pillow at the window with the soft red light. She was back with Greasy Gijs.

"Yoo hoo," she yelled as she sailed in. "Boy, do you look a sight! What's the matter? They starve you down in Spain?"

I laughed. She was a good kid, Skinny Suzie. I once had a brief but passionate affair with her bony body. Lots of laughs. When I kept getting visions of concentration camps every time I screwed her, I pulled out of our relationship. We were still good friends, though. I'd looked for her when I got back from Spain but couldn't find her. Lean Lilly and Clever Conny had taken her place at the window and all they knew was that she was gone off with a Negro somewhere.

Claudia knew all about Skinny Suzie and me. It was before her time and she was crazy about her.

"Do you want coffee?" Claudia asked Suzie.

"Sweetie pie," she squealed, "a cup of coffee or a good hot prick— it's all the same to me as long as I've got something hot inside!"

While Claudia puttered around in the kitchen she said "How's things with her ex? That bastard still on your tail?"

"No, it's okay," I said. "The divorce should come through any day now, I hope."

"She's a good kid, Claudia," she said. "Just your type. Better watch your step though. If you cheat on her, I wouldn't let her know if I were you. After all, we're none of us angels, are we?"

She winked at me.

"How's Greasy Gijs?" I asked.

"Aw," she said tenderly. "Gijs is a doll. I was really sorry I ran off with that black boy. Good thing we're back together now. Shoulda seen his face when I got back. I walked in the room and Gijs was sitting there reading his paper near the window with those crazy glasses on—you know, the ones we bought two years back on the Riviera. You remember when we all went with the bus and you and Barry was supposed to come in the Chevy with Greasy Gijs and the boys? God, did we ever laugh. Those were the days.

"Gijs says, 'Who's that knocking on my door? Suzie!' He couldn't believe his eyes. 'Are you back?' he asked and, man, he was surprised. 'Why?' he says.

" 'Why is the sky blue?' I says. 'If the sky wasn't blue it wouldn't be no sky. That's why!'

" 'Gijs,' I says, 'I'd be better off six feet under than in that guy's bed. I'm back. And I'll never leave you again. We belong together.'

"Gijs went out of his mind, and he says, 'Suzie, dreamboat, let's welcome you back with a little glass of wine and then fuck up a storm just like old times. Your bed's waiting for you. I'll tell Lilly and Conny to go in back for a while! And," she said, "Jan, I can't tell you how it felt when I had Greasy Gijs back in there again. We balled like nobody's business. It's a good thing he took me back, after the way I dropped him.

Like a ton of bricks. Who wants a girl who goes out peddling her wares for free?"

Claudia came in with the steaming coffee that tasted like rubber bands.

"I've got a surprise for you," Suzie said, and she took a silver flask of French cognac out of her alligator bag.

"Here, a little something on the side."

It tasted great. We gave Caramella a Life Saver and talked about old times. She told us about her daily life, a life I'd lost contact with ever since I was with Claudia. Sometimes I missed it. Simple honest hard-working people. Lots of laughs. A sense of humor is the most important thing in life.

"You two ever fight?" Suzie asked, bursting with curiosity.

Claudia smiled at me and said, "Now and then."

"Well, you gotta look at it this way," Suzie said good-naturedly. "Jan is a madman, but he's got a good heart. And don't forget that the guy that bothers you the most fucks you the best. And you're better off with a man you love than with some dried-up fig in a white shirt and tie who brings home a pay check every week and can't keep your feet warm at night. We all get slapped around sometimes, it's part of life. That's why I'm back with Greasy Gijs. I'd rather have him fucking the hell out of me than wasting that gorgeous prick of his pissing. And even if he gets cranky and moody sometimes and beats me black and blue when he's drunk, I still get hot every time I see him. He's my man. I know he's got something going with that actress bitch, nothing but a bag of bones as far as I can see, but he's after culture, that's all. So if he sees a play on TV he'll know what it's all about. He got her in trouble, too. I know it's my money he spends on all them fancy clothes, but what do I care? I love the man and when I'm on my back and some poor fool's lying there panting on top of me, I keep thinking: Rest you merry, gentleman, let nothing you dismay—or however the song goes.

"Well, I've gotta be going now," she said. "Promise you'll come around next week when I've got a night off. We'll all go out together and live it up. Gijs will be glad to see you. 'Good old Jan,' he always says, 'he'll make it someday. He's got the world in his hands.' He really admires you, you know. Okay, bye now!"

Skinny Suzie gave Caramella a kiss and said, "What a gorgeous little hunk of flesh." She smiled at us with her sweet face under all the make-up, then tore down the stairs, her skinny but nicely shaped legs tottering on her high heels, and left us in a cloud of Chanel.

"Great kid," Claudia and I agreed.

313

As usual the cupboard was bare.

"Doesn't matter," Claudia said. "I wanted to lose weight anyway."

314

I thought about how it used to be when I was a kid. My mother used to say, "There's nothing left, the Boogey Man ate it all up." An expression she picked up somewhere. Wow, I thought, and pictured a guy straight out of Mother Goose. A big fat man wearing a pointed cap with a feather in it, who chuckled as he stuffed the whole kitchen in his mouth. Just like Hansel and Gretel and the gingerbread house.

315

"Jantje Cremer, you're going to get what's coming to you some day," the teacher said when I said something smart. Aha, I thought, that's worth waiting for. So I hung around after school, waiting, long after the other kids were gone.

"What are you doing here?" the teacher snapped. "Out!"

316

Bread with slippery cheese, a thick slice of bread with a thin layer of margarine on it and a paper-thin slice of cheese that slid farther and farther away from your nose every time you took a bite.

My mother cut out pictures of delicious food and hung them up on the wall in the kitchen. I looked at them while I ate my mealy potatoes with half a spoon of gravy. It tasted like I was really eating all those fantastic things on the walls.

317

I went to a Catholic school and ate a sandwich during recess. One Friday I had a meat sandwich. We—my mother and I—usually had meat only on Sunday. It was a special treat for me to have meat in the middle

*of the week. It was the meat for Sunday but my mother didn't have any-
thing else to put on my sandwich so she gave me the meat.*

*Suddenly the teacher came over. With a whole bunch of kids who
had told on me.*

*"What kind of sandwich do you have there?" he asked menacingly.
"Meat!" he yelled as he ran his hands through his hair, horror struck.
"Meat on Friday! Give me that! That's a sin!" he roared and he snatched
the sandwich out of my hands.*

*He threw the sandwich on the ground and violently stamped the
Temptation of the Devil into the sand.*

Everything went red in front of my eyes.

I knew what meat meant to us.

*Before he knew it I gave him a nasty kick in the shin with the metal
tip of my shoe. He stood there writhing in pain and I kicked him in the
other shin.*

*I narrowly escaped a flying wedge of all the other teachers lunging
for me and got home with a torn jacket.*

*"You must never hit anyone," my mother had taught me. "Only if
they hit you first. Then you hit back twice as hard!"*

318

*We didn't have any food. I used to steal bread from the baker's cart when
he went inside to deliver his bread.*

"Where did you get it?" my mother used to ask.

"Fritsje's mother gave it to me," I fibbed.

*Fritsje's mother really did have a bakery. One afternoon when I was
on my way home I saw a cart, waited till the baker had started off with
his basket tucked under his arm and rung a doorbell to deliver the bread,
then I stole up, grabbed a loaf of whole wheat bread, and ran off as fast
as I could.*

*Suddenly I felt something swish past my head and bang down on my
neck. I turned around and saw a real live policeman jump off his bike.
He caught me under the front wheel.*

"I saw that," he roared.

*He lifted me up by the collar. I was still clutching the loaf of bread
to my chest. I was scared he'd lock me up.*

*"Why did you steal the loaf of bread when the baker turned his
back?" he asked sternly.*

*"Because my mother and I don't have any bread in the house," my
voice trembled.*

"Are you telling the truth?" he asked grimly.

"Yes, sir," I trembled.

"Here," he said and he took thirty-five cents from the wallet which he drew out of the hip pocket of his uniform. "Go to the baker and tell him you took the bread and you want to pay for it. And don't let me catch you doing it again!"

319

The winter was ice cold. In the morning we had to wait until the icicles on the window panes melted before we could see what kind of weather it was.

Claudia wore black stockings on her beautiful legs and over them a pair of black woolen knee socks. Her delicious baby-colored flesh bulged over the tops of her stockings in between the shiny black garters with tiny red roses embroidered on them. She wore a pair of beautiful light brown boots that she laced up with leather laces. They looked tremendously sexy on her beautiful, slightly chubby legs. I bought them as soon as I got my hands on some money because Claudia didn't have any shoes for the winter. They cost fifty guilders!

I also bought some paint and made pictures in bright poster colors. At that time Pop Art was just getting off the ground in London and New York. I entitled my creations: "Front Barrier at El Alamein," "Napoleon Rests at Waterloo," "House of Cards in Dixie," "Ray Charles Plays the Piano," "Algerian Diary," "Fidel Castro in the Bush," "Christine Keeler in the Woods," "Portrait of Jesse James."

Claudia became a devoted Trini Lopez fan. The Beatles arrived on the scene and with them Bob Dylan and the Rolling Stones.

A new period in history began. The Pop generation was soon to take over the world. I was to be part of it.

The Cold War babies, my generation, were to raise their voices and take over. I'm glad I was born in time for the Second World War.

All the houses around us were torn down. The Jewish neighborhood was being demolished bit by bit—the only neighborhood in Holland with a history all its own. The walls that had seen and heard so much were balled and clawed by huge cranes, battered with demolition hammers, and finished off with bulldozers.

Poverty was all we had, poverty and more poverty. The Fine Arts Subsidy Committee needed a year to investigate whether or not I was really a serious artist. By the time they came to a decision I didn't need them any more. A month later my first book was published. The first step on the hard road to the top, to world fame, to total domination.

Claudia's family didn't give up. We had a real blow-up once, Claudia and me. I was quick to use my hands when I wanted to end the conversation. I think working is more important than arguing. Women like to go on whining.

We always made up an hour later. "If a man is great, his temper is greater," I always say, and every good broad deserves a good beating now and then.

In panic Claudia would sometimes call up friends of mine. She'd say I wanted to murder her or that I was after her with a knife. Nonsense. I don't need a knife. My bare hands can serve as knives, hammers, and hatchets.

She does some pretty weird things sometimes, my Claudia. Punctuality is a concept completely unknown to her. If I asked her to be back in an hour, I was lucky if she was back within three. She'd stay away for hours on end and leave me to take care of Caramella when she was just going out to buy butter. She'd wander around the flea market or drop in on friends. When we had a fight and I wanted to be alone and get some work done, she'd go away mad but then she'd come back later ready to make up. I was used to it.

She told strange stories about me to our friends and then over they came to tell me I really ought to behave myself. Astonished, I listened to their advice.

I asked Claudia later, "Why did you tell them that story about me beating you up? You know it isn't true. Nothing happened that afternoon and you know it."

(I'd just been a little on edge and cussed her out.)

"You're right," she said.

"Then why did you tell them that story?" I asked. "You know they love any little bit of sensation or excitement and all they do is gossip. This is the way misunderstandings arise and it wasn't even based on anything."

"Yes, you're right," she said in the sad voice of hers, unsure of herself. "I thought if I walked in there and said I came over just because you cussed me out they wouldn't think I was interesting, they'd just think what a dumb broad, every time he swears at her she runs away. So I tell them a story. They really go for those stories."

"Yeah," I said, "but when it turns out they're not true, they'll think we're nuts. And every time you open your mouth they'll think you're lying."

"Yeah," she said, "I didn't look at it that way."

Slowly but surely Claudia was afraid to visit anybody. She became a real stay-at-home.

321

Her mother sometimes came to pick her up in the afternoon. The door-bell rang.

"Is Claudia home?" she screamed from downstairs.

"Your family," I said to Claudia.

"My mother wants to know if I want to go have a cup of coffee with her," Claudia said when she came back in from the hall. "She's got Lena with her."

"Do you want to go?"

"No," she said, "but I don't know how to say no. I'll be back in half an hour."

"Okay," I said. "A bit of talk will do you good. But remember, don't let them start picking at you. I'll take care of Caramella."

Hours later she came back, whipped and depressed. A few days later the truth came out. Her sister said she'd seen me dancing cheek to cheek with a beautiful girl, much more beautiful than Claudia, down in the whore's quarter.

Although I swore to God and God knows who else that it wasn't true, that it was completely impossible since I'd been at home with Claudia herself that evening, still the poisonous bites of the two serpents had the desired effect. Claudia was scared of losing me. She was very suspicious every time I went out shopping and stayed away too long.

"Bet you and your chick had a ball!" she screamed when I walked in and found her in tears.

"No woman in the world is more beautiful than you are, you know that. I was just playing billiards and lost track of the time."

I still loved Claudia as much as ever. Everything was against us. The house, a slum tenement with a depressing view. Late at night Claudia was afraid to go out on the street alone and if she looked out the window she saw strange figures scrambling around in the scrap iron. I made jokes about it although I was pretty suspicious of the whole set-up myself. If I came home alone at night I'd whistle a happy tune as loud as I could. I had a big blackjack under my jacket. There were two night watchmen at the yard. I brought them coffee at night in return for some wood for the stove. They said plenty of people had been attacked and robbed in and around the yard.

Once Claudia's folks tried to get me. Eight of them. Guys who worked at her mother's boyfriend's repair shop. They were going to teach me a lesson. With lead pipes and rubber hoses. They waited till I came out of the house. They were just about to get out of the car when the guys from the yard started getting very interested in that car. When they moved in, armed with a scrap-iron arsenal, Claudia's family's goon squad moved out fast.

I watched my step. More than once I barely escaped. I decided not to let them get me down, but also not to take any chances.

We went to the movies, Claudia and me, while Barry took care of Caramella.

The Birds, with the magnificent Angie Dickinson
glasses smashed
eyes pecked out
and Hitchcock and his two dogs strolling out of a bird shop.

We made up with the Zweeters. After all we'd all been a little quick to lose our tempers that day. And hadn't J. Christ given us a special message for that day—Peace on Earth, Good Will to All Men?

I had to finish my book. I did it at their house since it was impossible to get any work done at home. Our one room was our whole house and I couldn't concentrate. In the evening I went to the Zweeters. I watched television until eleven. Then when they went to bed I got down to work. Every night, night in, night out, for three weeks. In the morning when the kids woke up I stopped. I walked home, got a good whiff of fresh air along the Amstel River and slept till the next evening. No bar, no friend, no nothing could keep me from my work. I had to write my book. I dreamed of robber knights, cannibals, crusaders, sheeted ghosts, and headless horsemen. An avant-garde magazine published two chapters of my book. It caused quite a stir in the publishing world.

Our love life blossomed like never before. The morning when I came home after working the whole night and lay down next to Claudia in the warm bed, she whispered, "I'm going to have another baby."

"Well, bless my soul, another one?" I said. "And I've been taking the pill every night!"

322

I decided to become the Phenomenon of Publicity and Literature and write the best book in Dutch literary history. When I was a little kid I had only one goal in life: to be a reporter.

My father had been a war correspondent, a famous globetrotter. Right after I got back from Spain I met an old man in a bar where I came to get a few bottles of beer to take out. A man who'd been around the world more times than he could remember and who'd known my father well. They'd made lots of trips together. Full of admiration, he spoke of old Jan who'd written his memoirs, but unfortunately the manuscript disappeared in the war.

I decided that later, when I had more time, I would follow in the footsteps of old Jan Cremer. And of my grandfather, the English pirate Captain John Cremer, called Ramblin Jack for short, who wrote a book about his wild adventures at sea. I've always known there was pirate blood in my veins.

I wrote and wrote. As soon as the manuscript was finished and the contract signed, I collapsed. I'd pumped out every word I had in me. A psychiatrist had to be notified because I started seeing the funniest things and thinking about suicide. I needed medical help of some kind fast.

The evening the psychiatrist invited me to lie down on his leather couch and stare at the tip of his golden ballpoint in the bright light so he could hypnotize me, I saw a whole series of visions—Japanese prison camps, the third degree, the Gestapo, the electric chair, the FLN. I felt my eyelids getting heavier and heavier and it took all my will power to keep from falling sound asleep. After lying stretched out there for an hour, I looked up. The sandman hadn't gotten around to me, but the psychiatrist was snoring up a storm in the chair next to the couch. His mouth hanging open but the ballpoint still in his hand.

I decided to be my own headshrinker. I got a license to drive a truck, took lots of long walks, a course in body building. And of course there were the pills I got from the psychiatrist. Palfium, Librium, Dexamyl, and sleeping pills.

Claudia gave birth to another beautiful baby. This time a son, and I took care of the delivery almost singlehanded. I named him Cassius Cadwallader after my favorite boxing hero, the phenomenal Cassius Clay.

If I could have a little machine built into my head to take down all my thoughts I could write five enormous books a year.

323

When I was a kid I had a paper route. A good way to earn a little pocket money. When I was thirteen I became editor-in-chief of the City Boys' Daily *and even had an interview with the mayor of Amsterdam. I had my own paper too, the* Eager Beaver, *wrote all the letters to the editor, articles, jokes, serials, crossword puzzles, and news commentaries myself. I illustrated important news stories with pictures I took with my Brownie. I also wrote articles for the youth page of* Okido. *I had a press card and, in short pants, saw the world.*

I got my first publicity when I was ten. A couple of boys in my class belonged to the Men's Glee Club. When they gave a performance there were posters all over town with a photograph of the 484 members of the Glee Club. The boys in my class could show me exactly which ones they were. I decided to join the Men's Glee Club. I wanted to be in the picture, too.

I felt like a real star. I was a soprano, I always told everybody because I thought it sounded so funny. As crazy as being a piccolo player or a kettle drummer. We were going to be on the radio on Wednesday afternoon. For weeks I told my mother and all my friends to be sure to listen to the radio. I said I'd yell out a hello.

"Won't you get into trouble?" my mother asked, and my friends said, "You'll chicken out."

That afternoon in the radio studio when we'd just finished singing "Lady bug, lady bug, fly away" (it was a live broadcast) and the red light was still on, which meant we were still on the air, I shouted "YOO HOO" at the top of my lungs.

It sounded so loud in that quiet room that I jumped myself and blushed red as a beet. The Glee Club leader came back and gave me a whack and sent me out to stand in the hall. I wouldn't ever be able to sing with them again. On the bus home I had to sit all by myself on the back seat. The other boys from the Glee Club weren't allowed to talk to me. I had won all the bets, though, and my career as newsmaker was off to a start.

In my own paper I wrote the adventures of my hero Mok Griebus, a forerunner of James Bond. Mok Griebus and the Spanish Torero, Mok Griebus in China, Mok Griebus in the Wild West, Mok Griebus in Africa.

324

Until late at night I went around slipping flyers under people's doors. I had a cigarette lighter and warmed my frozen blue fingers over it so I could go on delivering. Thousands of flyers. They seemed like millions before I got home.

I had a tiny animal hospital in the barn where I nursed birds, butterflies, and pigeons who'd been run over or had fallen out of trees, or broken their legs or wings. I nursed a caterpillar for half a year. Every day I put it on a bottle top on the corner of the window sill where the sun shone. Just after it had finally turned into a butterfly it fell on the floor and my mother accidentally stepped on it. I cried for hours and refused to go to school.

Jan Cremer *The New Horatio Alger*

My father had enormous collections of stamps and butterflies. He gave the butterfly collection to the Museum of Natural History and I and my mother could get in for free for the rest of our lives. My mother saved the stamp collection for when I grew up. The collection included the first stamps in the world, stamps that fell apart when you touched them. Stamps with the personal postmarks of Attila the Hun and the Roman emperors. The most valuable specimens were appropriated long ago by philatelists and pseudofriends who supposedly wanted to take them home and study them to see how much they were worth.

They used to call me Jantje Goldfingers. In the summer vacation I'd pick flowers in the neighbor's back yard, put a rubber band around them and sell them for a quarter at the same neighbor's front door. I cut out paper dolls in traditional Vollendam costumes, stapled on a little calendar, and sold them for a quarter. I was the director and owner of the Circus Matador. I did anything for bread. I always had more money than any of the kids at school. After the war I guided American and Canadian soldiers down to the red light district for a small fee. I was on my way to becoming Horatio Alger.

325

Jantje Cremer, an unusually gifted child, and that's a fact.

326

stinkie stankie dingy hanky
stinkie stankie dingy poo
stinkie stankie dingy panty
stinkie stankie dingy foo

327

I set up a tent in the back yard. A teepee made out of two blankets and a broom. Me and my friends smoked a peace pipe full of dried leaves, after we'd cut the palms of our hands and traded a few drops of blood. We built our own oven out of big gray paving tiles and brewed our own brand of secret tea.

The Housing Bureau sent a circular around to everybody in the neighborhood. Too many tiles had been stolen from the pile stacked up to lay a new sidewalk. *The Housing Bureau said they knew exactly who had taken them and that if the tiles weren't all back on the pile by Monday morning they'd call in the police. All the neighbors had taken a few to pave the paths in their back yard gardens or the floors in their pigeon lofts.*

That Monday morning the whole pile was back—plus sixty-nine extra tiles.

328

*I'll never forget the name
Kaatje Mustert
a doll of 17
pimply face, big tits
sitting just behind me
at school
I 13
reached back through the boards
and felt her twat*

329

*a big fat spider
circles Kaatje's quim
ten times around
then right straight in*

330

I had a part-time job selling the monthly magazine Homes, Gardens & Kitchens *door to door. In grim winter weather. I rang the bell. The housewife who stuck her mop out the upstairs window along with her head, yelled, "No thanks, whatever it is I don't need any."*

"Lady, wanna fuck?" I yelled up to her.

"What?" she asked incredulously. "Hold on. I'll be right down."

"Good morning, madam," I said when she opened the door.

I showed her the magazine in a plastic cover.

"I have a surprise for you. I'm from the beautiful monthly magazine Homes, Gardens & Kitchens, *and . . ."*

Jan Cremer *The New Horatio Alger*

I rattled off the whole spiel. Told her she'd get the book Elizabeth Goes Skiing *for free if she bought a subscription to this beautifully illustrated magazine.*

If they stood there for a few minutes, I automatically gave them a subscription. I quickly filled in the name and address. Me and my pal Jopie Champignon used to meet at a luncheonette where we could warm our feet near the stove; we'd have some coffee and cake and make up a list of our fortunate subscribers. Less than five minutes at the door meant a three-month subscription, more than five minutes meant half a year, and the broads who slammed the door in our face got a whole year's subscription. We scribbled the signatures and handed the forms on to our employer.

"I've never had such splendid salesmen!" he said proudly.

"Aw," we mumbled, flattered, and pocketed our commissions. Plus a special bonus.

Sometimes we even managed to get in a little fucking. Another bonus.

331

At the Felix Cat Food office they gave me an address where I could pick up a nice kitten. For free. I got on my bike and went over. The house was in a little courtyard, everything painted white. I knocked on the door. A stooped little old lady wearing a white lace cap opened the door. Out of the room behind her came a stink that almost knocked me over.

"Good morning, madam," I said. "Felix Cat Food sent me."

The poor dame was stone deaf. "Yes, I heard all about it," she said. "Pity, isn't it?"

"Felix Cat Food," I repeated.

"But I don't know anybody named Felix," she said, peering at me suspiciously.

"I was supposed to pick up a kitten today," I said.

"Why should I have to pay? What for?" she asked, flabbergasted.

"Pick up pussy cat," I said, articulating very carefully.

"Why, you naughty rascal," she screamed, "you dirty thing you! Get out of here and fast or I'll call the neighbors."

332

We set up a press association. For next to nothing we rented a cubbyhole on the Rokin. Just for the swanky address. A little room, 6′ x 10′. The main office of THE DODGERS PRESS ASSOCIATION. Headquarters.

340

Willem van der Linden, my trusty photographer, and me. Willem, who could be trusted as long as he wasn't busy eating anyway. Put a dish of anything edible in front of Willem and he was gone to the world. The whole press association meant nothing anymore. Not even a scoop. Food was the magic word for Willem. Just mention the word and he lit up.

Our main office had four doors to closets, one to the toilet. We painted each door a different color and nailed up signs: PRIVATE OFFICE, EDITORIAL BOARD, ADMINISTRATION, and PHOTOGRAPHY DEPARTMENT.

All there was in the office itself was a cluttered desk. If prospective clients or acquaintances came in we put on a tape recorder in the closet —a whole tape with office sounds and the ticking of a typewriter. If it was a serious matter, one of us went and stood in the closet for ten minutes and then came back and announced that "the editor-in-chief does not wish to be disturbed at the moment."

Willem and I got a few good scoops and the press association would have become a booming industry if the approaching publication of my first book hadn't distracted me from my duties.

We did get to go to Lille with Armando. There was barely room in the car due to the enormous stock of food for the two-day trip. The Soggy Noodle wanted to set up a parachute club in Lille. We had everything we needed—uniforms, boots, and crash helmets. We named the club the NAPO.

They wouldn't let me jump. Before you could make your first jump out of the rickety old plane, you had to work your way through two thick technical books in French and take an exam in French. Count me out. In the first place I was never much for studying, and especially not in French. I'm great at English and German. If I like a language I can learn it without any trouble. When I was a kid I jabbered a mixture of Hungarian and Dutch, but I could always write Dutch without any mistakes.

The Noodle, who made a few jumps (in a fit of hysteria he lurched out of the flying machine screeching *love! love! love!*), did his best to bug me. After years of frustration he finally thought he'd got the better of me. He went around telling everybody about how I couldn't jump because I'd flunked the exam. Some guy that Noodle.

333

A new kick came to Holland. The health food kick. Special organic bread (whole kernels, inedible crusts), special healthy jam (wild rosehip jam), special healthy rice with a sprig of grass, kusa (a monstrous cucumberlike thing that they slice and treat like it was some kind of meat) with a pinch of deep sea salt, cooked on a special healthy gas stove which they light with special healthy matches so it wasn't any fun going out to eat at any-body else's house any more. I checked up before accepting any invitations because you never know what these beatniks are going to come up with, and if there's one thing I can't stand it's a plateful of seaweed. No matter how hip it is.

Simon and the Mole started the whole thing. Of course the Mole started first. Later he suddenly took off for India in his old Deux Chevaux when he heard the grass was so good there. He heard somebody talking about it. Allen Ginsberg had been there. The Mole never came back. Probably devoured by the holy cows, or maybe flattened by a lawn mower, or maybe drowned in the Ganges.

It struck me that the hippies who went along with the new fad seemed to be in pretty bad shape. Take Simon for example. At the age of forty suddenly, under the influence of unmentionable narcotics, he sets out to seduce Willem's sister. A nice girl of about 6'2" from a respectable fam-ily. He gets her to come up and live with him in the attic while downstairs his charming wife lives it up with an American who sits around banging his bongos all day long. She also submits to the Special Poetic Pen of visit-ing men of letters and poets. All of which Simon thought was very hip. Freeloaders were always welcome at his pad. Because Simon needed ma-terial for his new book. He called himself the Apostle of Marijuana and made a nuisance of himself with his corny cub scout games. He put marijuana in his teenage girlfriend's pocket book, spread the word far and wide, then acted very surprised and indignant when the long arm of the law finally grabbed him by his bony elbow and wouldn't let go. In the solitude of his cell Simon tossed off fourteen volumes all about love, love, love. Simon once said he needed marijuana to make love. No grass, no fuck. But even with grass he didn't have much going. Poor martyr.

334

The shock jolts the whole world. Kennedy is dead. John Fitzgerald Kennedy has been murdered. Shot and killed. The Young Eagle. The Spokesman of the Young Generation. The Phenomenon of the New World. America, the land of my dreams. My Valhalla. My Paradise. Where I want to be so I can fight for my life. Where I can have a future. Where History, Custom, and Traditions don't paralyze everything.

Now that Kennedy is dead the Foundation of the new Pop world has been swept away. The Eagle flew off in terror flapping his gigantic wings. How long will it take before he descends to sink his claws into America?

America, I'm coming. As fast as I can.

335

One more Christmas has come and gone and one more New Year's Eve. Claudia and I still live in our gloomy tenement in the old Jewish neighborhood. The demolition of the once so lively Jewish part of town goes on and the east wind plays all by itself in the hollow cellars where houses once stood, full of happy families observing the Sabbath.

In the Golden Age, Rembrandt lived right across from me. The American and English tourists look up in admiration as the lovely guide points out Van Rijn's house. It won't be long before this house becomes a national monument too, I thought.

It's almost time for Annual Readers' and Writers' Festivities. Cadwallader and Caramella are growing up to be two worthy descendants of the renowned Cremer lineage. My book is finished and at the printer's the rotary offset presses are finishing off the last few copies of the first printing.

Like always I'm the only one who believes in my creation. The publisher insisted on limiting the first printing to five thousand copies. "Breaks all the records for Dutch debuts," he says. I try to explain that he ought to start out with at least fifty thousand more. Didn't I write AN INEVITABLE BEST SELLER on the cover? He gazes at me in surprise, open-hearted and fatherly.

I designed the cover myself. There's a picture of me on my Harley. It's the first time a writer displayed himself on the cover of his book. And another picture of me on the back. Anything wrong with showing my face? What's wrong with it—not good enough? Just because I haven't got a good education, does that mean my book isn't a masterpiece?

I know my book will make me the most beloved and most hated Dutchman. There's no shutting me up. Nobody can push me around. I'll make it just by telling the truth, telling it like it is. I'm proud of the fact that lots of people hate and despise me. Their scorn and envy is what makes me strong. I thrive on contempt.

I was born too late or too early. I belong in the Wild West among the outlaws and the desperadoes. I belong with the knights at the tournaments. In the Middle Ages I'd be at the peak of my form. I'd be the most notorious robber knight in the Western hemisphere. Tromp and De Ruyter would have met their doom at my hands, just like many a poor soul at the hands of Ramblin' Jack, the English pirate. Or am I maybe a Sign of the Times? The Voice of the People, the Scourge of Civilization? The new Christ or the Anti-Christ? Jesus or Satan?

I dedicate my first book to Jayne Mansfield, the Sex Bomb of my dreams. We were born on the same day. We have the same tastes, the same preference for High Camp, and we're both crazy about animals.

Holland is such a tiny little country. If I had my say—with my brilliant talent as Self-Promoter the sky's the limit—I'd have one hundred thousand copies of my book printed right away, the first printing, so everybody would be able to buy it. The price would be much lower—dirt cheap. After all, I didn't write the book for capitalists and intellectuals but for the ordinary man in the street. The ordinary guy on land, at sea, or in the air.

336

I would organize an enormous publicity campaign like they have in America before the elections. Buttons with my picture on them and I LUV YA JAN CREMER to be handed out at all book shops and girls' schools. Or for sale in the department stores. I'd have special Jan Cremer sweaters made with a big picture of me and I LOVE YOU that all the girls had to wear when I came back from America, where I picked up Jayne Mansfield in her heart-shaped house in Hollywood.

The Jan Cremer prize would be presented by none other than Jayne. A silver statue version of the picture on the cover. Me on a Harley-Davidson in my uniform, dungarees, a denim jacket, and my favorite hat. And a generous sum of money. The prize would be awarded to the journalist or photographer whose book best explained the Phenomenon Jan Cremer. Favorable or unfavorable.

Jayne Mansfield and me would ride through the center of Amsterdam in a big Cadillac convertible accompanied by mounted policemen and heavily armed bodyguards. A Golden Book would be presented to me every time another one hundred thousand copies of my book were sold. A copy of the book in gold. Just like in the record business they give out golden records. I'd make a record of me reading parts of the book, or maybe a selection of my radio or television interviews. Since 1957 I've been interviewed dozens of times by Dutch and American broadcasting companies—me the barbarian, me the wild beast, the culture Provo.

I'd start off the day by giving a press conference when I landed at Schiphol with Jayne Mansfield standing at my side. Then we'd stop for lunch at the Hilton. A short visit to the printer. And to the publisher. Strut in and strut out.

Jayne Mansfield and me would stop off at the AKO in Reguliersbreestraat, the store that placed the biggest advance order for my book, and we'd autograph a few copies. In the meantime there'd be cameramen shooting scenes for mattress or lipstick ads. We're never against earn-ing a little something on the side. I'd sell exclusive rights to the whole story to the highest bidder. Photographers would crowd around for special shots of me and Jayne. I'd light up a Camel and say "Mmm good!"

No hang-ups. I'd hire helicopters and have them drop thousands of folders about my book in all the big cities. In recess at girls' boarding schools I'd come climbing down a rope ladder to give out autographs and kisses. Autograph pictures. Make a rock-and-roll record. My own radio program. Lifesize posters on all the billboards. The Jan Cremer cult would sweep the country. I'd hire Wim Wagenaar to do daredevil stunts over the crowded beaches in the middle of the summer in his American crate and a big banner fluttering behind it with the words I JAN CREMER. Special planes would write my name in the sky. My book would be taken out of circulation, the mayor would order it to be confiscated. Hell would break loose. The Revolution would start.

337

That evening, the last evening in February, Geert was going to give me the first copy after he picked it up that afternoon at the printer's. It's the day of the Grand Gala of Books. The Gala Ball where the Queen, Cabinet Members, and other Big Shots condescend to waltz around the floor with the merry book lovers.

The world was about to open up for me. I had to think about all the beautiful women I'd admired from afar. Lucia, who now worked as a fashion model for Pierre Cardin in Paris. Nico, the top mannequin, the beautiful bashful Polish girl who wandered around Ibiza in a dream, alone and lonely and unapproachable. Jayne Mansfield, of course, the voluptuous sex kitten from Hollywood. Claudia Cardinale, the warm Italian beauty. And Brigitte Bardot, whom I've always wanted to meet again ever since we danced together at St. Tropez when I, a young god of sixteen, was bashing my way around southern France for the first time.

My Super Star Claudia looked very appetizing. More beautiful than ever. The hard life at my side (it's not easy to live with a genius) had done her good. Her beautiful face had character now and she looked like a ma-ture woman.

We went to the public bath house and scrubbed ourselves clean. In separate showers, of course. I washed myself all over with a piece of Maya soap. Washed Long John, too.

Claudia bought a new dress that clung to her lovely curves like a good dress ought to. A low-cut neckline that accentuated her well-shaped breasts. I was proud of her. She was miles ahead of all the other women in the world.

On the way to the concert hall where the festivities were to take place, I whispered to her, "If things turn out the way I hope they will, the two of us will be off for a nice vacation in Napmaquac. If not, you can always get a job selling cotton candy at the circus."

"Okay," she said, and we burst out laughing.

Suddenly I saw a familiar figure shuffling along across the street. I couldn't believe my eyes. I peered at her in astonishment. It was really her. She saw me and smiled. A big warm grin on her toothless mouth with just that little tooth sticking up in it.

My navy blue suit didn't quite fit. I'd borrowed it from Willem, the waiter in the bar where all the journalists hang out. It was a little too big around the shoulders. The skimpy advance from the publisher barely took care of Claudia's dress and my shirt.

"Wipe that silly grin off your face, woman," I said to Claudia. "Try to look serious. This ball is a Book Ball, remember?"

New York, November 1966

TO BE CONTINUED
keep a look-out for
I JAN CREMER
Third Book

How Jan Cremer the poor kid became a millionaire
and how the millionaire became a poor kid all over again

346